SAFER ROADS:
A GUIDE TO ROAD SAFETY ENGINEERING

# Safer Roads:
# A Guide to Road Safety Engineering

K.W. OGDEN
*Institute of Transport Studies*
*Department of Civil Engineering*
*Monash University*
*Melbourne, Australia*

# Avebury Technical

Aldershot • Brookfield USA • Hong Kong • Singapore • Sydney

Published by
Avebury Technical
Ashgate Publishing Limited
Gower House
Croft Road
Aldershot
Hants GU11 3HR
England

Ashgate Publishing Company
Old Post Road
Brookfield
Vermont 05036
USA

Reprinted 1997

**British Library Cataloguing in Publication Data**

Ogden, K. W.
    Safer Roads: Guide to Road Safety
    Engineering
    I. Title
    625.7042

    ISBN 0 291 39829 4

**Library of Congress Catalog Card Number:** 95-80519

Printed in Great Britain at the University Press, Cambridge

# Contents

# List of tables

# List of figures

# Preface

Many professions have a direct responsibility for road safety. One of these is the road and traffic engineering profession. Various studies have indicated that perhaps 40 per cent or more of accident reductions which could reasonably be expected on the road system can accrue from the provision of safer roads.

Many of those responsible for road safety in a road or traffic engineering environment are employed by local government, a regional office of a state or national road agency, or a consultant working for these sorts of agency. Typically, road safety is only one of a number of their professional duties, and very often they need help in their attempts to provide a safer road environment within their area of responsibility.

It has been my experience over many years that engineers in this environment would welcome a concise, authoritative, and comprehensive source of practical information on the application of a range of road and traffic engineering treatments which can be applied to solve a road safety problem. Many times I have been asked what could be done in such and such a situation, and often I have been aware, through my research, of suitable treatments or strategies which may be applied to assist in that problem area. But usually the source of this information has been in a research report, an obscure publication, a conference paper, or some such source which the practicing engineer could not be expected to know about, or necessarily have ready access to it.

This book therefore is written primarily with this audience in mind. However, I expect that it would be directly relevant to an undergraduate or postgraduate course in road or traffic engineering, since safety should surely be one of the key considerations in such a curriculum. It is also, I hope, intelligible to the interested layperson, and should be of relevance to those with a responsibility for overall road safety policy.

In the course of writing the book, I have attempted to report world-best practice and have drawn upon a wide international range of source material, mainly (but not only) from the English-speaking world. As a result, the material in the book should assist in cross-fertilising concepts and practices from one country to another, because different countries are more advanced in some areas than another, and there are many opportunities to learn from the international focus which this book takes.

As a result, there is no one set of practices which forms the basis of the book. I am most familiar with practice and research in Australia, the United Kingdom, and the United States, but the book could not really be taken as representing current practice in any one of those places. Rather, as I have said, it attempts to draw upon the best which each of these (and other places) has to offer in the field of road safety engineering.

A substantive draft of the book was written in 1994-95 during a period of sabbatical leave from Monash University, spent at University College, London. I therefore wish to acknowledge with gratitude all of those who made this leave possible: Professor Richard Allsop at UCL, Eric Laurenson at Monash University, and my colleagues Bill Young and Geoff Rose for carrying my teaching and other workloads during my absence.

I am indebted to many people who provided direct or indirect input to the preparation of the manuscript. In Australia, these included many in State road and traffic authorities, particularly Phillip Jordan, John Cunningham, Michael Tziotis, John Griffith, Fred Schnerring, John Bliss, Gordon Lee, Peter Cleal, and Malcolm Smith; consultants including Robert Morgan, Ted Barton, Andrew O'Brien, Don Howie, Peter Sweatman, Bob Pearson and David Axup; my colleagues at the Monash University Accident Research Centre, Peter Vulcan, Bruce Corben, Max Cameron and Stewart Newstead; and my good friends at the Australian Road Research Board, Ray Brindle, Jim Jarvis, Deborah Donald, Peter Cairney, David Bennett, Samantha Taylor, Judy Tickner and John McLean. A special appreciation is due to David Andreassen, who more than any other has impressed on me and many others over the years the necessity for rigour and clarity in accident investigation and analysis.

In the United States, Donna Nelson, Martin Wallen, Bill Marconi, Kay Fitzpatrick, John Zogby, and Frank Haight all assisted directly or indirectly, as did Ian Appleton in New Zealand.

In the United Kingdom, there were many people who contributed to my understanding of practices and processes used in that country: David McGuigan, Miles Tight, Heather Ward, Steve Proctor, Martin Belcher, Andrew Walford, David Sherborne, Alan Ross, David Silcock, Michael

xvi

Kendrick, John Turner, Andrew Howard, Brian Langer, Tim Cheeseborough, Malcolm Baker, David Hook, John Devenport, Roger Legassick, David Lynam, Ken Huddart, Prof Chris Wright, Dr Oliver Carstens, Mike Goodge, Barbara Sabey, John Brownfield, Dick Rainbird, Malcolm Bulpitt, Andrew Evans, and once again, Professor Richard Allsop.

I acknowledge the following persons and organisations, each of which gave permission to use copyright material as noted at the appropriate places in the text: Standards Australia, American Association of State Highway and Transportation Officials, Cambridge University Press, Australian Road Research Board, David Andreassen, Her Majesty's Stationery Office, Institute of Transportation Engineers, and David McGuigan. I also acknowledge the contribution of Austroads and Robert Morgan for each providing a photograph.

I express my appreciation to Irene Sgouras who helped with word processing, Robert Alexander for preparing the line drawings, and Don McCarthy for preparing the photographic prints. I also thank John Hindley from Ashgate Publishing Limited for his encouragement, advice and support in this venture.

Finally, I thank my wife Elaine, and my sons Marcus, Matthew and Nicholas for supporting me during the time I spent writing and editing the manuscript.

*Ken Ogden*
*Melbourne*
*July, 1995*

# Glossary

In the course of preparing the manuscript for this book, it became clear that there were significant inconsistencies in terminology around the world for many items of road and traffic engineering practice and process. I therefore had to decide how to resolve this issue, since the book will fall short of its potential usefulness if it is not readily intelligible to the reader.

In some cases, when referring to a specific item, I have adopted a dual nomenclature, such as freeway/ motorway and GIVE WAY/ YIELD signs. But mostly, to avoid making the book very difficult and annoying to read, I have adopted a single term, and used that throughout. The term I have selected is the one which I hope and expect will be intelligible to all readers, even if in their own environment another term is more commonly used. For example, I use the term 'divided road' rather than 'dual carriageway', because those who habitually use the latter term will at least understand what the former term means. The reverse is not necessarily true, since the term carriageway is hardly used in America (I asked an American colleague what he thought it meant, and he surmised that it had something to do with horse-drawn vehicles!).

Fortunately, while there are many items for which there is different terminology, there are only a few where the same term means different things in different places. For example 'guard rail' in Britain means a pedestrian fence while elsewhere it is a roadside safety barrier, and 'passing' in some places refers to vehicles travelling in opposite directions while elsewhere it refers to vehicles travelling in the same direction (c.f. 'overtaking').

The following glossary therefore indicates in the first column the term that I have used in this book. The second column lists the words which have essentially the same meaning. There is no convention to this, i.e. I have not used, say the British or American or Australian terminology but rather, as explained above, the term which I think will be most widely understood.

| | |
|---|---|
| arterial road | trunk road, main road, distributor road |
| crash cushion | impact attenuator |
| cross intersection | 4-arm junction |
| divided road | dual carriageway |
| driver's side | far side |
| footpath | sidewalk, pavement |
| freeway | motorway, expressway |
| guard fence | guard rail (USA), median barrier |
| intersection | junction |
| kerb extension | build-out, peninsula, choker |
| leg (of an intersection) | arm, approach |
| median | central reserve |
| overtaking lane | passing lane |
| painted channelisation | ghost island |
| passenger's side | near side |
| pedestrian fence | guard rail (UK) |
| pedestrian underpass | subway |
| railway | railroad |
| railway crossing | level crossing, grade crossing |
| rear end accident | shunt |
| roadway | carriageway |
| roundabout | traffic circle, rotary |
| sight triangle | visibility splay |
| t-intersection | 3-arm junction |
| traffic calming | local area traffic management |
| truck | lorry |
| undivided road | single carriageway |

# 1 The nature and dimensions of the road safety problem

*In this introductory chapter, we discuss the nature of the road safety problem, establishing that it is a legitimate area of study by reference to humanitarian, public health and economic frameworks. The distinction is made between personal and societal perspectives, and the clash between society's demands for mobility on the one hand and the risk which that mobility creates on the other. Having established that there is a problem and briefly sketching its nature and dimensions, the remaining chapters systematically discuss solution strategies, focussing especially upon road safety engineering strategies.*

Each year, some half million people die and 10-15 million people are injured in road accidents worldwide. Road trauma is one of the significant diseases of industrial societies and is an increasing public health and economic issue in developing countries.

Travel is an inherently risky activity, because movement creates kinetic energy, and if there is an accident or collision, the energy exchange can be damaging to both humans and property. Travel, and especially road travel, is one of the more hazardous activities which people in developed countries undertake. Figure 1.1 shows the fatality rate for various modes of transport in Britain, expressed as deaths per 100 million hours of exposure (Evans, 1994). This shows the relative safety of land-based public transport modes (bus, coach, train), and risk experienced by so-called 'vulnerable' road users (pedestrians, cyclists), and the extreme hazard faced by motor cyclists. For comparison, the corresponding fatality rates for being at home and at work were 2.6 and 0.9 fatalities per 100 million hours respectively.

1

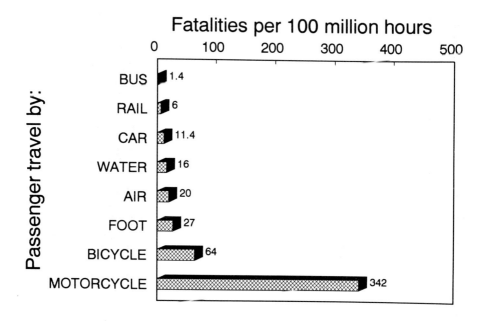

**Figure 1.1    Fatal accident rates for selected transport activities (UK)**

Source:    Evans (1994).

Not surprisingly, the faster we travel, and the more we travel, the more risk there is, all else being equal. For example, if we replace animal drawn transport with motorized transport, we increase both speed and mobility. It is primarily for this reason that death and injury on the road has become a major issue during the twentieth century. The experience in one country serves to demonstrate the point. In Australia, statistics first distinguished death by motor vehicle in 1925. Deaths from this cause increased steadily (with interruptions due to the Great Depression and World War 2) until by 1954 they exceeded deaths from all infectious diseases. They continued to rise until the late 1960s, but have been in decline since then (Trinca, et al, 1988).

About 3 per cent of all deaths in Australia occur on the road system, and these represent the major cause of death for people aged from about 5 to 35 years. However, this small percentage of fatalities masks the social and economic importance of road trauma. Since the age distribution of road accident victims is tilted towards the young, the reduction in length of life and hence loss of productivity is substantial, compared with the more frequent causes of death (cancer and heart disease) which are associated with old age.

The economic cost of road trauma in Australia has been estimated by the Bureau of Transport and Communications Economics (1994) as $AUD 6,100 million (about $US 4,900 million) in 1993. The figure itself perhaps does not mean very much, but the point to note is that it is about 1.6 per cent of Gross Domestic Product (GDP). This figure is typical of the economic significance of road accidents in other industrialized countries, even though different methods are used from place to place to estimate the costs of road trauma. For example, using standard UK accident costings, road accident costs in the UK in 1993 represented 1.7 per cent of GDP, while various US estimates reported by Haight (1994) would suggest an economic cost of between 1.0 and 1.5 per cent of GDP. These costs are not insignificant, and serve to underline the economic significance of road trauma. Thus, quite apart from any humanitarian concern for road trauma, there is a strong economic argument for tackling the problem. The components of the Australian estimate are shown in Figure 1.2. Once again, the amounts themselves are not so important as their relativity.

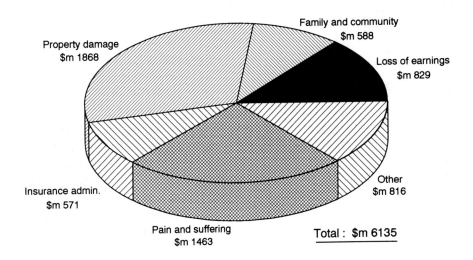

**Figure 1.2    Costs of road accidents by category (Australia)**

Source:    Bureau of Transport and Communications Economics (1994).

It can be seen that the major components are the costs of property damage, an amount to account for pain and suffering, and the loss of earnings of road trauma victims[1].

However, while the economic and public health issues may be significant, the problem as perceived by the individual traveller seems quite different. The chances of death on any given journey, no matter how hazardous, are extremely small. Lay (1986, p 556) for example has estimated that the probability of being killed in a road accident is about 1 in one thousand per year, or 1 in one million per trip or 1 in one hundred per lifetime. Similarly, the UK Department of Transport (1987, p 21) has estimated that in Britain the average motorist will be involved in an injury accident about once every 800,000 km (500,000 miles) or once every 35 years, while over a lifetime there is a 1 in 10 chance of being killed or seriously injured in a road accident. Even in fatal accidents (i.e. those where at least one person is killed), more people survive than die (Haight, 1987).

This contrast between the societal problem and the personal problem is at the crux of road safety policy. The personal problem may be measured in terms of the death rate per vehicle or per vehicle km (vehicle mile). Figures 1.3 and 1.4 respectively show these data for selected industrial countries over recent years[2].

It can be seen that by these measures, there has been an improvement. Indeed, by these measures, safety has steadily improved over time in all countries for which data are available. Some countries have recently shown a dramatic improvement; the risk of being killed per kilometre travelled in Australia for example fell by over one-half between 1982 and 1991.

Thus the personal risk problem, at least in developed countries, is improving; it is safer now to travel a given distance than it was in times past.

By comparison, the societal problem is best measured by the number of deaths per head of population. These data for recent years for the same countries are shown in Figure 1.5. It can be seen that although this situation is also generally improving, the rate of improvement is not so great as it is for the personal risk measures shown in Figures 1.3 and 1.4.

The implication of the above discussion is that as each kilometre of travel has become safer, demand for travel has increased, so the death rate per head has declined less dramatically. In fact, there is such a strong correlation between mobility and safety that we can confidently say as Haight (1987) has said that 'only mobility can be said to cause accidents.'

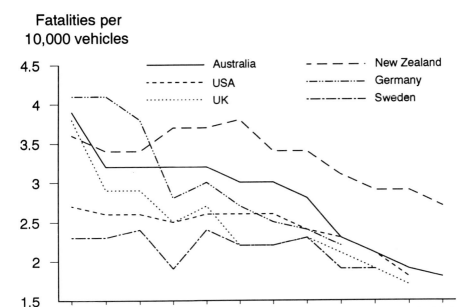

**Figure 1.3    Road accident fatalities per 10 thousand registered
vehicles, selected countries**

This dichotomy has also resulted in something of a paradox (Trinca, et
al, 1988, p 44): that on the one hand the lower rate of fatalities per
kilometre has meant that safety has tended to take second place to mobility
amongst *transport* decision makers, while on the other hand, the great
strides made by medical science in disease control has meant that road
trauma has grown as a *public health* issue.

There can therefore be a reluctance to accept safety measures if those
measures are perceived as compromising mobility. Examples of the
conflict between safety and mobility include (Trinca, et al, p 44; Evans,
p 363):

. speed limits,
. motor cycle helmets,
. land use planning (e.g. location and size of shopping centres),

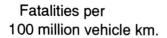

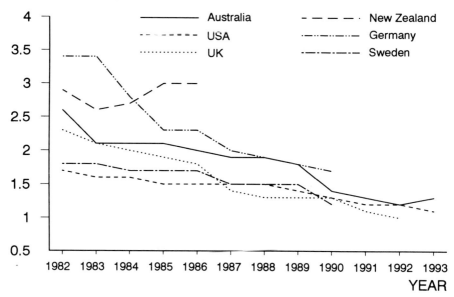

**Figure 1.4    Road accident fatalities per 100 million vehicle kilometres, selected countries**

- street layouts which restrict access (e.g. street closures),
- minimum age to hold a drivers license (or even the need to have a license),
- restrictions on novice drivers (alcohol, night time),
- graduated driver licenses for heavy vehicle drivers,
- road humps and other traffic calming measures, and
- fully controlled turn phases at traffic signals.

In each of these examples, there is (or has been in the past, depending on the country or jurisdiction concerned) resistance to the safety measure, or a compromise in its introduction or enforcement, because of the need to consider conflicts with mobility.

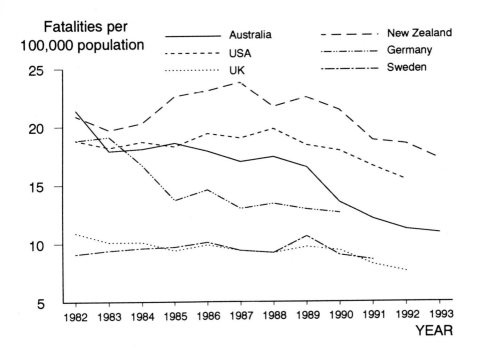

**Figure 1.5** **Road accident fatalities per 100 thousand population, selected countries**

Conversely, there are safety measures which do not conflict with mobility. These have found readier acceptance, except where there is opposition on other grounds, such as cost or inconvenience, in which case they may not have been adopted because of the very low level of risk perceived by travellers. Examples of such measures include (Evans, 1991, p 364):

.    active occupant protection devices (air bags),
.    passive occupant protection devices (seat belts),
.    vehicle safety improvements (e.g. crashworthiness),
.    safer highway furniture (frangible poles, etc),
.    improved emergency services,
.    passengers facing rearwards, and
.    passengers selecting rear rather than front seats.

Of course, there are measures which actually enhance both mobility and safety, and not surprisingly, these have been much more readily introduced. They include:

. upgrading roads (e.g. duplication, provision of freeways),
. improved vehicle performance and handling,
. safer vehicle types, and
. many traffic control devices (signals, roundabouts).

In the future, there are a range of emerging technologies which aim to enhance both mobility and safety, and on this argument, they are likely to find ready acceptance if they can be provided at reasonable cost. These include fatigue detectors, night time vision enhancement, car-following radar, on-board navigation systems, etc.

This tension between safety and mobility is particularly important for transport and traffic professionals, because their role is to attempt to promote both simultaneously, which, as we have seen, is not always possible. Indeed, Hauer (1993, p 3) has provocatively suggested that 'perhaps we transportation engineers cannot act in good faith as the custodians of traffic safety because the goals of safety and efficiency are too often in conflict'. However, he goes on to argue that engineers cannot evade their responsibilities in the safety area, and concludes (op cit, p 6) that 'within limits, highway traffic engineers can make roads safer or less safe' and therefore, most importantly, 'we must know the safety repercussions of our choices.'

*In summary, road trauma is a significant public health and economic issue in contemporary society. From a societal point of view, there are strong humanitarian and economic reasons to tackle these problems, but it must be recognized that the societal problem and the personal problem are not identical; from a personal viewpoint the risk of being in a road accident at a given time or on a given journey are very small and declining rapidly with time. Therefore mobility objectives rather than safety objectives tend to be more pressing. Safety measures are more likely to be accepted if they enhance, or at least detract little from, mobility objectives.*

**Notes**

1.  It should be noted that the Bureau of Transport and Communications Economics (1994) used the so-called 'human capital' approach to arrive at its estimate of the costs of road trauma. This approach focuses on the victim's potential output or productive capacity. There are a number of different approaches to estimating the cost of accidents (see Haight, 1994). Valuation of the costs of road accidents is discussed in more detail in Chapter 16.

2.  International or inter-jurisdictional comparisons of road accident statistics are not always easy to make, because of differences in definition, reporting thresholds, reporting scales, reporting rates, completeness of data, etc (Andreassen, 1985b, 1991; O'Day, 1993). However, comparisons of fatalities are more universally available and fairly reliable (Haight, 1987).

# 2 Safety management systems

*In this chapter, we provide an overview of the contemporary approach to the management of the road safety problem. We emphasize the necessity to base responses on a sound scientific footing, i.e. from an understanding of the nature of the problem and an ability to analyse it dispassionately and objectively, rather than judgementally or emotionally. Generic road safety strategies are defined, and policies and programs aimed specifically at road safety are discussed with reference to current activities in several countries. This leads to a discussion of how accidents happen within the road traffic system and its human-vehicle-road components, and from that, a description of the role and purpose of road safety engineering as one of the key components of a road safety management strategy.*

## Road safety analysis

In the previous chapter, the nature and extent of the road safety problem was discussed. These problems call for a response. Whether motivated by a humanitarian, public health or economic concern, there are several pre-requisites of a sound and effective road safety management program. These essentially call for a response based on a scientific analysis of the problem, not one based on judgement and emotion - or as used to be said, one based on the PHOG approach of prejudice, hunch, opinion and guesswork!

Haight (1983) has suggested that over time, our understanding of the road safety problem and the processes involved in its management has advanced in eight important ways, as follows.

*There is no 'cure'*

Road trauma is a result of the energy exchange involved when a vehicle, possessing kinetic energy, impacts another vehicle, a roadside object, or a human. It is an inevitable consequence of mobility.

We can certainly take steps to minimize these consequences, or the probability of a vehicle being involved in a hazardous situation, but while there is mobility it is probably impossible to eradicate accidents.

This realization is important, because it changes the focus from a problem that will go away if we devote enough resources to it, to one requiring on-going management. This management in turn requires the development of scientifically-based techniques, which will enable us to predict with confidence that safety resources are well-spent and likely to be effective - and that it is more cost-effective to spend them in one way rather than another. However, as with other areas of public health and safety, the target cannot realistically be to eliminate the problem, but to reduce it to acceptable and manageable proportions (Evans, 1994).

*Abandoning the concepts of 'cause' and 'blame'*

Concepts of 'blame' get us nowhere because they do not indicate how we may usefully develop safety programs.

An approach based on notions of cause and blame is simplistic in the extreme. It says that the 'right' person is absolved and the 'wrongdoer' is culpable so that he/she may be censured and punished. Then, to determine culpability, we select from a series of emotive phrases which are deemed to be adequate descriptions of the causal sequence (e.g. excessive speed, not keeping to the left, intoxicated, inexperienced, not keeping a proper lookout, inattentive driving, etc. - or in one infamous case, 'failure to drive safely.')

Of course, these things may happen, and they may have been contributing factors. We still see vestiges of them on police accident report forms. But subjective expressions like the above are judgemental and often misleading. More importantly, they reflect the belief that accidents are 'caused' by faulty - and therefore avoidable - behaviour alone.

Interestingly, such moralistic and judgemental attitudes have had exact parallels in other areas of public health - 'blame the victim'. For example, no progress was made in combating infectious diseases until this attitude was eliminated - e.g. 'They live in slums, which implies a sordid lifestyle, and this produces the disease'. Not 'provide a safe water supply.'

We did not make any progress to reducing road trauma until we abandoned the concepts of 'cause' and 'blame'. While we thought that way, road and traffic engineers, car manufacturers, law makers, police etc were absolved of the necessity to do anything.

However, once we moved away from that view, we saw the need to determine what a human was capable of, and found (for example) that humans need certain information to make decisions, that they take time to receive and process that information and arrive at those decisions, and that they sometimes make incorrect decisions. This puts the responsibility upon road authorities and others to design the system to accommodate the human, not the other way around. Lay (1986, p 554) has emphasized this point, noting that as a road accident is the consequence of a chain of events, those responsible for vehicle and road design must accept 'the near certainty of irresponsible, errant driver behaviour and design the road system to tolerate this less-than-ideal response. Indeed, the design professions have an obligation to design for human error and not to piously condemn the next round of accident victims.'

## Consequences, not accidents

In part, this follows from the previous point. While we conceptualized accidents as being the 'fault' of a human, we were inevitably led to think that the task at hand was to change the human so that accidents did not occur.

However, an alternative - and much more efficacious - approach is to replace the goal of reducing accident *frequency* with the goal of reducing *losses*: 'to control effectively the undesirable consequences of using the road transport system' (Haight, 1983). This sees that there are three phases involved in an accident - pre-crash, in-crash and post-crash. Rather than putting all of our focus on accident prevention, we also attempt to reduce the in-crash trauma if an accident should occur (e.g. seat belts) and provide post-crash treatment (e.g. emergency services). Neither seat belts nor emergency services *prevent* accidents from occurring, yet both have been very effective in reducing the extent and cost of road trauma.

Further, we need to recognize that particular countermeasures may reduce either the number of accidents or the severity of accidents, but rarely both. For example, Hedman (1990) notes that for a range of intersection safety measures, the only one to reduce both severity and frequency was grade-separation. If we were to concentrate only on reducing accident frequency, we would forego a lot of potential benefit that could be achieved from programs which reduce the severity of accidents.

## Exposure

Following from the argument, presented in Chapter 1, that mobility is the prerequisite for road accidents, it follows that accident losses can be reduced by managing mobility, i.e. by reducing exposure to hazardous situations. Thus an effective strategy can be to reduce the exposure of at-risk groups. This is particularly applicable to novice drivers (e.g. curfews or restrictions on alcohol use while driving).

Haight (1983) notes that the point about exposure is often mis-interpreted by using it as an index, for example as an accident rate. While, as we have seen in Chapter 1, accident rates can be a useful overall indicator of performance, they are of little value in selecting countermeasures or sites to target for treatment. It may be of little relevance that a particular site (e.g an intersection) has a 'good' accident rate if in fact it carries a lot of traffic and has a lot of accidents; it is the accident frequency that is important, not the rate. Similarly, a very lightly trafficked intersection may have a high rate, but if the frequency is very small because of the low traffic levels, treatment is not likely to be cost-effective (see Chapter 5).

## Statistical analysis

The importance of a scientifically-based analysis has been stressed above. This implies two things - a good data base, and skill in interpreting and analysing data. Our abilities in both these areas have progressed considerably over the years. Because this is so important, and fundamental in particular to road safety engineering, it forms a key structural component of this book.

However, we also need to be aware of the limits and pitfalls of statistical analysis. These include the limitations and shortcomings of the accident data bases, the difficulty of isolating one factor from others which may have also affected safety, and the dangers of 'regression to the mean' - the property that where there are random fluctuations in accidents occurring at a site, it is statistically probable that a period with a comparatively high accident frequency will be followed by one with a low accident frequency, even in the absence of some form of intervention. If we have intervened (e.g. with a traffic management treatment), we may incorrectly attribute the fall in accidents to the treatment.

*Outcomes may be counter-intuitive*

The next point made by Haight (1983) is that 'predictions of effects which are reasonably based on sensible hypotheses and known facts often go very far astray'. This may is a particular example of what is known as Forrester's Law (Forrester, 1969) that *in any complex system, the results of any action are always counter-intuitive!*

Haight quotes a number of examples where extravagant road safety claims were made for specific programs, based on extrapolation from groups where a measure had been found to be effective. He observed that 'road safety is a difficult and frustrating field of study, and most of us have learned from experience to be sceptical of claims for programs that have not been carefully and objectively evaluated. It is especially difficult to explain to laymen (sic) that perfectly sensible ideas may not work out in practice.'

*Evaluation*

The notion that we need to evaluate proposals in order to select those which are likely to be effective is important. As a result of this conceptual breakthrough, we now have reasonably good guides to what measures may be appropriate in response to given accident situations. This is particularly true in the road safety engineering area, and we will address this point in detail in later chapters of this book.

One of the most important developments in recent years in road safety has been institutional; the development of national and local integrated road safety strategies. An important consequence of this has been the potential for the provision of road safety resources on a more rigorous basis across program areas. However, there is still some way to go on this, and road safety resources still tend to be compartmentalized within institutional boundaries - vehicle engineering, road safety engineering, education, enforcement, etc - rather than allocated to areas where they potentially show the highest return. Resolution of this issue is likely to be one of the key road safety developments in the years ahead.

*Rational priorities*

In the real world, there are competing claims for limited budgets. This must inevitably extend to road safety budgets as well. Thus evaluation must be able to demonstrate, not only that a likely accident reduction will follow from implementing a given program, but that the benefits of such a program will exceed its costs, and that (if possible) expenditure in that area will be more beneficial than in another area.

## Historical development of approaches to road safety

The Organisation for Economic Cooperation and Development (1984) has summarized the development of the conceptualization of road safety problems, suggesting that over time we have progressed through six stages, each successively recognising the reality of road traffic as part of a system and acknowledging that solutions need to be sought in a systems context. These stages are as follows:

*Mono-causal casuistic approach.* 'Casuistic' means misleading or perverse. In the earliest phase of thinking, every accident was considered to be one too many and unique. Every accident was a problem and taking away the cause was the solution. No attention was paid to the difficulty that taking away one problem may produce others, or that another solution may be better.

However, it is obviously impossible to find a separate unique solution to every single accident. This philosophy induced perfectionism, and led to an attitude of 'blaming the victim', but by ignoring interactions between system components, the end result was often counterproductive.

*Mono-causal accident proneness approach.* For a while, the notion that certain people were 'accident-prone' had currency. The argument was that such accident prone drivers should be identified so that they could be kept away from traffic, or forced to improve themselves by punishment or retraining. However, this argument is spurious, since all attempts to identify in advance these accident prone drivers have failed (Haight, 1986)! Similarly, Hulbert (1982, p 213) quotes a US Department of Transportation report which stated that 'the negligence law usually treats driver error as both avoidable and unreasonable, and imposes liability pursuant to an objective standard to which all drivers are held. But ... a significant gap exists between the standard of behaviour required by the negligence law and the average behaviour normally exhibited by most drivers.' Hulbert concludes succinctly that 'the old concept of the accident prone driver is not supported by the facts'.

*Mono-causal chance phenomenon approach.* In reaction to the failure of the accident proneness approach, accidents then came to be considered as purely a matter of chance. Therefore, it was argued, they cannot be prevented because a chance phenomenon - fate - cannot be changed.

This approach led to a concentration on the consequences of accidents, e.g. frangible poles, crashworthy cars, etc. There are of course elements of good sense in the conclusions of these mono-causal approaches. Driver skill, attitude and behaviour are important, as are sound in-crash and post-crash countermeasures. However, they are all based upon a fundamentally unsound principle - single cause events - and thus must be limited in their effectiveness.

*Multi-causal chance phenomena approach.* From about the early 1970s, as scientific research and analysis was brought to bear on road accident research, it quickly became evident that accidents were rarely if ever the result of a single unique 'cause'. Rather, they are the outcome of a chain of events. Prevention or reduction of the end result of that chain - road trauma - meant finding the 'weak link' in the chain. This may be at some remove from the obvious 'cause'.

The multi-causal concept envisaged that anyone involved in traffic ran the risk of being involved in an accident. Several interdependent factors had a role, and the interactions between these factors (human-vehicle-road) were partly deterministic (and thus controllable) and partly stochastic (random). This led to the development of the need for extensive accident data bases and the development of sophisticated statistical techniques for identifying the interaction between these factors, and thus the deterministic ones.

Effectiveness, in terms of output indicators, became the leading principle for the management of road trauma, and the setting of priorities. It resulted in (for example) 'accident black spot' programs, targeted speed enforcement, concentration on at-risk groups (young, motor cyclists, alcohol-impaired, etc).

This approach led to great advances, and is essentially the state of current practice. This book, for example, emphasizes the need for a comprehensive data base in order to systematically identify and treat those aspects of the road and traffic environment which are shown to be more risky. However, in concept, its potential is limited because of the very thing that gives it strength - its foundation in a comprehensive data base. Clearly, the amount of data that can be collected about any accident in retrospect is limited, and thus the ability to model and evaluate all relevant interactions is limited. This realization has led, in principle, to the following refinements.

*Multi-causal static systems approach.* This approach attempts to focus more effort onto the nature of the problem. It differs from the above in that it is based upon a problem-oriented strategy of choosing the particular part of the problem which is of interest, and to bring resources to bear to attempt to examine it more closely. This has led to the development of 'in-depth' accident studies, in which an attempt is made to gather as much data as possible about not only the site and circumstances of the accident, but background information from the early stages of the 'chain', i.e. those circumstances which were in place before the accident itself.

*Multi-causal dynamic systems approach.* In principle at least, the defect of the static, multi-causal systems approach is that the dynamic character of transport and accident processes is passed by. We have a series of 'snapshots' captured by the in-depth data, but not a 'movie'. In every accident, the particular events (and thus the probability of failure) are partly the results of actions or circumstances which preceded them.

The dynamic systems approach thus, in concept, develops into a method to search for critical lines or sequences through all the processes leading to road trauma. In this way, the focus is not only problem-oriented and directed at effectiveness (as the other multi-causal approaches are), but additionally it aims at optimization (specific goals) and integration (all phases and countermeasures considered).

The Organisation for Economic Cooperation and Development (1984) suggests that the key links requiring investigation in order to operationalize this approach are:

. travel needs, which create the demand for mobility,

. predisposition, which includes those factors which increase the risk of travel, including road user factors (fatigue, urgency, use of alcohol and drugs, etc), modal factors (access, comfort), and environmental factors (weather, traffic volumes, road and traffic control characteristics),

18

. encounters, which are potentially risky traffic situations in which travellers find themselves, the outcome of which is determined by road user characteristics (experience, skills, motivation, risk-taking, etc), vehicle characteristics (manoeuvrability, braking, stability, etc), road characteristics (pavement surface condition, pavement friction, signing, access control, etc) and traffic factors (volume, stability of flow, intersecting traffic, conflicting manoeuvres, etc),

. incidents, which are encounters which are especially risky; most road users handle most encounters in a routine way, but those which call for extreme responses (heavy braking, swerving) or which result in undesirable vehicle behaviour (skidding, jackknifing, etc) may be termed incidents,

. accidents, which are incidents involving a collision; there is little discretion left to the road user at this stage, and the outcome of the accident is largely the result of the actions and conditions established in the preceding phases; death may occur at this stage but usually an accident will lead immediately to the next stage,

. injury and damage, which is the consequence of the energy exchanged in the accident, and

. recuperation, which involves attempts to save the life of any injured accident victim, physical and psychological recuperation of survivors, and repair/disposal of damaged property.

Thus, in summary, it was not until we moved away from mono-causal to multi-causal, systems-oriented approaches that we made significant progress in tackling road trauma, since more simplistic approaches overlook the essential interactions between the road user, the vehicle and the road system.

*Terminology*

Much of the above is reflected in the terminology we use. Words have a power to them, which convey impressions as well as meaning. Therefore, many people prefer to use the word 'crash' or 'collision' to 'accident'. The latter word conveys a sense that the losses incurred are due to fate and devoid of predicability. Similarly, a proportion of road accidents are

19

suicides, even homicides, which are certainly not 'accidental'. The word 'crash' or 'collision' indicates in a simple factual way what has happened. In related areas of road safety, the word 'accident' is not used; e.g. those working in vehicle design use words like 'collision avoidance', and while the word 'accident' is used in medical circles, words like 'road trauma' and 'injury prevention' are finding increasing currency (Trinca, et al, 1988; Langley, 1988).

However, in road safety engineering, the word 'accident' is in very common use, e.g. 'accident report form', 'accident statistics', 'accident type'. For ease of understanding then, although the author is personally inclined to prefer the word 'crash', we will in this book generally use the word 'accident', because it is readily understood by the likely readership.

**Road safety strategies**

Within the general intellectual climate described above, a wide range of possible road safety strategies, each addressing specific aspects of the road safety problem, can be devised. This raises two items for discussion: firstly, a generic overview of road safety strategies (which we present in this section), and secondly how these disparate approaches can be integrated into a coherent and systematic approach to the management of road safety, which we discuss in the next section.

Trinca, et al (1988) have usefully reviewed road safety *strategies* in five categories, each of which has a range of specific *programs*. These strategies are summarized below.

*Exposure control*

Gains in traffic safety can be achieved by reducing the amount of travel, or substituting safer forms for less safe forms of transport. It is thus a factor to be taken into account in transport planning and transport policy - but which rarely is! In highly motorized countries, the effect of such a strategy is likely to have limited impact, but it could be of major significance in industrializing countries. This strategy is clearly in conflict with some other values in society, such as freedom to choose where to live and work, freedom of movement, layout of cities, etc.

Specific program options include (Trinca, et al, 1988, p 89 ff):

. alternatives to road transport (e.g. rail, bus, air, telecommuting, etc),

. vehicle restrictions (limiting engine size - e.g. motor cycles),

. roadway restrictions (e.g. truck bans in local streets, pedestrian malls or precincts where pedestrians have priority over motorized transport, pedestrian and bicycle bans on freeways, etc), and

. user restrictions (e.g. driver licence age, limits on blood alcohol for novice drivers, limits on night time driving for novice drivers, graduated licences, etc).

## Accident prevention

Accidents may be prevented by better engineering or behaviour modification.

*Road engineering* can have a dramatic effect on road safety - a modern freeway can be 10 times safer per vehicle kilometre than an undivided 2-lane road, for example. Road design, construction, maintenance and management all contribute to safety.

However, the costs of this are high, and interestingly the adoption of high road design standards can rarely be justified on safety grounds alone. Safety benefits are typically of the order of 15 per cent of the total benefits of an urban road project and 5 per cent of the benefits of a rural road project - although since benefits usually outweigh costs by 4 or 5 to one, safety benefits are considerable (Lay, 1986, p 52).

Moreover, road infrastructure is long-lasting, and cannot be modified quickly in response to an emerging safety problem. Hence this strategy as a safety measure is a long term one.

Nevertheless, safety should be an important input to road decisions - whether they are built, their design, their construction standard, and their operation. The new field of road safety audit (see Chapter 15) attempts to focus on this potential.

Specific road-oriented safety programs are discussed in Chapters 8 to 14 below, and include:

. road design,
. intersection design and control,
. delineation, lighting and signing,
. road construction and maintenance,

. roadside hazard management,
. traffic management (including traffic calming),
. speeds and speed limits, and
. treatments directed at vulnerable road users.

*Vehicle engineering* affects safety, in relation to both the vehicle's initial design and its in-service condition. Design tends to be international, given the global nature of the car industry, while in-service condition varies considerably.

The future potential of safer vehicles is considerable, as electronic and information measures are increasingly available. By removing more of the decision-making from the driver and putting it onto machines, safety can be enhanced (e.g. route choice, car following, braking, etc). However, to be worthwhile, vehicle measures must apply to all or most vehicles, and this means that they are costly and take many years to reach worthwhile implementation. Programs related to vehicle engineering include:

. braking,
. lights, reflectors, etc,
. handling,
. driver controls,
. visibility,
. crashworthiness,
. heating and ventilation, and
. stability (especially heavy vehicles).

Note that in most countries, there are specific rules which mandate many of these for new vehicles. In some countries, there is also provision for periodic review and inspection of vehicles in service.

*Behaviour modification*

Notwithstanding the considerable resources devoted to various programs aimed at behaviour modification, its cost-effectiveness as a road safety measure is unproven. For example, in its major review of road safety in Britain, the Department of Transport (1987, p 13) concluded that 'common sense certainly suggests that ... driver training and testing, road traffic law or traffic education in schools must be in the interests of road safety, but no-one has yet been able convincingly to prove it.'

It is possible however to hypothesize that if they are to be effective, behaviour modification programs must be well-defined, realistic and aimed at identifiable problems, targeted at populations which lend themselves to educational intervention, and backed up by enforcement (Cameron and Newstead, 1993). In other words, to be successful, programs must be based upon a sophisticated understanding of the processes of human behaviour. In particular, successful behaviour modification appears to be capable of success if it aimed at affecting factors under the direct volitional control, of the driver - e.g. fastening a seat belt. Behaviour modification is less successful if it aimed at something which is infrequent. A driver may drive for many hours, even years, but be required to make a 'split second' decision in an emergency situation. There is no way that experience or training can prepare the driver for this, in such a way that a 'correct' decision is assured. Therefore the system should aim to minimize the probability that a driver will be in that situation, and be 'forgiving' if a wrong decision is made.

Typical programs related to behaviour modification include the following (Trinca, et al, 1988, p 94 ff):

*Pedestrian training* seems to be effective, perhaps because it is learned behaviour, instilled at childhood when a person is most susceptible to training and learning. The difficulties experienced by pedestrians when they go a country where the traffic drives on the 'wrong' side of the road underlines that pedestrian behaviour is deeply ingrained.

*Driver training* is not highly effective in producing safer drivers. Most training is directed more at encouraging compliance with laws than with conveying information about rules and procedures. Training aims to provide drivers with skills, which are then rehearsed again and again in the traffic stream. The driver becomes very good at these - but this form of training is of little benefit when confronted with an unusual situation. Overall, there is no evidence of a statistical correlation between driver training and subsequent accident involvement. (Although this is true for car drivers, it is probably less true for truck drivers, where the skill level is higher, broader, and responses to hazards are more commonplace, because of the size and mass of the truck.)

*Enforcement* can affect drivers in several ways: that a law will be enforced, that an offender will be detected, that the adjudicatory process will be swift and certain, and that punishment will follow conviction. Of these, the one that seems to most effect driver behaviour is the perceived probability of being detected (Axup, 1993). Police effort is directed mainly at two areas: speed and alcohol. These are both quantifiable (hence facilitating both detection and conviction), and they are related to road accidents. However, police resources are limited, so enforcement needs to be targeted at areas of highest risk.

*Injury control*

Injury control is a relatively recent development. It is based on the recognition that deaths and injuries can be reduced if the conditions which apply during the crash phase are modified. In other words, if the human is better 'packaged', substantial benefits will occur.

Programs here relate to both the vehicle the road, and include (Trinca, et al, 1988, p 97 ff):

- motor cars:
  - antiburst door locks
  - seat belt restraint
  - cabin structural integrity
  - laminated glazing
  - energy-absorbing steering column
  - 'forgiving' interior fittings
  - head restraints
  - exterior features (for pedestrian safety)

- bicycles and motor cycles
  - helmets
  - conspicuity

- buses
  - seat belts
  - 'forgiving' interior fittings

- road environment
  - similar to discussion under accident prevention (above)

*Post-injury management*

The post-crash phase involves efficient treatment and rehabilitation services to cope with the injured. Road deaths typically occur in three distinct time periods (Trinca, et al, 1988, p 72):

. In the crash or within minutes of it: death is usually the result of disruption to the brain, central nervous system, heart, or major blood vessel. Approx 50 per cent of road deaths occur in this period. However, it occurs in only about 5 per cent of casualty accidents. There is little that medical science can do for this group.

. Within the period 1-2 hours after the accident, where death results from major head, chest or abdominal injury or major blood loss. About 35 per cent of deaths occur in this period, from about 15 per cent of casualty accidents. Increased survival rates are likely to result from early and appropriate medical efforts.

. Within 30 days of hospital admission. Major causes are brain death, organ failure and infection. Approximately 15 per cent of deaths occur at this late stage. There is little that medical science can do to reduce this in developed countries, but it may be a major contributor in developing countries.

Thus the major impact of post-injury management is in the 1-2 hour period after the accident. It is primarily dependent upon roadside and hospital emergency treatment. Programs aimed at this strategy include (Trinca, et al, 1988, p 102 ff):

. training of care providers (not only emergency medical personal, but also first aid education for the general public, emergency services personnel training in roadside care, training of public utility workers and tow truck operators, etc),

. training of health professionals and hospital personnel in road trauma treatment,

. effective communication to notify the occurrence, location and nature of the accident,

. systems to ensure rapid response by para-medical services,

. efficient and effective transport of the victim to hospital,

. establishment of specialized trauma units at major hospitals,

. trauma registry (for information for research purposes), and

. rehabilitation.

This overview has been necessarily cursory. But it does serve to highlight that we are dealing with a complex and important topic, in which professionals from a range of disciplines have a responsibility. The balance of the book relates particularly to the role of the road and traffic engineer, but it is useful for the reader to have a glimpse of the bigger picture, so that the engineer's contribution can be seen in a broader context.

## Road safety policy and programs

Road safety is a complex issue, with many disparate activities and programs involved. Management of road safety therefore becomes a major challenge, and different countries have responded to this challenge in different ways (Organisation for Economic Cooperation and Development, 1994). In recent years, a number of countries (e.g. United Kingdom, The Netherlands, Australia, New Zealand) have developed comprehensive, coordinated national road safety strategies, aimed at achieving targeted reductions in road trauma and its costs. In other countries, notably the United States, leadership has been shown at the national level without the establishment of specific targets, with delivery through state and local agencies (Zogby, 1994). In this section, we will briefly describe three approaches, as used in the United Kingdom, Australia and the United States, and will then draw some general conclusions.

### United Kingdom

The Government in 1987 set a target of reducing road casualties by one-third by 2000 compared with the average for 1981-85 (Department of Transport, 1987, p 27). This indicated a reduction from 320,000 to 220,000 casualties per annum in absolute terms (Burrough, 1991). It was to be achieved despite an expected increase in traffic of over 50 per cent. The target of one-third was set as the result of research which indicated that such an outcome was achievable through the application of both then-existing measures plus the introduction of new measures (Sabey and Taylor, 1980).

Much of the responsibility for the delivery of these road safety targets in the UK lies with local authorities. In 1989 in response to the national goal, the Local Authorities Association (1989) produced a publication entitled *Road Safety Code of Good Practice*, outlining the components of a road safety plan. This suggested that such a plan had seven components:

. planning,
. information,
. engineering,
. education and training,
. enforcement,
. encouragement, and
. coordination of resources.

These plans are now in place, and local authorities in Britain are well attuned to the philosophy and implementation of road safety programs (Brownfield, 1993). Importantly, they have the legislative requirement (not just authority, but an obligation) to:

. carry out a program of measures designed to promote road safety,

. carry out studies into accidents,

. in the light of those studies, take measures to prevent accidents,

. in constructing new roads, take measures to reduce the possibility of accidents when the roads come into use, and

. carry out road safety audit on new road proposals.

*Australia*

Similarly, in Australia a national strategy, with the aim of 'reducing road crashes and their human and economic costs in real terms during the 1990s and into the next century' has been prepared (Federal Office of Road Safety, 1992). This followed the success of concerted but disparate road safety actions undertaken by the Federal Government, State Governments and local government. Further progress in road safety was seen to require a coordinated national effort. The strategy developed specific goals (e.g. to reduce road fatalities to 10 per 100,000 population by 2001 with corresponding reductions in injury), and specific priorities. There has been complementary development of road safety strategies in each of the States and Territories (see for example Ungers and Vincent, 1995), and a national action plan for road safety comprising 37 specific initiatives across eight strategic objectives, as follows:

. major stakeholder ownership and participation in road safety,
. road safety as a major public health issue,
. road safety as a major economic strategy,
. road safety as a priority in the management of transport and land use,
. safer vehicles, safer roads and safer road users,
. integrated framework for road safety planning and action,
. strategic research and development program, and
. rationalization of Federal, State and Territory programs.

*United States*

In the United States, the most recent initiative related to road safety management at the national level has been the requirement within the 1991 Intermodal Surface Transportation Efficiency Act (ISTEA) that States must develop management systems for seven areas related to highways, including the preparation of a safety management system (SMS). These were required to be developed by October 1994 and be fully operational by October 1996.

The program areas that need to be addressed in the SMS were developed through workshops conducted by the Federal Highway Administration, and include (Federal Highway Administration, 1991b; Zogby, 1994; Bray, 1993):

. coordinating and integrating broad base safety programs into a comprehensive management approach for highway safety,

. identifying and investigating hazardous or potentially hazardous safety problems, roadway locations and features, and establishing countermeasures and priorities to correct them,

. ensuring early consideration of safety in all roadway transportation programs and projects,

. identifying safety needs of special user groups in planning, design, construction and operation of the roadway system, and

. routinely maintaining and upgrading safety hardware, highway elements, and operational features.

*Summary*

In summary, although there are variations in detail, it is commonly recognised that management of road safety requires strong leadership at a national level and the development of a comprehensive strategy. The major components of such a strategy may be summarized as follows:

. a 'champion' in the form of an influential government department or office,

. establishment of short term and long term road safety goals,

. establishment of accountability across institutions,

. recognition of institutional and organisational initiatives, with commitment to cooperation at both policy and operational levels,

. collection, maintenance and dissemination of data,

. development of processes to assess needs, select countermeasures, and set priorities on a rational basis of cost-effectiveness,

. development and implementation of public information and education activities,

. identification of skills, resources and training needs,

. adequate guaranteed funding,

. monitoring the effects on safety of implementation, and

. an on-going adequately-resourced research program.

One important distinction between policy in different countries is whether or not specific targets for road safety improvements are set. The US approach does not feature specific national targets, but instead merely requires the States to prepare a safety management system. Individual States have flexibility as to how to do this, the only requirement being that each jurisdiction must employ a systematic approach, with an emphasis on integrating their safety management efforts with other stakeholders in the public and private sector (Zogby, 1995). For example, in New York State, regional safety targets are established in terms of a 'reduction in the number of high accident locations' (Hall, 1993, p 13).

By contrast, specific targets are included, as mentioned above, in the UK and Australian strategies, while these also feature in the road safety strategies of other countries[1]. Clearly, this is a matter for resolution in the country concerned, but it is perhaps salutary to note that the most spectacular recent gains in road safety have occurred in those countries which have established and set out to achieve specific targets for accident reduction (see Figures 1.3, 1.4 and 1.5).

## The road traffic system

Road traffic may be considered as a system, in which the various components interact with each other. This system is often described as comprising three components - the human, the vehicle and the road. An accident may be considered as a 'failure' in the system. Indeed, the UK Department of Transport (1986) in its *Accident Investigation Manual* defines an accident as a 'rare, random, multi-factor event always preceded by a situation in which one or more persons have failed to cope with their environment.'

In one of the early systematic approaches to road safety analysis, the American analyst William Haddon combined these three components with the three phases in an accident (pre-crash, in-crash and after-crash) to form what has since become known as the Haddon Matrix (Haddon, 1980). Each of the nine elements of the matrix represents a possible focus for road safety. An example of the Haddon Matrix is presented in Figure 2.1, showing typical countermeasures applicable to each cell of the matrix.

The relative contribution of human, vehicle and road factors to road accidents have been analysed in a number of studies. The results of two such studies, one in the UK (Sabey, 1980) and one in the US (Treat, 1980) are shown in Table 2.1.

| Element | Before Crash | In Crash | After Crash |
|---------|-------------|----------|-------------|
| Human | Training Education Behaviour (e.g. drink driving) Attitudes Conspicuous clothing on pedestrians and cyclists | In-vehicle restraints fitted and worn | Emergency medical services |
| Vehicle | Primary safety (e.g. braking, roadworthiness, visibility) Speed Exposure | Secondary safety (e.g. impact protection) | Salvage |
| Road | Delineation Road geometry Surface condition Visibility Road safety audit | Roadside safety (e.g. frangible poles) Safety barriers | Restoration of road and traffic devices |

**Figure 2.1   Haddon Matrix**

Source: Lay (1986), p 552.

Both studies involved in-depth analysis of a large number of accidents, with contributing factors being identified as related to the road, road user or vehicle, or interactions between them.

In total, the road contributed to 28-34 per cent of accidents, the human to 93-94 per cent and the vehicle to 8-12 percent. These results are valuable, because they highlight the key role of the road user. However, the high involvement of the human is not surprising - ultimately, perhaps we would expect that the user is involved in 100 per cent of accidents, because in almost every case, some alternative action is possible, and in any case, if we take a broader perspective, humans are also involved in vehicle and road design and provision.

**Table 2.1**
**Factors contributing to road accidents**

| Contribution | UK study | US study |
|---|---|---|
| road environment only | 2 | 3 |
| road user only | 65 | 57 |
| vehicle only | 2 | 2 |
| road and road user | 24 | 27 |
| road user and vehicle | 4 | 6 |
| road and vehicle | 1 | 1 |
| all three factors | 1 | 3 |

Source: Sabey (1980) (UK); Treat (1980) (USA).

While such studies are of value, they are of limited use in developing *countermeasures*, for several reasons. First, these analyses are based on the premise that the outcome would have been different if a particular feature had not been present. This gives rise to some problems of interpretation. For example, a head-on accident on a dry well-lit roadway would likely be regarded as having entirely a road user contribution. But it could well be argued that the accident would not have occurred if it had happened on a divided highway, i.e. there is a road countermeasure potentially available. Similarly, outcomes are not directly related to contributory factors - the same accident, with identical factors, could have different outcomes depending on such things as vehicle size, belt use, emergency services, etc.

Moreover, factors which contribute to an accident do not necessarily point in the direction of cost-effective countermeasures. Commenting on this point, the UK Department of Transport (1986, p 2.12) in its *Accident Investigation Manual* noted that:

'When considering remedial measures to reduce accidents it must be borne in mind that the most effective remedy is not necessarily related directly to the main 'cause' of the accident and may even lie in a different area of the road, vehicle or road user. This is particularly true of accidents in which the road user fails to cope with the road environment; in many accidents the primary cause may be said to be the driver's lack of skill, but engineering remedies to improve the road are cheaper and easier to effect than training the driver to the necessary degree of skill.

Further, even in circumstances in which human error or impairment has been judged to be the sole contributor, it may be possible to influence human behaviour more readily by engineering means than by education or enforcement or legislation. There is also considerable potential for injury reduction even when accidents cannot be avoided.'

Hauer (1993, p 4) in an excellent discussion of this issue, points out that notions of 'cause' almost always focus upon the conditions immediately proximate to the accident event itself. However, he argues persuasively that 'the concept of cause has meaning only if we think by it something which, had it been done differently, would have affected the outcome.' He then points out that altering road and traffic engineering features or traffic control will usually affect the probability of accident occurrence or severity, so that there is no useful distinction between roads as a cause or human factors as a cause: 'there is just a causal chain in which the road, its environment, markings and signs affect what road users do.'

Moreover, Rumar (1982) makes the important point that 'the human component (of the road traffic system) is the most difficult one to change or modify, therefore the human characteristic should be the determining variable in the building of the system... man (sic) has several basic limitations which must be recognized and taken care of in the technical design of road geometry and surface, signs, signals, lighting, vehicles, etc.'

From a road safety engineering viewpoint, the important point to note from the above is that since the driver is the key, the engineer must be aware of human factors and realize that traffic engineering applications and countermeasures work through their influence of human behaviour. Thus, it needs to be emphasized that although road-related factors may contribute to only 25 per cent or so of accidents, road and traffic engineering countermeasures have a much greater contribution to play that just affecting that 25 per cent, since these measures act, in many cases, by assisting or influencing the behaviour of the dominant factor, namely the driver. This was well-expressed by the New South Wales Roads and Traffic Authority (1992), where it referred to 'developing and applying traffic control systems, such as signals, signs and line marking *to help road users drive safely*' (our emphasis). Almost all traffic engineering and

33

management measures work through their influence on human behaviour, and therefore they are an important component of an overall road safety strategy. Indeed, the UK Department of Transport (1987) in its major review of road safety policy reached the conclusion that 'accident investigation and prevention work ... remains by far the most cost-effective means of reducing casualties yet identified.' Similarly, the US Department of Transportation (1991) has developed a list of eleven 'priority short term countermeasures (which) ... should be emphasized for implementation on a national basis'. Of these eleven, six were within the responsibility of the road safety engineer[2].

We have previously referred to a road accident as being the consequence of a chain of events, involving human, vehicle and road factors. The challenge in road safety is to identify what is common about that causal chain across a range of accidents, and to apply measures which will 'break' the chain for a number of accidents. This is the power of the road safety engineering approach; where a common road-related feature can be identified across a range of accidents, remedial action to remove or modify that feature is likely to be highly cost-effective. These remedial treatments are discussed in detail later in this book, but for illustrative purpose might involve road design features (e.g. the provision of a divided road), intersection treatments (e.g. the installation of signals to fully control turns), the provision of improved delineation such as raised reflectorized pavement markers, the provision of high-friction pavements, the removal of roadside objects at hazardous locations such as the outside of a curve, application of appropriate speed limits, the installation of traffic calming devices to slow traffic in residential streets, or the provision of pedestrian facilities.

This notion of accidents being the result of a chain of events is a very valuable one in developing a safer road network. It is also recognized and applied in other fields of risk analysis and transport safety, such as aviation (Johnston, McDonald and Fuller 1994). Reason (1990) for example uses a somewhat different analogy than a 'chain' and refers to a 'trajectory of accident opportunities', as shown in Figure 2.2. Reason suggests that these trajectories must 'penetrate several defensive systems' which in our context are the human, vehicle and road systems, with the outcome depending upon their 'penetration' of the pre-crash, in-crash and after-crash phases as well. For example, the vast majority of decisions made by a driver do not result in any sort of hazard; the 'trajectory of opportunity' does not penetrate the first barrier (human, pre-crash). If the driver does make an error (i.e. the first barrier is breached), in most cases, good vehicle design (e.g braking, handling) will ensure that the second barrier is not breached, or good road design (e.g. wide shoulders, good surface friction) will assist in preventing an accident; this is depicted as the third barrier. Similarly, in the in-crash and after-crash phases, a succession of barriers must be breached if the outcome is to be a casualty accident. Reason points out that 'the chances of such a trajectory of opportunity finding loopholes in all the defences at any one time is very small indeed', an observation that applies also to the road traffic system.

## Role of road safety engineering

### Road safety engineering

As noted above, road safety strategies may involve strategies aimed at exposure control, accident prevention, behaviour modification, injury control, or post-injury management. Road safety engineering falls mainly within the second of these categories, and partly within the third.

Road safety engineering may be defined as a process, based on analysis of road and traffic related accident information, which applies engineering principles in order to identify road design or traffic management improvements that will cost-effectively reduce the cost of road accidents.

The opportunities for road safety engineering in general apply at four levels (Ross Silcock Partnership, 1991, p 10):

.   safety conscious planning of new road networks,
.   incorporation of safety features in the design of new roads,
.   improvement of safety aspects of existing roads to avoid future problems, and
.   improvement of known hazardous locations on the road network.

The potential for road safety engineering is well-recognized. For example, in the UK program established in 1987 to reduce road accident casualties by one-third by the year 2000, road safety engineering measures were expected to deliver at least one-third of this target reduction (Burrough, 1991). The potential of road safety engineering is therefore considerable. This potential has not been realized except in a few places because, as the Institution of Highways and Transportation (1990a, p 2) observe, 'few administrations have a systematic procedure for identification of hazard and selection of appropriate treatment for them (and) even fewer authorities have a systematic checking that safety principles are applied in new construction and road improvements.' There is also strong community support for the provision of safer roads; a major European study found that 53 per cent of drivers supported higher standard roads as a road safety strategy, compared with 34 per cent supporting driver training and 33 per cent supporting enhanced enforcement (Barjonet, Benjamin and Wittink, 1994).

### Accident investigation

The process of road safety engineering, as defined above, is based upon accident investigation and prevention, that is, the analysis of data on road accidents. From a road safety engineering viewpoint the purpose of such investigation is to determine the factors involved in accident(s) so that appropriate road or traffic engineering remedial or preventative measures may be applied.

There is often a parallel activity undertaken by the police aimed at determining fault (in a legal sense) so that charges can be laid against a guilty party. Unfortunately, the aims and intentions of the police and the road safety engineer are not the same and are often in conflict. The police are concerned with exercising their responsibility to bring criminal charges against a road user considered to have broken the law, and thus wish to gather supporting evidence. The road safety engineer is not concerned with fault, but with establishing the features and processes which led to the accident, realising, as discussed above, that there are usually many factors involved in an accident, not just those which relate to actions on the part of one individual.

This difference in role between the police and the road safety engineer can carry over into data collection. Since the police usually collect the initial data (see Chapter 4), if they conclude that there are no charges to be laid (e.g. the person legally at fault has been killed), there can often be a paucity of data in relation to that accident.

Accident investigation can be carried out at three levels. The first level, which is the routine level of accident investigation, involves the analysis of the mass accident data base, i.e. the data base which stores information based primarily upon routine police accident reports. By examining these data, problem locations on the road network can be identified and the broad characteristics of the problems at any site, or across a range of sites, can be established.

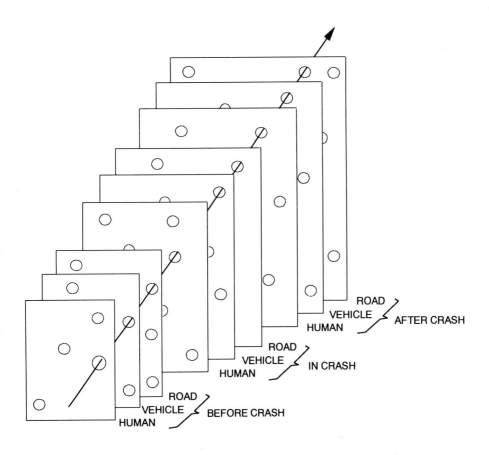

**Figure 2.2   The dynamics of accident causation**

Source: Reason (1990), p 208. Copyright 1990 by James Reason.
Reprinted with the permission of Cambridge University Press.

The second level of analysis involves the collection and analysis of supplementary data, i.e. data which are not routinely collected by the police. The supplementary data may be aimed at getting a better understanding of particular accident problems, including those related to a particular type of accident (e.g. run-off-road accidents), a particular type of road user (e.g. pedestrians) or a particular type of vehicle (e.g. heavy vehicles).

The third level involves an in-depth multi-disciplinary investigation, requiring the analysis of in-depth data collected at the scene of the accident and subsequently by multi-disciplinary teams. The aim is to develop an understanding of the factors and mechanisms involved in the pre-crash, in-crash and post-crash situations. The team may comprise specialists from a range of disciplines including medicine, human factors, vehicle engineering, road or traffic engineering, police, etc.

Accident data usually need to be aggregated for analysis. There are two prime ways in which this may be done, by location and by some common feature of the accident.

Aggregation by location is necessary to identify clustering of accidents in order to identify and prioritize sites for treatment. There are four prime applications (Institution of Highways and Transportation, 1990a, p 10):

. single sites: treatment of specific sites or short lengths of road at which accidents are clustered (often referred to as black spots or black sites),

. route action: application of remedial treatments to a road which has an abnormally high accident experience,

. area action: application of remedial measures over an area (e.g. a residential precinct) which has an abnormally high accident experience, or

. mass actions: application of remedial measures to locations having common accident features (e.g. skidding on approach to intersection, treatment of railway crossings, pedestrian facilities, etc).

Aggregation by some common feature of the accident is a useful way to investigate the nature of such accidents and develop countermeasures. Typical examples may include aggregation by:

. accident type, such as head-on, run off road, etc,

. road feature, such as road shoulders, bridge approach, etc,

. vehicle type, such as trucks, bicycles, motor cycles,

. road user type, such as pedestrians, young drivers, elderly drivers,

. common feature, such as speeding, fatigue, alcohol or drug involvement, and

. major event (e.g. newsworthy or politically sensitive) such as accidents involving a bus, a vehicle carrying dangerous goods, multi-vehicle accidents, or accidents with multiple fatalities.

It can be seen that the process is data-driven. Methods of collecting and analysing accident and other data are discussed in Chapter 4. Monitoring the effectiveness of schemes, and application of statistical techniques to determine the effectiveness or otherwise of measures is discussed in Chapter 17.

*Remedial and preventative measures*

As noted above, there are four opportunities for the application of road safety engineering. The first two of these (safety conscious planning of new road networks and new developments, and incorporation of safety features in the design of new roads) relate to the design and implementation of new projects, and we will consider these in the discussion of *road safety audit* in Chapter 15.

The third application (improvement of safety aspects of existing roads to avoid future problems) and the fourth (improvement of known hazardous locations on the road network) are closely related, but differ in one important respect, namely that one is pro-active, aimed at accident prevention, while the other is reactive, focussing upon remedial treatments at sites which are known hazards, based upon their accident history. Together, these form the basis of *hazardous road location (HRL) programs*.

The rationale for remedial programs is obvious; if a location has an accident history that is statistically significant (i.e. not likely to be the result of mere chance), then resources should be directed towards correcting it, if possible. The maximum reduction in road trauma and its associated costs will result from a concentration of resources on known problems.

However, this implies that locations without an accident history are 'safe'. In reality, this is not necessarily so, as the features which result in one site having accidents may be also present in other sites, although these other sites may not (yet) have experienced a significant number of accidents. This is the rationale for the preventative approach. It is based upon attempting to identify site features which are associated with accidents (such as low pavement friction, roadside objects, road geometry, poor sight distance, intersection configuration, etc), and treat them before their inherent hazard is revealed in accidents (Zegeer, 1986, Chapters 1 and 2; Institution of Highways and Transportation, 1990a, Chapter 8). An example of such an approach is presented by Ogden and Howie (1990) who examined the features associated with accidents at bridges, and developed guidelines for treating other bridges (i.e. those which did not have a poor safety record, but had similar characteristics to those which did), including a priority ranking.

The distribution of resources between remedial programs and preventative programs is a matter of judgement. However, there is general agreement that resources should primarily focus upon sites with a poor accident record (if such accidents are amenable to safety engineering treatments). This will maximize the immediate safety benefit. The resources directed to preventative programs will likely increase over time, since an agency which has had a major remedial program under way for some time should find that it has been successful in identifying and improving the worst sites. Remaining accidents are then likely to be more diffuse, so resources can be shifted towards preventative programs. This is the basis of the road safety audit process as applied to the existing road network (see Chapter 15).

*Hazardous road location programs*

The notion of hazardous road locations was introduced in the preceding section. More formally, a HRL program may be defined as a process which aims to identify locations within the road system which are hazardous, in order to develop appropriate and cost-effective treatments.

For simplicity, the HRL program is summarized in its most simple form (i.e. without showing the interactions and feedback loops between the different elements) in Figure 2.3.

In essence, this approach gradually sieves out accidents and/or sites from consideration, as the analysis homes in on those sites which have a demonstrated priority for treatment. This process is illustrated diagrammatically in Figure 2.4:

.   The assignment of accidents to a data base (see Chapter 4), as a sub-set firstly of all accidents (dependent upon reporting criteria), and secondly of reported accidents (dependent upon recording criteria). This provides the data base for subsequent analysis.

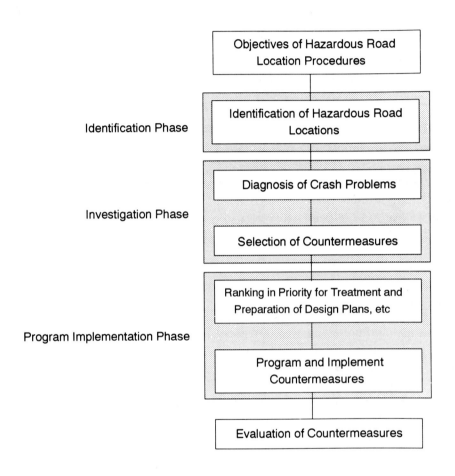

**Identification Phase** — Objectives of Hazardous Road Location Procedures / Identification of Hazardous Road Locations

**Investigation Phase** — Diagnosis of Crash Problems / Selection of Countermeasures

**Program Implementation Phase** — Ranking in Priority for Treatment and Preparation of Design Plans, etc / Program and Implement Countermeasures

Evaluation of Countermeasures

**Figure 2.3   Hazardous road location program elements**

Source: National Association of Australian State Road Authorities (1988a), p 18.

- The identification of those sites at which the potential for accident reduction is high (see Chapter 5).

- Diagnosis of accident patterns, to identify those sites where there is sufficient commonality in the accident pattern to indicate that remedial treatment may be available (see Chapter 6).

- Development of countermeasures aimed at reducing the frequency or severity of accidents, and hence determining which sites are treatable (see Chapters 7 through 14).

- Economic appraisal and development of priorities, to develop a measure of the worth of undertaking remedial works at each site (see Chapter 16).

- Works programming, which involves the implementation of the most cost-effective or economically worthwhile program (see Chapter 16).

Most of the remainder of this book is taken up with a discussion of the elements of this program. *Objectives* and the *identification of hazardous sites* will be discussed in Chapter 5, and the *diagnosis* phase in Chapter 6. *Countermeasure selection* is discussed in general terms in Chapter 7, while Chapters 8 through 14 discuss the application of specific countermeasures. Chapter 15 is concerned with road safety audit, while in Chapter 16 we discuss *implementation and program appraisal*. Finally, *monitoring and evaluation* is discussed in Chapter 17.

Before commencing this detailed exposition of the components of the HRL program, there are two prior considerations that must be discussed. Firstly, as we have emphasized throughout this chapter, road safety engineering largely works by influencing or responding to human behaviour. It is essential therefore that the road safety engineer has some working knowledge of *human factors in the road traffic system*. This is provided in Chapter 3.

Secondly, again as emphasized in this chapter, the whole HRL process is data-dependent, and therefore it is necessary to outline *data and information needs* in relation to road safety engineering and to discuss the limitations of data. This is presented in Chapter 4.

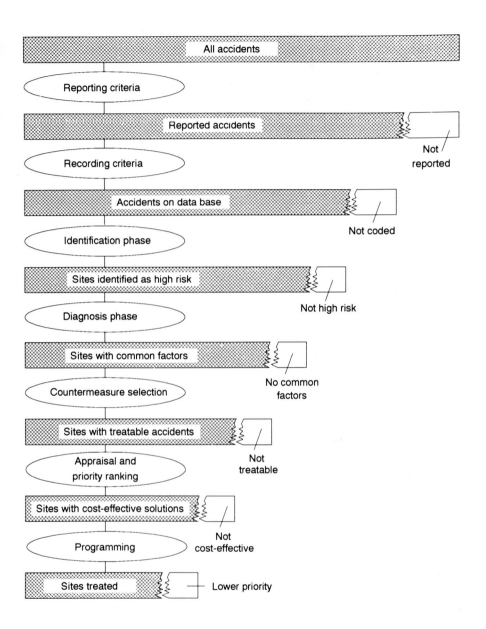

**Figure 2.4    A staged approach to accident investigation and project appraisal**

Source: adapted from McGuigan (1990).

**Notes**

1.  For example, in The Netherlands, targets have been set for a 50 per
    cent reduction in fatalities and a 40 per cent reduction in hospital
    injuries for 2010 compared with 1986 (van de Watering, 1993). In
    Denmark, a target for the year 2000 is to reduce the number of persons
    killed and injured in road accidents by 40-45 per cent (Herrstedt,
    1992). In New Zealand, a target of a 50 per cent reduction in fatalities
    and a 48 per cent reduction in injuries has been set for 2001 compared
    with 1991. In addition, New Zealand has set specific safety-related
    road performance targets, including a 40 per cent reduction in the
    percentage of fatal accidents involving alcohol, a reduction in rural 85
    percentile speeds from 120 to 110 km/h (75 to 68 mph), an increase in
    front seat restraint use from 89 per cent to 98 per cent, and an increase
    in the bicycle rider helmet wearing rate from 50 per cent to 90 per cent
    (Ministry of Transport, NZ, 1993).

2.  The eleven priority countermeasures developed by the US Department
    of Transportation (1991) included six which were within the field of
    road safety engineering: pedestrian facilities; improved signing,
    marking and delineation; work zone safety; removal or relocation of
    hazardous utility poles; identification of high-accident locations for
    corrective action; and corridor improvement projects.

# 3 Human factors in road traffic

*Road safety engineering measures work largely through influencing human behaviour. It is essential therefore that the road safety engineer has a knowledge of some fundamental aspects of the human factor in the road traffic system, in order that traffic management and control strategies can be effective and operate with safety in the required manner. In this chapter, three key aspects of human performance are reviewed, namely information processing, visual characteristics, and information needs of drivers[1].*

## The human in the road traffic system

As we noted in Chapter 2, the road traffic system may be considered as comprising three elements - the human, the vehicle, and the road.

This system is inherently unstable, and is maintained in equilibrium only by the frequent intervention of the human (usually as a driver of a vehicle, but also as a pedestrian or cyclist).

Knowledge of human performance, capabilities and behavioural characteristics is thus a vital input to much of the road and traffic engineer's task and a prerequisite to understanding how human behaviour may be influenced. That is, road safety engineering is concerned with various aspects of traffic control, but such control is often introduced through, or relies upon, influencing human behaviour. For example, traffic signs and signals of themselves are useless if drivers do not see, interpret, respond to, and obey them.

The safe operation of the road system consequently depends fundamentally upon the road user - driver, rider and pedestrian - making a series of sequential decisions, which need to be correct, or if incorrect, implemented in a forgiving environment. The road and traffic engineer has a vitally important role to play in assisting the road user to make correct decisions, both by helping to control the rate of decision-making to that which the human is capable of accommodating, and by presenting traffic information in such a way that it facilitates rapid and correct decisions. The function of much of traffic engineering, such as signs, signals, line markings, etc, is to help road users travel safely.

However, road users are not homogeneous in their characteristics, and we must be conscious of the need to design for a range of human characteristics and a distribution of responses. For example, there are substantial differences between experienced and inexperienced drivers (Drummond, 1989), with the latter:

. having difficulty in judging speed, distance and reaction time,
. tending to concentrate on near objects,
. missing important information, because its relevance is not appreciated,
. having poor perception of how hazardous a situation can become,
. fixating the eyes on an object for a longer period,
. having difficulty in integrating information,
. under-estimating the risk of accident involvement, and
. making less effective driving decisions.

At the other end of the spectrum, older drivers, whose visual acuity and information-processing capability have deteriorated, can have difficulties with situations where rapid decision-making is required (especially at intersections), take time to absorb traffic control information on road signs, have more difficulty at night due to lower light levels and problems of headlight glare, and are more readily fatigued. On the other hand, they are not over-represented in accidents because they tend to make adjustments in behaviour, such as time of day, speed and route of travel, avoidance of congested areas, seeking longer gaps in traffic, etc (Schlackman and Winstone, 1988; Transportation Research Board, 1988).

## Information processing

*The driving task*

Driving can be considered as comprising three essential tasks (American Association of State Highway and Transportation Officials, 1990, p 43):

. navigation: trip planning and route following,

. guidance: following the road and maintaining a safe path in response to traffic conditions, and

. control: steering and speed control.

These tasks require the driver to receive inputs (most of which are visual), process them, make predictions about alternative actions and decide which is the most appropriate, execute the actions, and observe their effects through the reception and processing of new information (Lay, 1986, p 317).

There are numerous problems inherent in this sequence of tasks, arising from both the capabilities of the human driver, and the interfaces between the human and the other components of the road traffic system (the road and the vehicle). These include (Lay, op cit):

. there may be inadequate or insufficient input available for the task at hand (e.g. during night time driving, as a result of poor sight distance, or because of complex intersection layouts),

. drivers have difficulty in handling extreme inputs or uncommon events,

. drivers may sometimes sample inappropriate inputs or process them too slowly,

. when they become overloaded, drivers shed part of the input demand to deal with that judged to be more important,

. driver stress, arousal, conditioning, inexperience, and poor motivation can all lead to errors and misjudgments, or

. drivers are imperfect decision-makers and may make errors.

*A model of the driving task*

Provided that the driver is not called upon to receive and process information too rapidly, the driver can remain in control of the vehicle, and hence ensure equilibrium in the road traffic system. However, human beings have essentially a one-track (single channel) mind, so they must divide attention while driving, and process information sequentially (Hulbert, 1982, p 214; Wickens, 1984, p 12). Hence, if the rate at which decisions need to be made (the rate of input) exceeds the driver's capability (the maximum rate of output), the resulting stress could cause an error which may lead to a faulty navigation, guidance or control action, which may in turn lead to an accident.

Recognising that drivers have a finite limit to their ability to process information is crucial to the provision of a safe road environment. In the words of the American Association of State Highway and Transportation Officials (1990, p 49):

'A common characteristic of many high accident locations is that they place large or unusual demands on the information-processing capabilities of drivers. Inefficient operation and accidents usually occur where the chance for information-handling errors are high. At locations when the design is deficient the possibility of error and inappropriate driver performance increases.'

A simple, though very useful, model of information processing is presented in Figure 3.1 (Cumming, 1964; Cumming and Croft, 1973). This plots the rate at which tasks are presented to the driver (i.e. the rate of input demand) against the rate at which decisions are transmitted (i.e. the output performance).

It can be seen that when demand is low, output equals demand, i.e. all inputs are processed correctly, and all decisions are appropriate.

However, as demand increases, there comes a point (A) at which the rate of output starts to fall below the rate of demand. Beyond A, if demand is increased still further, output also continues to increase for a time, but at a lesser rate than demand - i.e. there is a gap between input and output. The driver's output continues to increase till it reaches a peak (B), after which it actually starts to fall away with the information overload resulting from a continued increase in demand.

For a driver who has been significantly overloaded (C), there is a residual effect on performance even after the demand is reduced. This is shown by the lower curve CA on Figure 3.1.

The gap between input and output (i.e. between line AD and line ABC) may be indicated by an error, input information which is not detected, or information which is selectively and deliberately shed.

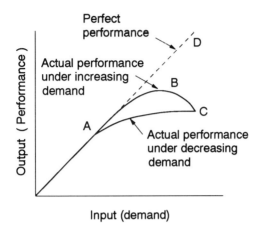

**Figure 3.1 Information processing model**

Source: Cumming (1964). Copyright. Reprinted with the permission of the Australian Road Research Board.

Ideally, the road traffic system should encourage and permit the driver to do the third, i.e. shed information which is not immediately relevant to the driving task. In other words, if part of the demand at point A is optional (e.g. listening to the radio, engaging in conversation), then ideally this part of the task should be discarded if a new task is interposed, so that overall demand does not increase beyond A.

However, there can be a problem here, because of the phenomenon known as self-pacing. Drivers tend to set a goal for themselves at a level just above what they know that they can achieve. This self-challenge is a common observation in psychology and is 'highly motivating, and is no doubt one underlying reason for the rate of progress in so many aspects of life' (Cumming, 1964). In performing a skilled task such as driving, the rate of output may be set by the person (self-paced) or by external factors (externally paced). With self-paced tasks the 'self-challenge' effect tends to apply, so that people set a pace for themselves at or slightly beyond the rate at which they can perform without error, i.e. near point A on Figure 3.1. Thus a driver in a traffic situation where the external pacing is at a low level (e.g. a lightly trafficked rural road) will seek to impose a self-paced load by such means as increasing the driving task (e.g. increasing speed, tailgating, precision steering on the centre line, etc) or by attending to extraneous matters (e.g. listening to the radio, engaging in conversation, looking at the scenery, or concentrating on matters unconnected with the driving task).

Since drivers are usually operating at or near A, the sudden imposition of a new demand must result in an error, a missed signal, or a degree of load shedding, as described above. The mark of skill is the ability to determine what must be attended to and what can be shed. As Cumming (1964) has noted, 'examples of load shedding in driving are commonplace: the switch of attention from a conversation to concentrate on a sudden development in traffic, or from the traffic situation to manoeuvre around a pot hole which has suddenly come into view. Accidents can follow incorrect shedding, as, for example, in allowing attention to be diverted from the traffic situation to retrieve a dropped cigarette or to attend to an outburst from children in the back seat.'

The potential for driver distraction and overload has led to the development of standards dictating the maximum number of destinations on a direction sign and regulations in many countries about roadside advertising signs (Dewar, 1993). However, Andreassen (1985a) in a review of the effect of accidents and advertising signs concluded that 'there is no current evidence to say that advertising signs, in general, are causing traffic accidents'.

Of course, drivers are not all identical in their capabilities or habits. Driver behaviour seems to vary between individuals according to two factors: ability and motivation (Naatanen and Summala, 1976). Behaviour is dependent upon both what the driver is *able* to do and what the driver *chooses* to do, and the degree of difficulty depends upon the latter. For example, a driver can choose to drive faster or slower, can choose to overtake or not, can choose long headways or short, and so on. Thus, there is little correlation between driver skill and driver accident experience (Williams and O'Neill, 1974).

It can be seen that it is important that the road traffic system allows and assists drivers to adjust their pace downwards, by shedding extraneous tasks. This process depends upon (indeed is almost a definition of) experience; an experienced driver knows what effects any controlling action is going to have, and is thus able to select and limit the information sought and processed.

The driver can be assisted to do this in several ways, for example:

.   provide trend information where possible (e.g. the series of signs on an approach to a freeway exit ramp, which progressively provide advance warning, designation of the ramp, and directional instructions at the terminus of the ramp),

. avoid the sudden imposition of demand, or the introduction of extraneous demand when loads on the driver are already high (e.g. speed limit signs should be a distance upstream or downstream of an intersection, not at the intersection itself),

. limit the amount of information presented, e.g. avoid putting too much detail on a direction sign,

. require a series of simple decisions rather that a single complex decision (e.g. use fully controlled turns at traffic signals, rather than requiring drivers to select gaps in oncoming traffic - see Chapter 9), and

. control the rate at which drivers are required to make decisions.

*Expectancy*

The importance of experience in relation to the driving task was mentioned above. Prior experience is critical in reducing reaction times and enabling drivers to adjust their pace downwards when a new driving task is imposed. These experiences develop, over time, into a set of workable expectancies which allow for anticipation and forward planning, and which enable the driver to respond to common situations in predictable and successful ways. If these expectancies are violated, problems are likely to occur, either as a result of a wrong decision or of an inordinately long reaction time (Shinar, 1978; American Association of State Highway and Transportation Officials, 1990, p 49). There are three types of driver expectancy (Naatanen and Summala, 1976):

*Continuation expectancy*. This is the expectation that the events of the immediate past will continue. It results, for example, in small headways, as drivers expect that the preceding vehicle will not suddenly change speed. One particularly perverse aspect of continuation expectancy is that of subliminal delineation (e.g. a line of poles or trees) which suggests to the driver that the road continues straight ahead when in fact it veers left or right (Figure 3.2). These indications are subtle, but should always be looked out for on a site visit, especially if there is a history at the site of

51

vehicles going straight ahead on a curve. They can usually be countered with positive delineation devices such as chevrons or curve alignment markers (see Chapter 10).

**Figure 3.2    Subliminal delineation**. Drivers may follow roadside visual cues such as a line of trees or poles, and this should be countered with strong formal delineation such as chevrons.

*Event expectancy*. This is the expectation that events which have not happened will not happen. It results, for example, in disregard for railway crossings (see Chapter 9), and perhaps for minor intersections as well, because drivers expect that no hazard will present itself where none has been seen before. A response to this situation is more positive control, such as an active warning device at railway crossings which requires that the driver respond to the device, not to the presence of a hazard.

*Temporal expectancy*. This is the expectation that where events are cyclic (e.g. traffic signals), the longer a given state occurs, the greater the likelihood that change will occur. This is of course a perfectly reasonable expectation, but it can result in inconsistent responses. For example, some drivers may accelerate towards a green signal, because it is increasingly likely that it will change, whereas others may decelerate. A response to this is to ensure, to the extent possible, that there is consistency throughout the road traffic system, for example with the yellow and all-red periods at traffic signals, to encourage predictable and consistent driver behaviour.

Lumenfeld and Alexander (1984) have summarized driver expectancies and the traffic design response to them as follows:

. drivers tend to anticipate upcoming situations and events that are common to the road they are travelling,

. the more predictable the roadway feature, the less likely will be the chance for errors,

. drivers experience problems when they are surprised,

. drivers, in the absence of counter evidence, assume that they will only have to react to standard situations,

. the roadway and its environment upstream of a site create an expectation of downstream conditions; drivers experience problems in transition areas and locations with inconsistent design or operation, and

. expectancies are associated with all levels of driving performance and all aspects of the driving situation. This includes expectancies relative to speed, path, direction, the roadway, the environment, geometric design, traffic operations, and traffic control devices.

In essence, provided that the driver receives information in the expected form and events occur in accordance with that information, then the driver's performance is very likely to be error-free. However, when the information does not match the driver's expectations, system failures in the form of accidents and incidents are much more likely to occur.

It is very important therefore for the road and traffic engineer to realise that driver behaviour is largely governed by habit, experience, and expectation, and that any design or operation which violates these considerations is likely to be unsatisfactory, and possibly unsafe. We should therefore attempt to ensure that:

. drivers' expectations are recognised, and unexpected, unusual or non-standard design or operational situations avoided or minimized (e.g. avoid situations where a 'Keep Right' sign is required if traffic drives on the left, and vice versa, because this is unusual and calls for unfamiliar behaviour),

. predictable behaviour is encouraged through familiarity and habit (e.g. there should be a limited range of intersection design formats, each appropriate to a given situation, and similar designs should be used in similar situations),

. consistency of design and driver behaviour is maintained from element to element (e.g. avoid significant changes in design speed along a road), and

. the information which is provided should decrease the driver's uncertainty, not increase it.

*Reaction time*

Information takes time to process. The term reaction time is used to describe the period between the occurrence or appearance of a 'signal' (usually a visual stimulus - see below) and the driver's physical reaction to it. It is an innate characteristic which increases with increased decision complexity and information content. A complex or unexpected decision with several alternatives takes considerably longer than a simple, anticipated decision. Long processing times also decrease the time available to attend to other information, and thus compound the chances for error (Lumenfeld and Alexander, 1984).

Reaction time is usually considered to comprise four elements (Garber and Hoel, 1988, p. 44):

. perception: the use of vision capabilities to see a visual signal,

. identification: the driver identifies the signal and thus understands the stimulus,

. emotion: the driver decides what action to take in response to the stimulus (e.g. to apply the brakes, turn the steering wheel, etc.), and

.  volition: during which the driver actually executes the action decided upon.

Expectancies, as described above, reduce reaction times because drivers respond through familiarity and habit. However, different drivers will have different reaction times, because reaction time is affected by a wide range of individual characteristics, such as experience, skill, degree of alertness, motivation, risk-taking behaviour, blood alcohol level, etc. These are not under the control of the road and traffic engineer, but the engineer must recognize that these variations exist, and design the traffic system for as wide a range of driver abilities as possible.

Studies of driver reaction to stimuli have shown that, for many situations, an average reaction time of around 2.5 s is typical, but that the variance of the distribution of reaction times is very high (McCormick and Sanders, 1982; Garber & Hoel, 1988, p. 45). Thus, traffic design and operations should aim to reduce both average reaction times and (perhaps more importantly) reduce the variance of reaction times, especially inordinately long reaction times.

Ways in which these objectives may be pursued include (Cumming, 1964; MacDonald and Hoffman, 1978; American Association of State Highway and Transportation Officials, 1990, p 46):

*Encourage familiarity*. This relates to the above discussion on expectancies; drivers will react much more quickly to a familiar stimulus. Therefore, as noted above, unfamiliar situations (e.g. unusual intersection layouts or other traffic management treatments) or unexpected responses should be avoided.

*Minimize the number of alternatives*. The reaction time increases with the number of alternative courses of action that are available, because the driver has to process more information. Therefore, the number of alternatives should be limited. Preferably there should be only two options, e.g. to maintain the status quo, or to be presented with a single alternative to it.

*Provide positive information*. Ideally, the driver should receive positive information, i.e. be told what to do, not what not to do; this minimizes the time taken to search for alternatives. This is not always possible or sensible, but is revealed in the use, for example, of 'Wrong Way Go Back' rather than 'Do Not Enter' signs (Figure 3.3).

**Figure 3.3** **Positive information**. The human responds more quickly if told what to do (Wrong Way; Go Back), rather than what not to do.

*Provide prior warning.* The reaction time can be reduced if the driver is prompted to expect the event to which the reaction is required. However, a prior warning without a context is likely to be ignored, so the warning should either call for a response (e.g. change lanes), or alert the driver to a situation which is already visible (e.g. a roadworks warning sign should be located where the roadworks are visible).

*Provide clear sight distance.* Clear sight lines and adequate decision sight distance provide time for decision making and allow margins for error and recovery (see Chapter 9).

*Use symbolic signs.* Certain signs, including warning, direction and regulatory signs, may have either a symbol or a written legend, or both (Figure 3.4). Practice varies between countries, and national uniformity is important. However, there is evidence to suggest that the reaction time for symbolic signs is less than for written legends (Ells and Dewar, 1979), while also being more readily understood across language barriers (Donald, 1995).

**Figure 3.4** **Symbols and written legends**. Signs may have either a written legend, a symbol, or both. The symbols for hospital and airport are international, while this sign for a railway station is well understood in Britain.

*Short term memory*

The human memory may be considered as having three stages (Lay, 1986, p 321; Wickens, 1984, p 12):

. Sensory memory, which is momentary and sensitive to incoming stimuli. Sensory memory does not store information for very long; information will decay in about a second and will be replaced rapidly by new inputs. Only a small fraction of stimuli will be acted upon and transferred to the short term or working memory.

. Short term memory, also known as the working memory, is where information which requires processing is temporarily stored. It has a very limited capacity and information is lost after about 30 s unless it is actively reinforced by repetition or by use in some other activity. Information cannot be recalled once it has faded.

. Long term memory, where information persists, and can be recalled after the event.

Most inputs received by a driver do not pass beyond the sensory memory, since they do not require any processing. Similarly, most of the signs, signals, pavement markings, other vehicles, pedestrians, etc which a driver encounters require only routine processing, which is performed using the short term memory. That is, most of the driving task is performed by processing information which never leaves the short term memory, and after use (if any) is made of the information, it fades from memory, without entering the long term memory.

Information in the short term memory fades (or is replaced) if another task is interposed. Thus there is an interaction between perception and short term memory, with the result that if a driver is trying to recall something in the short term memory, the driver's perceptual ability is lowered, and thus a 'signal' may be missed. Alternatively, if the driver attends to the signal, the information in the short term memory may be lost (Cumming, 1964). This factor has implications for traffic design. For example:

**Figure 3.5    Immediate response**. Warnings should require an immediate response, while the information is still within the driver's short term memory.

. warnings should require an immediate response (Figure 3.5),

. drivers should be frequently reminded of control information which varies along the road (e.g. speed limits), and

. the rate of information gathering which is required should be limited to ensure that the driver has time to respond to one stimulus before the next one is imposed.

*Hysteresis effects*

In the model of the driving task described above it was shown that there is a hysteresis effect as demand is taken off an overloaded driver, such that the driver's output is less than it was for the same level of demand as the task was increasing. This was shown in curve CA in Figure 3.1. There are some implications of this observation for traffic design, for example (Cumming and Croft, 1973):

59

.   the ability to process information may be lower on the departure side of an intersection than the approach side, perhaps explaining higher pedestrian accident rates on the downstream side of intersections,

.   the use of 'before and after' methods of assessing traffic design features may be affected since 'an accident due to poor performance following overload will not necessarily occur at the feature giving rise to the overload' (op cit), and

.   pedestrian crossings, bus stops, etc, should not be placed immediately downstream of an uncontrolled intersection.

**Visual characteristics**

As noted above, the driving task is information-driven, and requires the driver to select and sample 'signals' or inputs from the road traffic system. About 90 per cent of the information used by the driver is visual (Lay, 1986, p 321); other inputs are audible (sound), tactile (touch, such as vibration), vestibular (affecting balance, such as stability and acceleration), and occasionally olfactory (smell).

Since vision is so important to the driving task, and indeed is the only way that information provided by the road and traffic engineer using traffic signs, signals, pavement markings and delineation devices actually gets to the driver, it is necessary to have some awareness of the visual characteristics of the human. This section briefly reviews some of the key aspects; for a more extensive treatment, refer to Cole (1972) or Lay (1986, Chapter 16.3 and 21.2).

*Visual field*

If a visual signal is to be seen, it must be within the driver's visual field. For reading purposes, the visual field is quite narrow - 3° to 10°. However, objects outside this field can be detected: signs and signals within 10°-12° of the line of sight can be seen and understood, while objects can be detected in peripheral vision to 90° left and right, 60° above the line of sight, and 70° below the line of sight.

These values are for a stationary observer. At speed, the eye focuses further ahead and so the visual field narrows. For example, at 30 km/h (about 20 mph) the lateral (left-right) angle of the visual field decreases to about 100°, and at 100 km/h (about 60 mph) it reduces to about 40° (compared to 180° at rest) (Cole, 1972).

The visual scene perceived by the driver of a moving vehicle is changing in a complex fashion, with oncoming objects 'expanding' in the driver's perception. The driver must sample this changing scene (because it cannot all be taken in) and select cues to make decisions about vehicle guidance and control (Hulbert, 1982, p 214). Within this visual field, objects which are moving relative both to each other and to the visual field will appear as discontinuities, and will be detected, provided that they are within the driver's visual field as specified above.

However, if they are not within that field, the driver must turn the head to look in an appropriate direction. This means that drivers must be given an indication and a motivation to turn the head to look in appropriate directions, for example by the provision of warning and control signs, and having adequate sight distance at intersections or railway crossings.

The driver may also be stimulated to seek the object by detecting it in peripheral vision. Objects within the peripheral limits defined above can be detected readily, if they are sufficiently stimulating. Such stimulus may be provided by movement of the object across the visual field, by brightness, or by a pulsation (e.g. rotating beacon on an emergency services vehicle or a flashing railway crossing warning). It is salutary to note that two vehicles on a collision course maintain a constant bearing with respect to each other, and so there is no relative motion. They will not therefore be detected in peripheral vision unless there is some other stimulus; this is the rationale behind daylight use locomotive headlights, for example.

These considerations have direct implications for traffic design, including:

.   traffic signs and traffic signals must be within the driver's field of view, having regard to the speed of travel,

.   drivers need to be alerted to the presence of uncontrolled intersections, so that they will be prompted to move the head to seek vehicles on conflicting courses, and

.   particular attention needs to be given to railway crossings with passive control only (see Chapter 9) as trains will be less visible in peripheral vision; this is exacerbated by the above notion of event expectancy, which leads to disregard for lightly trafficked railway crossings.

*Eye and head movement*

The main constraint on the rate of information gathering is the rate at which the eye can move from one object to another, and re-focus.

Filmed records of eye movements indicate a maximum possible rate of about 4 fixations per second (Cole and Jenkins, 1982). However, this rate cannot be sustained for a long period, and perhaps 2 fixations per second would be the usual maximum rate for an alerted, busy, driver. For normal driving, in which the driver is attending to other tasks as well, a rate of 1.0 - 1.5 fixations per second would be reasonable. (In passing, it is interesting to compare this rate with the maximum rate of human sensory processing in the brain of some $10^9$ bits per second; clearly the rate of driver decision making is most critically affected by the rate at which the eye can gather information.)

Thus, for traffic design, it is necessary for 'signals' to be separated in time. If the vehicle is in motion, it is also necessary that they be separated in space. For example, at a vehicle speed of 100 km/h (60 mph), a driver would be able to view a 'signal' only once in every, say, 20-28 m (about 60-90 ft), at a rate of information gathering of about 1.0-1.5 fixations per second. If the 'signals' (i.e. traffic signs, traffic signals, information signs, etc) are closer than this, some will be missed because the driver is physically incapable of sighting them. Further, if the 'signals' are provided at this spacing, and all are viewed, the driver will not be able to attend to any other control or navigation information, such as viewing other vehicles, pedestrians, etc. Drivers tend not to look very far ahead of the vehicle to seek 'signals' which affect the driving task. Cole and Jenkins (1982) have found that traffic signs beyond 100 m (about 330 ft) are rarely noticed.

Although eye movements can be made over a field of about 50°, it is rare for that full range to be used. Rather, the driver will move the head to focus on a new object, such that eye movements are limited to about 15° left or right (Lay, 1976, p 325).

*Illumination*

The human visual system is capable of operating over an enormous range of illumination, from $0.75 \times 10^{-6}$ cd/m$^2$ (a very dark night) to $10^5$ cd/m$^2$ (a beach on a bright day) - a range from the darkest to the brightest varying by a factor of over $10^{11}$!

This enormous range is attributable to two factors. First, the pupil of the eye (aperture) can contract or dilate to let in more or less light. Second, after a period of relative dark, receptor cells in the retina of the eye begin to regenerate. The result is that, due to the latter effect, the eye increases its sensitivity to light by a factor of about $10^7$ over a period of about 30 minutes after exposure to dark (Cole, 1972).

However, in a traffic stream, transient changes in illumination caused by exposure to relative light and dark as the vehicle progresses along the road are the relevant issue, rather than long term changes in the ambient light level.

On exposure to brightness after darkness, the pupil diameter contracts at a rate of about 3 mm/s, whereas on exposure to darkness after brightness, it is much less responsive, dilating at about 0.5 mm/s (Cole, 1972). In other words, the eye can adjust to sudden brightness more rapidly than sudden dark. Therefore, in tunnels or long underpasses, artificial illumination should be provided at a higher level at the tunnel entrance. The lighting level can be reduced within the tunnel as the eye adjusts to the lower level of illumination, and there is no need for a higher level of illumination at the tunnel exit as the eye can adapt rapidly to the daylight (Schrueder, 1991).

Another aspect of illumination is glare, both from street lighting and from oncoming headlights. Both types of glare result in a decrease of visibility and discomfort to the driver. It is particularly important for elderly people and is one of the main reasons why the elderly have much less vision at night (Garber and Hoel, 1988, p 43).

Glare effects from street lighting can be kept to a minimum by reducing luminaire brightness, increasing mounting height, and increasing the background brightness. Glare from oncoming headlights can be minimized by plantations or fencing in the median of divided highways. Illuminating the roadway is also effective in reducing headlight glare since drivers do not have to use their headlight high beam.

*Visual disabilities*

About 2.5 per cent of the adult male population has colour impaired vision, such that they cannot discriminate red, yellow and green (as in traffic signals), or indeed any three-colour combination (Lay, 1976, p 325). Further, about 2.5 per cent of the adult male population has a reduced sensitivity to red - they need about 4 times the intensity required by unaffected observers (Johnston and Cole, 1976). Also, some people experience blurred vision such that their legibility distance is reduced. About 5 per cent of the population is visually impaired with respect to detecting low luminance contrasts; visual sensitivity declines with age and the detection threshold of elderly drivers is about double that of younger drivers (Lay, 1986, p 325).

These findings have important relevance to traffic design, especially for traffic signals. For example:

. signal lanterns should be located in a standard fashion, with red on top, yellow in the middle, and green at the bottom; this applies also to coloured turn arrows,

. the intensity of traffic signals, and the actual colours used need to be closely specified (Lay, 1986, p 448), and

. these considerations also affect the size of traffic signs and the letters on them.

It is of interest to note that no correlation has been found between poor visual performance and driver safety, suggesting that drivers with visual disabilities compensate in their driving behaviour or in other ways (Cole, 1972).


**Information needs of road users**

The success of many traffic engineering measures and the safety and efficiency of the road traffic system depends to a large extent on successfully conveying information to drivers to aid them in their navigation, guidance and control tasks. The key needs of road users in relation to traffic control information are (Lay, 1986, p 424, 386):

. conspicuity (the 'signal' must be seen),
. legibility (its message must be able to be read),
. comprehensibility (the message must be understood), and
. credibility (the message must be perceived to be true).

*Conspicuity*

The detection of a visual 'signal' involves recognising it against its background. Conspicuity is affected by several factors, including (Cole and Jenkins, 1980):

. size (larger signs are more conspicuous),
. brightness (brighter signs are more conspicuous),
. boldness (larger letters are more conspicuous),
. edge sharpness (a line around the edge of a sign),
. contrast (high contrast, especially contrast in brightness),
. visual simplicity (a simple background makes a sign conspicuous), and
. eccentricity (a 'signal' is unlikely to be detected if it is more than 6°-7° from the line of sight).

There are a number of direct implications of these principles which affect various aspects of traffic engineering and road safety practice. These include:

. influence on the size, colour, layout and location of traffic signs,
. legislation for control of roadside advertising,
. reflectorization of signs, pavement markings, etc,
. illumination of signs (especially direction signs),
. roadworks signing and work site protection and
. promotion of safety yellow raincoats for pedestrians and brightly coloured vests for road maintenance crews.

*Legibility*

A visual 'signal' is legible if enough detail within it is sufficiently visible to allow its message to be interpreted (Lay, 1986, p 426). Increasing the size of a sign will increase legibility distance and give a driver more opportunity to observe and read the sign. Thus signs which need to contain a lot of information need to be larger (e.g. direction signs).

*Comprehensibility*

The driver must perceive the importance of a 'signal'; if the driver does not do so, the 'signal' will be ignored. The vast majority of the roadside visual 'signals' which confront a driver on a trip are simply ignored because they (correctly) are not perceived as being relevant or important to the driver. Therefore, those 'signals' which are important (including those provided by the traffic engineer) must be presented in such a way that the driver appreciates their relevance. Of prime importance is that the driver perceives that the 'signal' affects his or her own well-being.

For this reason, within any country, traffic signs and signals are of a standard shape and colour, with a recognisable legend and/or symbol. There are, broadly speaking, two systems in use worldwide, one based on US practice and one based on a United Nations convention. These are usually specified in codes and standards within any country, and that country's practices should be adhered to.

The message on some types of sign (particularly warning and regulatory signs) may be either symbolic or written. As noted above, there is some evidence that reaction times are less with symbolic signs. They also tend to be more legible and conspicuous due to the larger sign elements (Cole and Jenkins, 1982). A well-designed symbolic sign is quicker and easier to comprehend than its corresponding written form, although in real-world driving situations, both are retained equally well in the short-term memory (Lay, 1986, p 429).

It is also important that road and traffic engineers realise that much of the information conveyed to the driving public is not well understood (Cairney, 1984). As a result, only standard signs, messages, formats, etc should be used. Unconventional treatments, using 'home made' signs and formats are likely to be incomprehensible to a majority of drivers and should be avoided.

*Credibility*

Credibility refers to the extent to which drivers believe that a 'signal' is both true, and refers to them. Credibility is affected by the context of the 'signal', how it is used in other contexts, and how it is used in relation to other traffic control devices.

The traffic engineer can aid credibility, and also contribute to the overall credibility of the traffic system, by ensuring that the use and application of traffic control devices (especially, but not only, traffic signs) is strictly in accord with current practice as set out in the relevant national codes or standards. This would include, for example, the following:

**Figure 3.6    Credibility.** The road clearly bends left, yet one sign indicates that it goes straight ahead, and the other indicates that it bends right!

.   ensure that the sign or device is credible in its context (Figure 3.6),

.   ensure that sign selection, colour, and shape conform with national standards,

.   avoid the unnecessary use of signs and other traffic control devices,

.   avoid unnecessarily restrictive signs; the over-use of STOP signs in particular detracts from their credibility at sites where it really is important that vehicles come to a standstill, and thus many STOP signs should be replaced by GIVE WAY / YIELD signs (see Chapter 9),

.   important messages should be adequately displayed (e.g. speed limit repeater signs should be used; advance direction signing should be consistent and prominent),

. speeds on advisory signs should be realistic and consistent, and

. assist the driver to distinguish between important and relatively unimportant information by consistent use and avoidance of poor practice; the latter may involve removal or replacement of signs or devices currently in place.

## Notes

1. This chapter is an update and revision of a paper published in the *ITE Journal*, Volume 60(8), pp 41-46 (Ogden, 1990). It is presented here with the kind permission of the Institution of Transportation Engineers, 525 School Street, SW, Suite 410, Washington DC, 20024-2797, USA. Fax (+1) 202 863 5486.

   The material is inevitably an overview only; for a more extensive review of these issues, refer to Cumming and Croft (1973), Forbes (1972), Shinar (1978), McCormick and Sanders (1982), Lay (1986), Hulbert (1982), Transportation Research Board (1993).

# 4 Data needs and limitations

*Central to any systematic scientifically-based analysis of the road accident situation and the development of rational countermeasures is the availability of reliable data concerning accidents and other relevant factors. In this chapter, we review what data are needed, how it is generated, and briefly overview its management. This material is necessary at this point, as subsequent chapters concerned with details of road safety engineering implicitly or explicitly assume the availability of this sort of information.*

## Information requirements

### The need for information

A common factor of central importance in road safety management is the collection and use of accurate and comprehensive data related to road accidents. The interpretation of those data can lead to a better understanding of operational problems, is a pre-requisite for accurate diagnosis of accident problems, assists in the development of remedial measures, and allows us to evaluate the effectiveness of road safety programs.

This requirement is often reflected in legislation. For example, in Britain, local authorities are required to report periodically to central government details of accidents which involve personal injury. This has led to the development of a standard national reporting form (the so-called STATS19 form - see Langan, 1992) around which each local authority has built its own data collection and analysis system. In the US, Federal regulations implementing the requirements of the 1991 Interstate Surface

Transportation Efficiency Act mandate each State to establish a Highway Safety Management System (see Chapter 2) which will, among other things, include procedures for 'the use of data bases with common or coordinated reference systems and methods of data sharing.' (Code of Federal Regulations, Part 500, Title 23, Sub-part A).

Curiously perhaps, although the need for data is universally recognised, there is currently little consistency or commonality in the data which is collected or the definitions and criteria used. For example, Ercoli and Negri (1985) in a comparative study of eleven European countries found that only two variables (date and hour of the day) were collected in all eleven countries, only 7 percent of items were recorded in three countries, and 70 per cent of items were recorded in only one country. Similarly, in the US, there has been no nationwide accident data reporting system, and little commonality amongst or within States upon data elements which are recorded (Zegeer, 1982).

In part, these variations no doubt reflect the historical development of data collection and analysis systems, and the practices which have evolved over time. Importantly however, they are significantly affected by the relative influence of the various parties which are potential users of the system. As we shall see in a moment, there are many potential users, and their needs are not identical, and in many cases may even be in conflict. Moreover, data collection and data management systems are expensive, and the relative priority given to data collection and data base management varies from place to place. Many jurisdictions for example do not require the reporting of property damage accidents (i.e. an accident where no-one is injured) and thus these are not included on the data base even if reported to police for other reasons (e.g. for insurance purposes). Other jurisdictions, particularly in the US (O'Day, 1993, p 25) require the reporting of all casualty accidents, with a cost-of-repair threshold for property damage accidents.

More importantly, even within the road safety engineering field, there are significant variations in the data which analysts find useful in the diagnosis of accidents and the development of countermeasures. One particular inconsistency is with the use of information relating to accident type, i.e. information which precisely defines the traffic manoeuvres leading to the conflict situation (see below). Those countries which do not use this tool, or which do so in only a rudimentary way, such as the UK, generally claim that their system is adequate without it (although interestingly, a number of UK local authorities are beginning to make more use of detailed accident type data), while those jurisdictions which do use it, claim that it is a vital tool and central to their accident investigation process.

What this probably indicates is that we are still at a rather early stage in the professional development of road safety engineering in general and accident investigation in particular. More research, including comparative research between different countries, is necessary to determine what data are really needed, what tools are most effective, what data management and analysis processes are efficient, and what countermeasures are most cost-effective.

For this reason, in the following discussion, we must recognise the disparate practices in use worldwide. An attempt will be made to identify the common ground, if it exists, while at the same time acknowledging that this is a field in which there is still much fundamental work to be done.

## Users and uses of information

There are numerous parties with an interest in the use of road accident data. For example:

. road safety engineers, for the purposes of the development of remedial or pro-active road and traffic measures,

. police, for the purpose of charging a person with a criminal offence in relation to a specific accident,

. lawyers acting for clients in civil litigation (especially compensation for injuries and other losses),

. insurers, seeking facts before settling an insurance claim,

. those with responsibility for road safety education or publicity, who may be concerned to ensure that their efforts are well-targeted,

. police, in relation to enforcement activities, such as the location of speed cameras or breath testing stations,

. safety administrators, exercising a duty to report statistical information on road accidents,

. researchers, who need access to a good reliable data base in order to conduct rigorous research projects, and

. vehicle or component manufacturers, and suppliers of highway materials, who wish to assess the safety of their product, perhaps from the viewpoint of litigation, marketing, or product enhancement.

The list could go on. It can be seen that there are potentially many uses and users of accident data, and that their needs are not coincident.

One basic and fundamental distinction is whether the user is seeking information about one specific accident (e.g in relation to civil or criminal legal proceedings) or whether the need is for basic and common information about a large number of accidents. The road safety engineer usually (though not always) wants information of the second type, e.g. in relation to hazardous road location (HRL) analyses. Many other users are only interested in data related to specific accidents.

This puts considerable pressure on those designing an accident data collection and management system: what data to collect, what data to code, how to manage the data base, and how long to retain the data. Similarly, the different requirements put pressure on the person who initiates the data collection process - almost always a police officer - in terms of the amount of information he/she chooses to collect, the accuracy with which it is measured, and the extent to which it is verified.

In particular, those jurisdictions which allow for the inclusion in the data base of accidents which were not attended by a police officer must inevitably be less robust than those where only those accidents attended by police are included. This issue tends to relate to the severity of accidents which are reported and/or recorded. If there is a facility for a person to literally walk in to a police station and report a property damage accident (e.g. for insurance purposes), and if that accident is then included on the data base, then this must affect the reliability and consistency of the data base. A problem for the user of the data is that there is usually no way of knowing whether the data on a particular accident is in one or other of these categories.

Thus, a key question in the development of an accident data base is that of which accidents to include, which is related to the question of which accidents are legally required to be reported. (Needless to say, this implies a further question, namely whether accidents are actually reported even if there is a legal requirement to do so.) There is a wide divergence of practice from jurisdiction to jurisdiction around the world on these questions. Practice ranges from a requirement to report (and record) all accidents no matter how slight, to a reporting (and recording) threshold which may be set at various levels, e.g. where at least one person in the accident is medically treated, admitted to hospital, etc. From an analysis viewpoint, what all of this means is that there is a very clear tradeoff between quality of information and quantity. That is, if the data base is large then the data about many accidents must be suspect, while if it is small it will be more accurate about those accidents which are included but will have no information about many accidents which have actually happened.

The road safety engineer must be aware of these factors, and as one of the users of an accident data base should seek to influence decisions about both the reporting level and (more importantly) the data elements which are included in the data base. However, as there are many users, decisions about these questions will usually involve a compromise between the needs of the different parties, and the resulting data base may be less than ideal for HRL purposes.

*Information requirements*

To develop a robust and effective road safety management system, information is needed not only on road accidents, but on other pertinent factors as well. We will consider information needs in relation to road accidents later, but for completeness it is appropriate to mention here the other data bases which are relevant. Ideally, all of these data bases should be integrated, and be able to talk to each other - an ideal which is not always achieved (Harris, 1986)!

As a good example, the American draft guidelines for implementation of a Safety Management System provide a useful description of a safety-related integrated data base (National Highway Traffic Safety Administration, 1994). The suggested elements of the data base include:

. an accident file, including data on the 'time, environment and circumstances' of an accident,

. a driver file, including data on personal identification, license type and status, violations, accidents, and safety education,

. a vehicle file, including data on identification, type and vehicle inspection,

. a roadway file with information about road characteristics, classification, traffic volumes, etc, all tied to a location reference system,

. a commercial vehicle file, including information on configuration, body type, hazardous materials, and operator,

. a citation/conviction file which identifies the violation, violator, and 'adjudication action and results',

. an emergency medical services file, including information about emergency care and victim outcome, and

. provisions for file linkages.

In the remainder of this chapter, we review the three phases of accident data processing - its capture, its coding and its management - and then consider supplementary data sources apart from the accident data itself. The limitations of accident data then considered.

Discussion of the other safety-related data bases mentioned in the above list is beyond the scope of this book. Useful sources for this information include Zegeer (1982, 1986), O'Day (1983) and Hummer (1994a).

## Accident data capture

*Accident data*

In Chapter 2, four basic strategies for accident reduction through road safety engineering were described: single site actions, route actions, area wide actions and mass actions. All of these (and also by implication pro-active approaches such as road safety audit) rely on the availability of data describing accidents and their location. This information must describe:

. *where* the accident occurred: location by map co-ordinates or node/link identifier, road name, road classification, road layout and type of traffic control,

. *when* the accident occurred: by year, month, day of month, day of week and time of day,

. *who* was involved: people, vehicles, animals and roadside objects,

. *what* was the result of the accident: fatal, personal injury, or property damage,

. *what* were the environmental conditions: light condition, weather and pavement surface condition, etc, and

. *how* did the accident occur.

*Police accident reports*

The source of most accident data is a police report form. Most jurisdictions have their own report form, and usually every accident attended by a police officer results in an accident report form being generated.

Most jurisdictions have criteria which provide directives or guidelines to the police concerning which accidents that they will attend. In general, police will attend accidents where there is a fatality or serious injury, but often these outcomes are only known after the event, so police will sometimes attend relatively minor accidents, and (less often) not attend serious accidents. Some jurisdictions have further criteria, e.g. that police attend an accident where one or more vehicle is towed away, or where the amount of property damage exceeds some threshold value (O'Day, 1993, p 25).

Because of the critical role of the police in data capture, it is important to recognise the circumstances under which the police officer obtains information to complete the report. Firstly, at the scene of the accident itself, there will often be more pressing matters to attend to than form-filling, such as helping other emergency services, directing traffic, collecting witnesses statements, etc. The police officer may lack local knowledge, meaning that certain data items may be inadequately or incorrectly entered. Accidents do not always fit 'standard' formats, and it cannot be assumed that the accident report form will report a completely accurate description of all that happened. The completion of the accident report form may in fact take place some time after the accident, and often back in the police station. And finally and perhaps most importantly, the police officer attending the scene and completing the report is not necessarily well-motivated to fill in the form, often tending to see it as just another bureaucratic piece of paperwork.

The implication of these points is that police accident reports are inevitably imperfect, even with goodwill on the part of the police. They remain however the best and only form of basic data generation on accidents in most jurisdictions. It should also be mentioned that there is much merit in having active police involvement in accident data analysis if for no other reason than that it indicates to the police that the 'paperwork' which they generate is valuable and is used for legitimate purposes; ensuring that the police are active stakeholders in the accident investigation process is perhaps the best way of generating good input data.

Some jurisdictions also have the facility for the generation of an accident report form in respect of accidents not attended by the police, e.g. if an accident is reported at a police station; often this form is of a different and less detailed nature that the one which is filled out by a police officer attending an accident site.

However, in either case, data from the accident report form will only be entered into the mass accident data base if it satisfies that jurisdiction's criterion for entry.

Data extracted from police accident reports generally answer the where, when, who and what questions but not the how. There is also information in most reports in the form of narratives which can give a lead to an understanding of the contributory factors involved in an accident, while some report forms still retain an option for the police officer to enter a subjective 'cause' of the accident. However, such information is not generally included in the mass accident data bases because of the difficulty of coding narrative information. This means that very often, when particular accidents are being investigated, it will be helpful to go back to the original police accident report form or report book maintained at the police station to obtain information which is not inserted into the mass accident data base.

*Technology*

The traditional method of data collection involves police completing a standard form. However, a range of new technologies for data capture are in the process of being developed and these are likely to find increased use in the years ahead as they offer potential for more streamlined reporting or efficiencies in data processing (O'Day, 1993). They include:

. use of Global Positioning Systems (GPS) or satellite navigation systems for accurate determination and reporting of the location of an accident,

. use of geographic information systems to record accident locations (see below),

. use of scannable accident report forms, to minimise costs and potential for error in accident coding, and

. use of laptop computers in police cars, with menu-driven accident data capture and allowing for in-built logic or consistency checks on the data as it is entered.

*Accident data elements*

Each jurisdiction will have its own set of data requirements, in reflection of local tradition, needs, and the influence of the various data users. As noted above, there is wide variation in the extent and detail of data collected, and similarly there is a wide variation in the data format. Nevertheless, there is some coalescence of data between different agencies in the same country. In Britain for example, each County collects its own data on its own report form, but these all tend to be variations or extensions of the national STATS19 form issued by the UK Department of Transport for the purpose of collection of national road accident statistics (Langan, 1992). In the United States, although there is considerable variation in both the format of the report form and the information required to be collected, there is widespread use of the American National Standards Institute standards, and a likelihood of increased commonality of variables, such as those recommended by the National Highway Traffic Safety Administration (1992) (NHTSA) in its CADRE (*Critical Automated Data Reporting Elements*) program (O'Day, 1993). There is also a requirement for standardised reporting of fatal accidents, to enable the preparation of the national FARS (Fatal Accident Reporting System) report by NHTSA (Bryer, 1993).

However, in general, three types of data are required for the purposes of hazardous road location investigations: accident data, road data and traffic data. Typical data elements within each are set out in Tables 4.1, 4.2 and 4.3.

77

**Table 4.1**
**Typical accident data elements**

| Item | Description |
|---|---|
| General description | location, intersection/midblock, date, day hour, location, accident type and/or vehicle manoeuvres, number of vehicles, accident severity, number of injuries, object hit |
| Administrative | reporting officer, accident file number, details of vehicle owner, witnesses names and addresses, time police arrived |
| Vehicles (for each vehicle involved) | licence number, vehicle owner, type, make, year of manufacture, loaded/empty truck, skidding, instability, defects, towed/not towed away |
| Persons (for each person involved) | name, address, sex, age, alcohol, injuries, position in vehicle, seat belt use, pedestrian location and movement |
| Environment | natural light, street lighting, weather, road surface condition |
| Sketch and narrative | includes site details, movements of vehicles and pedestrians, vehicles speeds, collision sequence |

Most of these elements are entered by the police officer as alphanumeric codes, except for the narrative description of the events leading up to the accident (describing the actions and manoeuvres of all of the vehicles etc involved), and a sketch, showing the layout of the site and the paths followed by each of the vehicles etc in the course of the accident event. Street names must be marked on the sketch, and the location of any pertinent road features (e.g bridges, utility poles) must be clearly indicated.

**Table 4.2**
**Typical road data elements**

| Item | Description |
|------|-------------|
| Road description | classification, divided/undivided, number of lanes, speed limit, adjacent land use |
| Geometric details | curve, grade, sag, crest, lane and shoulder width, shoulder type, median width, sight restrictions |
| Road surface | type, macrotexture, microtexture |
| Traffic control devices | signs, markings, delineation, channelization, street lighting |
| Intersection control | uncontrolled, GIVE WAY / YIELD signs, STOP signs, signals |
| Roadside objects | signs, poles, guard fencing, street furniture, fixed objects, bridge, culvert, rail crossing |
| Intersection | type, configuration, number of legs, sight restrictions |
| Roadworks | yes/no, in progress/ not in progress, type of traffic control |

**Table 4.3**
**Typical traffic data elements**

| Item | Description |
|------|-------------|
| Traffic volume | daily, hourly, seasonal |
| Composition | cars, trucks, buses, motor cycles, bicycles |
| Pedestrians | volumes, age groups represented |
| Vehicle speed | mean, 85 percentile |
| Parking | yes/no, type |

These two items are of immense value in accident investigation, and enormously enhance the alpha-numeric information which can be coded and put on the data base. As such, their use should be strongly encouraged or mandated, and needless to say, they should be accurate. The importance of providing this information should always be stressed in discussions with police on the question of data collection.

*Definitions*

It may be an obvious point, but it needs to be stressed that each item in the data base needs to be explicitly defined, so that the resulting data base is robust and reliable. It is also very helpful if the definitions are reasonably consistent with those used in other jurisdictions, to smooth the transfer of knowledge and experience in the road safety field; as noted above, we are currently a long way from achieving this aim.

Most of the terms listed in Tables 4.1, 4.2 and 4.3 need explicit definition. (A useful discussion of this question is presented in Andreassen, 1994). Even the most basic items like 'road' and 'accident' need to be defined. (For example, when does a public road become a private driveway? And how serious must the damage be for the event to be entered onto the data base?)

It is important to bear this point in mind in any work dealing with analysis of accident data, and particularly when making comparisons between different jurisdictions.

*Minimum data requirements*

Having said that the actual data which is collected and coded varies from place to place, it can nevertheless be suggested that there is a minimum set of data which is necessary to form the basis of a sound and satisfactory accident investigation for a hazardous road location program. This information, which is presented in Table 4.4, can be discerned from examination of the literature (e.g. Institution of Highways and Transportation, 1990a; Andreassen, 1989, 1994; National Highway Traffic Safety Administration, 1992; Transport Research Laboratory, 1988; Ercoli and Negri, 1985).

## Accident data coding

*Data coding procedures*

Accident data obtained from police accident report forms is coded for purposes of efficient computer storage and retrieval. Microfiche or digitised copies of the original forms, perhaps without confidential information such as names of individuals, may also held for later reference. Narratives from witnesses and those directly involved in the accident are held in police files. Access to these can usually be arranged for accident research and investigation purposes.

The alpha-numerical coding of accident data can sometimes give the impression of accuracy which is not deserved. An understanding of the methods by which the data files are prepared is therefore necessary if it is to be used for research and investigation.

Data are coded at two stages of the reporting process, at the accident scene or shortly afterwards at the police station, and subsequently at the point of data entry. Some of the key decisions at each of these points are briefly described below.

At the accident site and later at the police station, the reporting officer fills out a codified form. For many of the data fields, the officer can select from a list of responses on the form. For most accidents, the selection of an appropriate response will be straightforward. However, there will be a proportion of accidents where the answer is unclear or ambiguous.

The next stage of coding occurs at the point of data entry. At this point, additional information to that shown on the police accident report form may need to be accessed and inserted into the data file for each particular accident. This data may include, for example, the results of any blood alcohol tests that may have been conducted.

In addition to this information and the coding of data provided on the police accident report form, the data coder has to use the information provided on the form to determine four very important pieces of information. These four items, namely the location of the accident, whether or not the accident occurred at an intersection, the accident type, and the accident severity, are described below:

**Table 4.4**
**Suggested minimum data for hazardous road location programs**

| Item | Description |
|---|---|
| *Road user* | For each person involved: name, address, sex, date of birth, casualty class |
| | For each driver: license type (motorised vehicles only), seatbelt/helmet wearing, alcohol test and result |
| | For road users who are not vehicle occupants: alcohol test and result |
| | For non-driver occupants: age, sex, seating position in vehicle, casualty class, seatbelt/helmet wearing |
| *Vehicle* | For each vehicle in the accident: registration number, vehicle type, make, year of manufacture, defects, where impacted |
| *Accident scene* | Location: street names and/or distances to nearest intersection or reference point, speed limits, road classification, road type, number of lanes and lane/shoulder width, land use, roadside objects |
| | Intersection: type, configuration, number of legs, traffic control |
| | Mid-block: traffic control (e.g. pedestrian crossing, railway crossing), driveway, curve, grade, bridge, tunnel, roadside objects, traffic calming device |
| | Day, date, time, light conditions, street lighting |
| | Road conditions: wet/dry, road surface type, road surface condition |

**Table 4.4 (continued)**

| Item | Description |
|------|-------------|
| *Speed* | mean, 85 percentile |
| *Parking* | yes/no |
| *Sketch* | Showing the movements of the vehicles and other road users leading up to the accident, and any subsequent events. All objects and vehicles involved in the accident to be shown. |
| *Narrative* | Events and movements to be described, including those not involved in the collision, but which indirectly contributed (e.g. other vehicles or pedestrians, animals, roadside objects, sight distance restrictions, etc) |
| *Accident type* | Based upon the sketch and the narrative, the accident type can be coded using standard codes (see for example Figures 4.1 and 4.2) |

*Location*

One of the key pieces of information required by the road safety engineer is *precise* knowledge of the location of the accident. Since much of the work of the analyst involves relating accidents to sites, it is clearly essential to have accurate information about the location of the accident.

This means firstly that the police office has to provide clear and accurate data on the police accident report form. Vague, ambiguous or incorrect information is of little value. The information must be provided in such a way that the person coding the information can locate it on a map or road network. Thus the information ideally is of the form 'm metres north-east of the intersection of X street and Y street', or 'outside Number n, Z Street', or at location a.b metres on Highway A (where a and b are specific distance markers on the highway). Vague information like '3 km east of town B', or incomplete information like 'between town C and town D' is unhelpful. Some sites are difficult to code precisely, for example, sites within a roundabout. Various reference methods in use for location of accidents are described by Zegeer (1982, p 5).

The coders task, having received the accident report form with the location information on it, is to translate that information onto a referencing system. There are two basic options:

. a coded road network, where each node (intersection) is numbered; accidents at nodes are coded according to the relevant node number, while those between nodes (mid-block or link accidents, or accidents at minor, un-numbered intersection) are coded with reference to the adjacent node(s), or

. a grid reference system, based upon a national geographic grid.

A number of authorities are now beginning to include their accident data using a Geographic Information System (GIS) or digital mapping system (McGuigan, McBride and Ryall, 1994; O'Day, 1993). This enables accident data to be incorporated within a relational data base, allowing accident sites to overlaid on plans showing other geographic information, such as highway features, traffic flows, intersection layouts, land uses, etc.

*Intersection definition*

Intersections are very important in accident analysis because a high proportion of total road accidents occur there. Thus, analysts are particularly interested in knowing whether an accident occurred at an intersection (which may also be called a junction or a node) or away from an intersection (variously referred to as a link or a mid-block accident). Usually, the definition includes that area bounded by the extension of the building lines of the intersecting roads (and thus includes footpaths or sidewalks as well as roadways). In some jurisdictions it also includes a short length (say 10 m or 30 ft) along each of the intersecting road reserves, to include accidents resulting from conditions at the intersection but where the collision occurs a little way away (e.g. a rear end accident at a traffic signal). It can immediately be seen that there is a certain arbitrariness about just what constitutes an intersection.

*Accident type classification*

Accident type is a very useful concept and a valuable tool in developing countermeasures. The accident type is based upon the traffic movements leading up to the conflict situation which results in the accident. Coding of road user movements requires skilful interpretation of sketches and written descriptions provide by the police officer. Practice varies between jurisdictions, although there is a general tendency toward the matrix type of code which presents diagrammatic representations of various vehicle-to-vehicle and vehicle-to-other-road-users movements. A good example is that recommended in the Australian model guidelines (Andreassen, 1994). These are reproduced in Figures 4.1 (for vehicles driven on the left side of the road) and 4.2 (for vehicles driven on the right side of the road).

*Accident severity and casualty class*

An important area, but one where there is often a degree of subjectivity, is accident severity and casualty class. The latter refers to a person, while the former refers to the accident, and is classified according to the most severe casualty sustained by any person involved in the accident (e.g. if one person was killed in an accident, it would be classed as a fatal accident, irrespective of whether there were also people involved in the accident who were not killed).

Severity is important because it is often used to rank accidents, and in some places different money values are placed on accidents of different severity for the purposes of evaluation. In many jurisdictions (including most US States - O'Day, 1993, p 8) the five-point scale often referred to as the KABCO scale defined by the American National Standards Institute (1989) is used:

K  person with fatal injury
A  person with incapacitating injury
B  person with non-incapacitating evident injury
C  person with possible injury
O  no injury (property damage only)

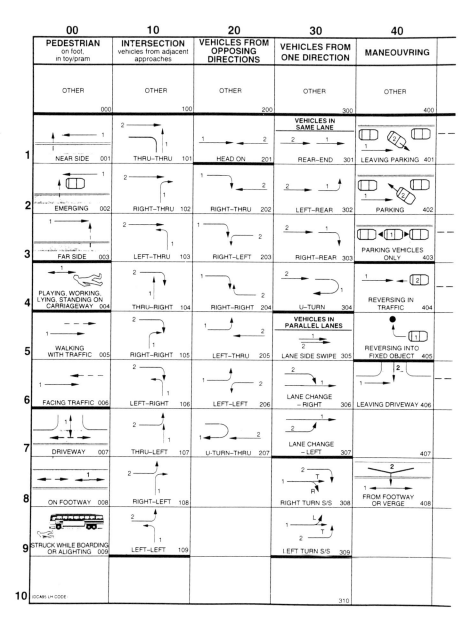

**Figure 4.1    Accident type classification: vehicles driven on the left side of the road**

| 50 | 60 | 70 | 80 | 90 |
|---|---|---|---|---|
| **OVERTAKING** | **ON PATH** | **NON-COLLISION, ON STRAIGHT** | **NON-COLLISION, ON CURVE** | **MISCELLANEOUS** |
| OTHER 500 | OTHER 600 | OTHER 700 | OTHER 800 | OTHER 900 |
| HEAD ON 501 | PARKED 601 | OFF CARRIAGEWAY TO LEFT 701 | OFF CARRIAGEWAY RIGHT BEND 801 | FELL IN/FROM VEHICLE 901 |
| OUT OF CONTROL 502 | DOUBLE PARKED 602 | OFF CARRIAGEWAY TO RIGHT 702 | OFF CARRIAGEWAY LEFT BEND 802 | 902 |
| PULLING OUT 503 | 603 | LEFT OFF CARRIAGEWAY INTO OBJECT 703 | OFF RIGHT BEND INTO OBJECT 803 | HIT TRAIN 903 |
| CUTTING IN 504 | CAR DOOR 604 | RIGHT OFF CARRIAGEWAY INTO OBJECT 704 | OFF LEFT BEND INTO OBJECT 804 | HIT RAILWAY XING FURNITURE 904 |
| PULLING OUT REAR END 505 | HIT PERMANENT OBSTRUCTION 605 | OUT OF CONTROL ON CARRIAGEWAY 705 | OUT OF CONTROL ON CARRIAGEWAY 805 | HIT ANIMAL, OFF CARRIAGEWAY 905 |
| OVERTAKING – RIGHT TURN 506 | HIT ROADWORKS 606 | LEFT TURN 706 | | PARKED VEHICLE RAN AWAY 906 |
| | HIT TEMPORARY OBJECT ON CARRIAGEWAY 607 | RIGHT TURN 707 | | VEHICLE MOVEMENTS NOT KNOWN 907 |
| | ACCIDENT OR BROKEN DOWN 608 | 708 | 808 | |
| | HIT ANIMAL 609 | | | |
| | LOAD HITS VEHICLE 610 | | | © D ANDREASSEN |

Source: Andreassen (1994). Copyright 1994 by David Andreassen. Reproduced with permission.

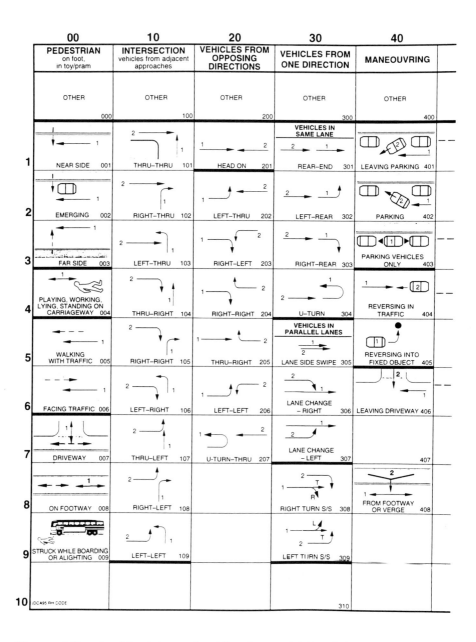

**Figure 4.2    Accident type classification: vehicles driven on the right side of the road**

| 50 | 60 | 70 | 80 | 90 |
|---|---|---|---|---|
| OVERTAKING | ON PATH | NON-COLLISION, ON STRAIGHT | NON-COLLISION, ON CURVE | MISCELLANEOUS |
| OTHER 500 | OTHER 600 | OTHER 700 | OTHER 800 | OTHER 900 |
| HEAD ON 501 | PARKED 601 | OFF CARRIAGEWAY TO LEFT 701 | OFF CARRIAGEWAY RIGHT BEND 801 | FELL IN/FROM VEHICLE 901 |
| OUT OF CONTROL 502 | DOUBLE PARKED 602 | OFF CARRIAGEWAY TO RIGHT 702 | OFF CARRIAGEWAY LEFT BEND 802 | 902 |
| PULLING OUT 503 | 603 | LEFT OFF CARRIAGEWAY INTO OBJECT 703 | OFF RIGHT BEND INTO OBJECT 803 | HIT TRAIN 903 |
| CUTTING IN 504 | CAR DOOR 604 | RIGHT OFF CARRIAGE-WAY INTO OBJECT 704 | OFF LEFT BEND INTO OBJECT 804 | HIT RAILWAY XING FURNITURE 904 |
| PULLING OUT REAR END 505 | HIT PERMANENT OBSTRUCTION 605 | OUT OF CONTROL ON CARRIAGEWAY 705 | OUT OF CONTROL ON CARRIAGEWAY 805 | HIT ANIMAL, OFF CARRIAGEWAY 905 |
| OVERTAKING – LEFT TURN 506 | HIT ROADWORKS 606 | LEFT TURN 706 | | PARKED VEHICLE RAN AWAY 906 |
| | HIT TEMPORARY OBJECT ON CARRIAGEWAY 607 | RIGHT TURN 707 | | VEHICLE MOVEMENTS NOT KNOWN 907 |
| | ACCIDENT OR BROKEN DOWN 608 | 708 | 808 | |
| | HIT ANIMAL 609 | | | |
| | LOAD HITS VEHICLE 610 | | | © D ANDREASSEN (DCA95 RH CODE) |

A fatal accident is usually defined as one in which death occurs within a given period of time as a result of injuries sustained in the accident. Although a 30 day period is common, it is not universal. Suicides are generally excluded; a suicide is usually only recorded if a coroner so determines (which may actually under-state the extent of suicides and thus over-state accidental death since coroners will usually only reach a finding of death by suicide if there is clear evidence to that effect). Similarly, a coroner may determine that a person in the accident died before the accident occurred (e.g. through a heart attack), in which case the accident would not be coded as fatal since the accident was not the cause of death.

The American National Standards Institute (1989) defines incapacitating injury (level A) to include severe lacerations, broken limbs, skull or chest injuries, abdominal injuries, unconsciousness, inability to leave the accident scene without assistance, etc. Non-incapacitating injuries (level B) include a lump on the head, abrasions, bruises, minor lacerations, etc. Possible injuries (level C) include momentary unconsciousness, limping, complaints of pain, nausea, hysteria, etc.

Some jurisdictions use a full five-part classification of this sort, but in many there is a truncation. In the UK for example, there is a four-part classification: fatal, serious injury, slight injury, and not injured. The distinction between 'serious' and 'slight' is left, perhaps surprisingly, to the police officer who completes the form; there is no independent medical determination. In some Australian states, all injuries, even those not requiring medical treatment, are included - i.e a 3-part code (fatal, injury, non-injury) is used. Conversely, in some American states, a more detailed code than the above 5-part code is used (O'Day, 1983).

**Accident data base management**

Management of the data base is a significant task, discussion of which is beyond the scope of this book. However, the prime characteristics of an accident data base management system (O'Day, 1993) are:

. competent accident reports, supported by training and supervision,
. a report form attuned to users' needs,
. attention to detail in the preparation of reports,
. accurate data entry and processing,
. free-flowing output to interested parties, and
. feedback of user comments to induce system improvement.

Attempts should be made to keep the data base as up to date as possible, with all accidents entered no more than a few weeks after their occurrence (bearing in mind that accident severity may need to be changed, as described above).

The data base is today almost invariably computerised, and increasingly there is scope for down-loading data onto personal computers. In many jurisdictions, data-specific software is used to manipulate data in a way tailored to meet the needs of a particular user, and present reports and outputs in specified formats.

In general, three sets of output are required, and these are often reflected in distinct data files: data pertaining to the accident, to vehicles in the accident, and to persons in the accident. The structure of the data files must enable these data outputs to be generated, but must also enable them to be related (e.g. to identify whether a particular person was a pedal cyclist, or to determine which street a particular vehicle was travelling on). These data files in turn may be used to produce routine periodic reports, for example (Zegeer, 1982, p 24):

.   lists of accidents by location; these are monitored to detect emerging problem sites;

.   lists of high accident locations; these are monitored to develop priorities for treatment,

.   detailed summaries of accidents that have occurred at each high accident location; these are used to prepare collision diagrams,

.   detailed summaries of variables coded from the accident report forms (e.g. accident type, pedestrian accidents, alcohol, vehicle type, time of day, etc); these are used for countermeasure development,

.   summaries of accident types which may be susceptible to enforcement (e.g. speeding, alcohol impairment); these are used by police in planning enforcement strategies,

.   summary reports, e.g. for dissemination to the media or for the preparation of official statistics,

.   statistical summaries produced by the central agency for distribution to local government, pertaining to accidents within jurisdictional boundaries; these may relate to any or all of the above, depending upon the jurisdiction's responsibilities in the road safety area,

. summaries of accidents involving particular hazardous features (e.g. roadside objects, railway crossings); these are useful for planning pro-active or preventative programs, and

. information for research studies.

**Supplementary data sources**

While the police accident report is the basic source of accident data, there are some other sources which may be useful and applicable in certain circumstances. These include the following:

*Local knowledge* is an important source of information about safety problems in the road network. Obviously, opinions and anecdotal information about accident problems must be regarded as subjective, but this information can be used as a pointer to problems. People who can be tapped for this information are local government staff, emergency service personnel, local safety groups, residents, and local businesses (Bryer, 1993; UK Department of Transport, 1986, p 4.19).

*Interviews* of road users, including people who have been involved in an accident at a site of interest, in a structured format have been a source of useful information for traffic authorities in the development of accident countermeasures (Carsten, et al, 1989; Bui, Corben, Leeming and Brierley, 1991).

*Special surveys* such as in-depth studies of particular groups of accidents (e.g. single vehicle fatal accidents) have been used to gain a better understanding of the nature of accidents. These surveys can be very costly but have the potential to obtain more useful data than is available from police accident report forms.

*Traffic conflict surveys* may be used where the collection of accident data is not practical or the period of evaluation is too short to collect sufficient samples. These involve field observations or video recording of conflicts (near misses) (Organisation for Economic Cooperation and Development,

1976; Glauz and Migletz, 1980; Transport and Road Research Laboratory, 1987; Hummer, 1994b). The information gained in this way is valuable in getting a sound understanding of the dynamic traffic operation and the interactions which occur between traffic streams at the site. As a proxy measures of safety, assumptions must be made about the relationship between the proxy measure (conflict) and accident rates.

*Coroner's reports* can be a useful source of additional information concerning specific fatal accidents.

*Site investigations* are a necessary component of a countermeasure development program and will often yield insights into the accident situation (see Chapter 6).

## Data limitations

Although data on accidents is an essential input to a systematic HRL program, there are some limitations and problems with such data. These include:

*Systematic reporting bias.* This arises from the regulations covering the reporting of accidents. Reporting criteria vary between jurisdictions, and thus accident experience is not comparable. Within a jurisdiction, the lack of a requirement to report accidents (and the policy of not coding accidents of low severity even if reported) means that the data base is not always truly reflective of the road accident situation. Numerically, property damage accidents constitute the bulk of accidents, and if these are not on the data base, the accident picture is incomplete and systematically biased.

*Random bias.* It is now well-established that certain accidents are significantly under-reported. In a comprehensive international review, James (1991) found that accidents involving children, pedal cyclists, pedestrians, and minor injury were all substantially under-reported. In a comment on the American situation O'Day (1993, p 26) coyly remarks that 'people in many State data processing offices believe that their missing data are negligible... the literature review suggests that this is an area that requires more than a casual observation to support such a belief'! Under-reporting can result in a distorted picture of the road accident situation, not only numerically, but in relation to the nature of the accidents that are occurring, and hence the allocation of resources for their treatment.

Similarly, there may be biases within the data records themselves. For example, if a particular factor is not recorded, this may mean that it was not present, or that the police officer completing the report did not know that it was not present, or that he/she was not able to find out if it was present, or that it may have been present but the police officer did not think it was important. All of these situations mean that the data are incomplete and the analyst may come to a misleading conclusion. Unfortunately, such situations are common, in relation to some human factors (e.g. alcohol and drugs) and roadway factors (e.g. the presence of roadside features such as culverts).

*Coding errors.* These can occur throughout the process from the filling out of the police accident report form to the data entry at the computer terminal. These types of error are difficult to estimate but are generally considered to be present in about 5 per cent of accident files. They are not identified unless revealed when the data are used for detailed investigation of accidents at individual sites. Typical problems range from errors in filling out the police accident report form (e.g. getting the north point wrong) to errors in data transcription or coding.

*Location errors.* The location of an accident may easily be incorrect or imprecise in the original police accident report form, and if so this will be carried over into the data base, resulting in inconsistencies or inaccuracies in the accident history of a specific location. In some cases, the location reference system itself may be imprecise, which may mean that the exact location of the accident cannot be accurately determined.

*Discontinuities.* Definitions or interpretations of field data may be changed over time by those responsible for coding and recording, meaning that data from one time period cannot be compared with that for another time period, or worse, the user may be unaware of the presence of a discontinuity and as a result the analyses may be incorrect. In fact the road safety analyst should take particular care to inquire about any such discontinuities. An abrupt change in accident experience at a site should also lead the analyst to inquire about any discontinuities or other inaccuracies in the data.

*Delays.* Agencies responsible for data processing may not be sufficiently resourced, and as a result it may be many months before information is available for analysis. This means that countermeasure development is responding to historical accident patterns which may be out of date.

*Hidden problems.* The implicit assumption in the process described in this chapter is that the accident data base is a good indicator of road safety problems. Generally this is probably true (subject to the qualifications made in the previous paragraphs). However, it may be masking other problems, for example if pedestrians avoid using an area because of a perceived safety problem; in this case the safety issue has resulted in lack of amenity rather than the occurrence of accidents.

The road safety engineer needs to aware of these limitations and drawbacks. However, at the same time, a good data base is a necessary prerequisite for tackling *real* problems, and must be used to address those problems. Other problems, of the sort mentioned above, may need to be tackled in other ways, for example through a road safety audit (see Chapter 15) or identified through community consultation.

# 5 Hazardous road locations

*As discussed in Chapter 2, hazardous road location (HRL) programs may be directed at single sites, routes, areas, or mass application programs. In this chapter, we examine firstly the objectives which may be set for programs in each of the four categories, and then the criteria for identification of hazardous locations.*

## Hazardous road location programs

In Chapter 2, we introduced the concept of hazardous road location as one of the two prime applications of road safety engineering (the other being road safety audit, to be discussed in Chapter 15). A hazardous road location (HRL) program is a formal process which aims to identify locations within the road system which have an unacceptably high incidence of road accidents, in order to develop appropriate treatments to reduce the cost of accidents.

The process involved in HRL has been summarized in Figure 2.3. The initial stages in that process were *specification of objectives* and *identification of hazardous road locations*. These two aspects are discussed in this chapter.

The HRL process is predicated on being able to identify a specific site or groups of sites where some form of remedial road or traffic engineering treatment may be applied in order to reduce the number of accidents occurring at such sites, or reduce their severity. As noted in Chapter 2, few treatments will reduce both accident frequency and accident severity; most reduce only one or the other, but either outcome is a benefit since both will reduce the cost of accidents at the site.

The purpose of these initial phases of the HRL process is to identify sites which should be subjected to further study (Figure 2.4). The immediate outcome of such study is to determine which sites have a high risk, i.e. which sites have a high probability that improvement will occur as a result of the application of the remedial measures to be discussed in Chapters 7 through 14.

Accident histories usually need to be aggregated in order to have some confidence in the beneficial effects of such measures. For example a single accident at a site is a poor indicator of what may happen in the future, but if there are several accidents of the same type occurring at the site, we can be more confident that a remedial measure focussed on that particular accident type will be effective. Appropriate aggregations include:

. accidents clustered at intersections or on short lengths of a road (hazardous sites, or 'black spots'),

. accidents clustered along routes or sections of routes (hazardous routes),

. accidents clustered within an area (hazardous areas),

. groups of accidents for which there are known effective treatments, occurring across several sites,

. groups of accidents of a similar type, occurring across several sites,

. a series of accidents that have common features, such as road features (e.g. bridges), vehicle features (e.g. bicycles), road user features (e.g. pedestrians) or contributory features (e.g. driver fatigue), or

. a series of 'high profile' accidents such as those involving vehicles carrying dangerous goods, or accidents at railway crossings.

These last four examples may lead to some form of mass action program, aimed at applying known engineering remedies across a range of affected sites. For example:

. accidents involving loss of control on rural roads with the vehicle running off the road; remedial programs include shoulder sealing, treatment of hazardous curves, and treatment of fixed roadside hazards,

. accidents at signalized intersections; remedial programs include the installation of fully controlled turn phases, installation of red light cameras, and replacement of signalized intersections with roundabouts,

. overtaking accidents on 2-lane rural highways, a treatment for which is the provision of overtaking lanes,

. wet weather accidents, the remedial treatment for which may be the provision of skid resistant pavements, and

. accidents involving pedestrians and cyclists, for which a range of treatments aimed at these vulnerable road users is available (see Chapter 14).

**Objectives of hazardous road location programs**

The overall goal of an HRL program (Sanderson and Cameron, 1986) is to:

. identify locations at which there is both an inherently high risk of accident losses and an economically justifiable opportunity for reducing this risk, and

. to identify countermeasure options and priorities which maximize the economic benefits from the HRL program.

To operationalize this goal, specific objectives, or quantified targets should be set. For example, the Institution of Highways and Transportation (1990a, p 14) have suggested the following objectives as being realistic and achievable for the four types of action defined in Chapter 2:

. single site:
  . to achieve an average accident reduction of 33 per cent
  . to achieve a first year rate of return of 50 per cent

. route action:
  . to achieve an average accident reduction of 15 per cent
  . to achieve a first year rate of return of 40 per cent

. area action:
  . to achieve an accident reduction of 10 per cent
  . to obtain a first year rate of return of 10-25 per cent

. mass action:
  . to achieve an average accident reduction of 15 per cent
  . to obtain a first year rate of return of 40 per cent.

It can be seen that higher rates of return are expected from single site actions, with lower rates as the focus of the action becomes more diffuse. This is hardly surprising, since the most effective actions are likely to be those which target a specific accident type at a specific site. As these sites are dealt with, the program is likely to focus on routes, where the accidents are somewhat dispersed along a road, and then following this to areas, where the accidents are even more dispersed. The challenge as we move away from sites therefore is to identify the locations where known remedial measures are likely to be cost-effective.

It should also be noted that the economic criterion mentioned above (first year rate of return) is extremely crude, although useful for an initial sieve. The UK Department of Transport (1986, p 3.16) in its *Accident Investigation Manual*, noted that while this criterion was a 'useful practical objective', 'schemes should finally be evaluated more thoroughly by looking at the discounted value of the full time stream of benefits rather than the first year benefits only, in order that comparisons between options and schemes with different life spans can be made.' The question of economic appraisal of remedial measures is taken up in Chapter 16.


**Identification of hazardous road locations**

In order to identify a hazardous road location, it is necessary to:

. *define* the site (or route or area),
. have explicit *criteria* for such identification,
. in some cases, the criteria will require the use of a measure of *exposure* to risk at the site(s) in question,
. take account of accident *severity*, and
. consider the *time period* for the analysis.

These five aspects are discussed in this section, with distinctions being drawn where necessary between their application to sites, routes, areas and mass action HRL programs.

## Sites, routes and areas

*Sites.* Hazardous site analysis involves an examination of the accident patterns at a specific location, such as an intersection, a short length of road (e.g. a bend) or a specific road feature (e.g. a bridge). For the purposes of analysis, it is therefore necessary to define the road length, or in the case of intersections, to be specific about the definition.

With the subdivision of roads into sections, it is important that roadway and traffic factors be fairly uniform within the section, and that the section length should is in keeping with the level of precision and degree of error in reporting accident location. Statistical reliability is also important. It is obvious that as the section length gets very small the probability of either zero or one accident in the period must tend towards unity. Conversely, as the section length gets very large, the effects of isolated hazardous features will be submerged and lost. Zegeer (1982, p 37) suggests that data for road segments of less than approx 0.3 miles (0.5 km) or carrying less than 500 veh/d are unreliable.

Intersections are usually defined as the area bounded by the projections of the property boundaries, plus a certain distance (typically between, say, 10 m and 30 m (say, 30-100 ft)) of the approach roads. Accidents occurring within this area are classified as intersection accidents, and all others as 'link' or 'mid-block' accidents.

*Routes.* By definition, routes are longer than the sub-division of roads into discrete sections that may be considered as a single 'site'. Routes will therefore be relatively long, typically from about 1 to 10 km (0.6 to 6 miles).

*Areas.* An area needs to be reasonably uniform and homogeneous in its characteristics, such as land use, density, and street configuration. Typical applications relate to the development of a HRL program within a local residential or commercial area, so the boundaries of the site will be dictated by the extent to which a comprehensive traffic management plan can be developed for the area. A typical area may be 5 square km (2 square miles) or larger.

*Mass action.* Mass action investigations usually focus upon the application of treatments at sites or routes (and occasionally areas), so the definitions just given apply to these investigations as well.

*Criteria*

A number of criteria have been used to identify hazardous *sites and routes*[1]. The principal methods are:

. The number of accidents (or accidents per unit length of road) in a given period exceeding some set level (e.g. 3 per year). This takes no account of exposure.

. The rate of accidents for a given period exceeding some set value. This does take account of exposure. Rates are usually expressed in terms of accidents per million vehicle kilometres (vehicle miles) for road sections. For intersections, a variety of exposure methods have been used (see below).

. The number and rate of accidents both exceeding some defined threshold value.

. The rate of accidents exceeding a critical value derived from statistical analysis of rates at all sites. This method, sometimes referred as the rate quality control (RQC) method, determines whether the accident rate at a site is significantly higher than a predetermined rate for locations of similar characteristics, based upon a Poisson distribution (Zegeer, 1982, p 32).

. The potential accident reduction (PAR) method. This is the difference between the observed and expected accident experience calculated from the site and traffic flow characteristics, with the selection criteria being to select sites which will maximize the accident reduction if their accident history can be reduced to the expected value (McGuigan, 1981, 1982). It is essentially the RQC method using frequencies not rates.

. Rating by accident severity method. In this approach, past accidents are weighted according to their severity to produce an index, the index being used as the selection criteria (Zegeer, 1982; Turner and Hall, 1994).

. The hazard index method, which is a variation on the above in which a number of factors are calculated (such as rates, frequencies, severities, and perhaps site data such as traffic flow or site distance). A composite index, which is a weighted average of these factors, is then calculated (Khisty, 1990, p 637).

. Rating according not to accident history, but by site features. These typically include road features (curves, grades), roadside features, and traffic features. A composite index, based upon a weighted sum of the value of each of these features at any given site, is then calculated to give an indication of priority for site treatment (Zegeer, 1986, p 8 ff).

. The current annual cost of accidents occurring at the site, based upon an average cost of accident by accident type. This takes account of different severities, but does so in a way that relates directly to evaluation without having to take recourse in arbitrary weights as the previous two methods do (Andreassen, 1992a,b,c).

For hazardous *areas*, Nicholson (1990) notes that as this is a relatively new area of study, there is some doubt about the criteria which ought to be used. Possible criteria include:

. the number of accidents per square kilometre (square mile) (this does not take account of variations in the length of road and traffic flows),

. the number of accidents per head of population (ditto),

. the number of accidents per kilometre (mile) of road (this takes no account of traffic flow),

. the number of accidents per vehicle owned or available to the population (this attempts to take account of traffic flows in a crude manner), or

. the annual cost of accidents occurring within the area.

Whether we are dealing with sites, routes or areas, there is little consensus on which criteria are most appropriate. Proponents of approaches using accident frequency argue that it focuses attention upon the locations where most accidents occur, and hence a program based on this criterion has the most potential to reduce the number of accidents and their cost. Also, this approach will tend to focus upon sites on high volume roads which have a large number of accidents. Proponents of approaches using rates argue that they identify sites where there is something truly unusual, not just a high level of traffic. This approach will lead to site selection on lower volume roads having fewer accidents and therefore possibly less potential for improvement. Proponents of the PAR and RQC methods claim that it focuses attention upon sites where there is the greatest likelihood that remedies may be effective.

Hence, those criteria which combine both frequency and rate have some attraction in that they lead to identification of sites that have a high risk (in terms of accidents per unit of exposure) and where there are relatively large numbers of accidents.

The key issue in all of this is how the criteria adopted direct the analyst to consider sites, routes or areas which contribute to the overall road safety goal, namely the reduction of the cost of road accidents, or more precisely the maximization of the benefit of road safety treatments (Chapter 2). Sanderson and Cameron (1986) examined this question, using a sample of 198 intersections in Adelaide, Australia. They determined that *casualty accident frequency* is an adequate basis for identification of hazardous road locations, but economic benefits are maximized when sites are identified on the basis that their *casualty accident rate is significantly greater than the system average casualty accident rate* for that intersection type. However, a *combination method* based on ranking by casualty accident rate and then casualty accident frequency is nearly as good. (In this study, the casualty accident rate for intersections was defined as the number of casualty (fatal plus injury) accidents divided by the square root of the product of conflicting flows, while for road sections it was the number of casualty accidents per kilometre.)

McGuigan (1981, 1982) has reported on a somewhat similar study using data for intersections and road links respectively. In both cases, he demonstrated that the potential for accident reduction is maximized by using the potential accident reduction criterion.

These are important conclusions, and lend support to the use of either the potential accident reduction (PAR) method or the rate quality control (RQC) method. However, Maher and Mountain (1988), while acknowledging the theoretical superiority of the PAR method, claim that it does not necessarily perform better than a method based simply upon accident frequency because of 'inaccuracy of the estimation of the expected accident frequency at a site required in PAR'. In part, this is because the PAR method should make a correction for the 'regression to the mean' effect, which is discussed in Chapter 17.

However, all of these methods are proxies, since the 'ideal' method would be one which enables the maximization of the benefits of road accident countermeasures to be estimated directly. This has not hitherto been possible, because such a method requires knowledge the cost of accidents which are actually occurring on the site/route/area in question, not an index figure based upon a global average cost of accidents. However, cost data of this form are now beginning to become available, and have begun to be used for direct identification of hazardous road locations, for example in Australia (Ogden, 1994a). The development of accident type costs, which forms the basis of this approach, is discussed in Chapter 16.

In practice, all of the above methods are in use, either alone or in combination. For example in the *United States*, Zegeer (1982) in a survey of the practices used by State highway or safety agencies, reported that:

. accident frequency was used by 89 per cent of agencies on major roads and 73 per cent on minor roads,

. accident rate or rate quality control as used by 84 per cent of agencies for major roads and 50 per cent for minor roads, and

. accidents were stratified by severity by 65 per cent of agencies for major roads and 45 per cent for minor roads.

In the *United Kingdom*, Silcock and Smyth (1984) found that among local authorities (excluding London Boroughs):

. 74 per cent used accident frequency,

. 6 per cent used accident frequency weighted by severity,

. 4 per cent used an accident rate,

. 13 per cent used a 'multi-factor' approach, in which various components (e.g. pedestrian accidents) were differently weighted,

. 11 per cent used a 'subjective' method, and

. 6 per cent used 'other' methods.

In a survey of the methods used in *Australia*, Ogden (1994a) found that accident frequency was most widely used for identification of hazardous intersections, and methods similar to the PAR method were in wide use for the identification of hazardous routes. However, as noted above, several jurisdictions have recently introduced a cost criterion to identify sites or routes which, when treated, will maximize the economic benefit resulting from the remedial program.

Whichever method is used to determine whether a location is 'hazardous' or 'high risk', it is important that the sites, routes or areas which are being compared are truly comparable. Safety expectations vary with road and intersection type, as well as location (Deacon, Zegeer and Deen, 1975). Thus it would be unreasonable to compare, for example, a 2-lane undivided road with a 4-lane divided road, as there is no expectation that the former could be upgraded to have the safety performance of the latter. Similarly, accident patterns and safety standards will differ between urban and rural areas, and between high speed and low speed situations.

*Exposure measures*

Several of the above criteria for identification of hazardous sites, routes, or areas require the calculation of a rate, that is the accident frequency normalized by some measure which is intended, directly or indirectly, to account for exposure.

This problem of accounting for exposure to risk of a road traffic accident is one of the major theoretical and practical problems facing safety analysts (Organisation for Economic Cooperation and Development, 1984, p 6). In principle, the concept of 'exposure' is relatively simple: the more a person is involved in road traffic (e.g. amount of travel), the more likely it is that the person will be involved in an accident. Furthermore, the differential involvement of participants in the road traffic system points to the need for a meaningful basis for assessing the relative safety of the system. This is most evident when comparisons are made, for example, between different groups of drivers, or across time periods, etc.

For HRL analysis, a measure of exposure may be used directly, or a proxy measure in terms of an index might be used. Typical measures are discussed below, differentiating between exposure measures for links (routes) and exposure measures for intersections (nodes).

*Links or routes.* The simplest exposure measure for links is the length of the link, i.e. the longer the length of road, the more accidents to be expected. Accident rate is expressed as accidents per kilometre (mile) of road.

However, this takes no account of flow, and if such a measure is used (e.g. in the absence of traffic flow information), it will be necessary to group road segments by some proxy measure for traffic flow (e.g. minor 2-lane rural roads; residential streets, freeway lanes).

Where traffic flow data are available, this is a better measure, and is commonly used to define exposure. The typical measure is the total traffic flow expressed as average annual daily traffic (AADT). The accident rate would then be expressed as annual accidents per vehicle kilometre (AADT x 365 x length of section, usually expressed as accidents per $10^8$ vehicle km of travel (VKT) (or $10^8$ vehicle miles of travel (VMT)).

However, traffic flow is a crude measure of exposure, because different accident types relate to flow in different ways; single vehicle accidents for example may be expected to be somewhat proportional to traffic flow, but head-on accidents may be expected to be proportional to a power of traffic flow. Over the years, a number of empirical studies relating accidents to measures of traffic flow on links have been conducted. These reveal that accidents on links are *not* linearly related to traffic flow. For example, Satterthwaite (1981) after a review of such models, concluded that:

. the single vehicle accident rate per vehicle km (vehicle mile) deceases with increasing flow rate,

. the multi-vehicle accident rate per vehicle km (vehicle mile) increases with increasing flow rate, and

. overall, the accident rate varies in a U-shaped pattern with flow rate.

These results are important, because they indicate the importance of disaggregating accident data by accident type. For example, Taylor and Barker (1992) found that quite different factors were involved in different types of accidents on rural single carriageway (undivided) roads in the UK. Some studies, such as those by Silcock and Worsley (1982) and McGuigan (1982) have involved classifying roads according to factors like land use and roadway type, and then identifying, for each category, the relationship between accidents and traffic flow.

*Unsignalized intersections or nodes.* For unsignalized intersections, safety theoretically relates to the number of gaps in the opposing traffic flow, and the success of the driver in finding those gaps. Various studies have attempted to relate accidents to measures of traffic entering the intersection. The most common are the sum of entering flows (Sanderson and Cameron, 1986), the product of conflicting flows (Tanner, 1953), the square root of the product of conflicting flows (Tanner, 1953; Bennett, 1966), or the mean (or the geometric mean) of the average entering flows (Chapman, 1973).

An early study by Tanner (1953) developed the so-called 'square root law', namely that accidents were related to the square root of the product of the intersecting flows:

$$\sqrt{\frac{V1 + V3}{2} \times \frac{V2 + V4}{2}}$$

> where V1 … V4 are the entering flows sequentially around the legs of an intersection (4-leg intersection - variations for 3-leg and other intersections).

Various attempts have been made to refine this simple model, allowing for other geometric variables, intersection type, etc. For example, research at the Transport and Road Research Laboratory in the UK developed equations for 4-arm roundabouts (Maycock and Hall, 1984) and rural T-junctions (Pickering, Hall and Grimmer, 1986). These were generally of the form of accidents as a function of entering volumes. Several statistically significant models relating accidents to traffic flow were developed, but it was found that accidents were more closely related to a root of the product of conflicting flows than to the product or sum of the conflicting flows, thereby tending to confirm Tanner's earlier 'square root law'. The best-fit models were:

For *roundabouts* (Maycock and Hall, 1984):

$$A = kQ^a$$

where k and a are constants for a given accident type, and Q is the entering flow, e.g.:

for entering-circulating accident, $a=0.52$ and $k=0.090$ (small roundabouts) or 0.017 (conventional roundabouts),

for accidents on the approach to the roundabout, $a= 1.58$ and $k=0.0025$ (small) or 0.0055 (conventional),

for single vehicle accidents, $a=1.20$ and $k=0.0068$ (small) or 0.0164 (conventional).

For *rural T-junctions* (Pickering, Hall and Grimmer, 1986):

$$A = 0.24(QP)^{0.49}$$

where A is the number of accidents occurring within 20 m (66 ft) of the intersection, and Q and P are the traffic flows on the major and minor legs of the intersection, measured in thousands of veh/d.

*Signalized intersections.* The concept of exposure, and relating accidents to some measure of entering traffic, is much more difficult for signalized intersection. A comprehensive review of conflict analysis at signalized intersections by Hughes (1991, p 4) described some of the difficulties of applying the concept of exposure to signalized intersections:

'The complex nature of vehicle interactions and traffic control confuses the concept of exposure at traffic signal controlled sites. Some accident types such as rear end accidents exhibit the same number of opportunities as if signals were not a feature. However, the existence of signals alters the likelihood of certain other accidents occurring.'

Once again, a number of empirical studies relating accidents to traffic flows have been conducted. Perhaps the most comprehensive is that undertaken at the University of North Carolina for the US Federal Highway Administration by Council, Stewart and Rodgman (1987). The outcome of this work was a series of empirically-derived regression equations expressing exposure for several specific accident types (e.g. head-on, rear-end, sideswipe, etc) and intersection characteristics (unprotected, fully controlled or partially controlled turns, etc). The independent variables in these equations were items such as intersection width, cycle length, number of lanes, traffic flows and green splits.

This work, although probably the most comprehensive effort in terms of attempting to quantify exposure at signalized intersections (albeit empirically) is difficult to apply because of the data requirements - both flow data and accident data need to be heavily disaggregated by type and movement. It also assumes fixed cycle times, which lessens its value in networks controlled by adaptive traffic control software like SCOOT or SCATS.

A second study, undertaken in Toronto, Canada, by Hauer, Ng and Lovell (1988), also related particular accident types (e.g. rear end, angle, turning, sideswipe, approaching) to the traffic flows to which the colliding vehicles belonged. They built several models relating the number of accidents at an intersection to the relevant measure of traffic flow, and on this basis were able to estimate the number and type of accidents that could be expected at any given intersection. Comparing this with the actual accident experience at that site enabled sites which were 'deviant' to be identified (c.f. PAR approach discussed above). Their model, like the Council, Stewart and Rodgman (1987) study just described, depends upon the availability of traffic flow data (including turning volumes) and intersection accident data for a wide range of intersections.

A less data-hungry model has been developed for cross intersections in Britain by Hall (1986). Several variants were produced, but the basic model which caters for both pedestrian and vehicular flow was:

$$A = 0.023QT^{1.28}(1+PT^{0.30})$$

where A is the number of reported accidents, QT is the total vehicle inflow (i.e. sum of entering vehicles), and PT is the total pedestrian flow (i.e. sum of entering pedestrians).

A fourth study, conducted in Australia by Hughes (1991), developed models for accident frequency (for various road user movements) in terms of various measures of exposure, and examined the predictive power of the resulting equations. The conclusions may be summarized as follows:

'Three typical measures of exposure were explored - total entering traffic, product of the average traffic on the intersecting roads, and the square root of this product. In support of Chapman (1973), a detailed comparison did not discern a great difference between the validity of any of these. Any one should not be preferred over the others since none had a strong theoretical basis. It was suggested that the sum of the entering traffic was preferred since it was the simplest to calculate and avoided any misunderstanding.'

*Severity*

In some of the HRL criteria discussed above, accidents are stratified by severity, where, as described in Chapter 4, the severity of an accident is based upon the most severe injury sustained by any person involved in the accident. Severity classifications may be used in an attempt to identify those sites having a high number and/or high rate of serious accidents.

One way of doing this is to give each accident a weight representing the average cost of accident in the severity category in which it falls. This leads to fatal accidents typically having more than 10 times the weight attached to injury accidents.

If this is done, fatal accidents often dominate the identification procedure. The problem here is that the circumstances which lead to fatal accidents may be very similar to those which produce injury accidents, the severity outcome being a matter of chance. Concentration on fatal accidents alone (which are also a statistically rare event) may lead to spurious conclusions, i.e. the selection of sites which do not in fact have a high accident risk. Hence, a compromise approach is to weight the more severe accidents, but not with the extreme weights calculated in direct proportion to the average cost. Typically, fatal accidents are weighted at 2 to 4 times the influence of injury accidents. Such procedures have been used in the United States (Zegeer, 1986), Australia (National Association of Australian State Road Authorities, 1988a, p 19), and various developing countries (Ross Silcock Partnership, 1991, p 137).

While this is pragmatic, it is essentially arbitrary, and there is no theoretical basis for the weights. Indeed, such arbitrary approaches are

111

likely to be find lesser use in the future, since recent developments are allowing the use of average accident costs by type of accident directly; these have the implicit effect of weighting the more severe accident types, because they will, by definition, be more costly. Australian work in this area is reported in Andreassen (1992a,b,c), and it's use will be described in Chapter 16.

*Time period*

In any study of accidents occurring at a site, route, or area, a basic question which needs to be addressed relates to the time period of the analysis, i.e. how much historical accident data should be used in order to assess the location. Various factors affect the choice of time period, the main ones being (Nicholson, 1990):

.   attempt to avoid having environmental (e.g. traffic growth) and other trends affecting results,

.   use annual accident count data to avoid the effects of cyclic or seasonal variations in accident occurrence,

.   computer storage and processing costs, and

.   changes in data base definitions introducing discontinuities in the data.

With hazardous *routes* (as distinct from sites) a shorter time period may be appropriate, because data for several sites are being aggregated. Although accident frequency for any specific site may be very variable, the frequency for an aggregation of sites (i.e. the route) will be much less variable. Hence a shorter time period is required for equivalent precision. On the other hand, with the analysis of hazardous *areas*, because reported accidents may be quite few in number, a longer time period may be required to ensure a statistically significant sample size. If there have been traffic management works in the area over the time period concerned, allowance must be made for this.

In practice, time periods rarely exceed five years. Zegeer (1982, p 39) found that in the US, the time period ranged from one to five years, with one year or three years being most common. Similarly, in the UK, Silcock and Smyth (1984) found three years to be by far the most common.

From the viewpoint of statistical reliability, five years is most suitable (Nicholson, 1987), giving both a larger sample size and a smoothing of short term fluctuations. However, a shorter period will perhaps lead to the early detection of any sudden changes in the accident rate. For this reason, many authorities have established systems to detect substantial short term fluctuations. Any sites thus identified are examined to see if circumstances have changed. If so, they may be corrected immediately, but if there are no obvious reasons for the short term fluctuation, the site is kept under review, but action need not be taken immediately. Thus Zegeer (1982, p 39) recommended that 'dual time intervals (such as 1-year and 3-year periods) be used whenever possible for purposes of identifying and analysing hazardous locations'.

*Identification of sites for mass action*

The previous discussion has detailed the requirements in respect of HRL programs for sites, routes and areas. The fourth type of program, namely mass action programs, is based upon finding sites or routes where remedial measures which are known to be effective may be applied. For this reason, the previous comments in this section concerning criteria, exposure, severity and time period are all applicable to mass action programs also.

*Clustering of accidents*

Central to the concept of HRL is that certain types of accidents are over-represented at specific sites. In order to identify this clustering, and thus develop a program to treat high accident frequency sites, a cluster analysis needs to be performed.

This takes the form illustrated in Figure 5.1 (Andreassen, 1989, p 6). The cumulative percentage of accidents and the cumulative percentage of sites (e.g. intersections) are plotted. (The former is produced by the product of the number of accidents per site and the number of such sites). The example in Figure 5.1 shows that 50 per cent of these particular accidents (accidents at intersections) occurred at about 23 per cent of the sites, and that these sites averaged about 2.4 accidents per site.

This sort of clustering is important to identify, because when a relatively few sites account for a large proportion of the accidents, improvements at these sites is most likely to give a big overall reduction in accidents.

113

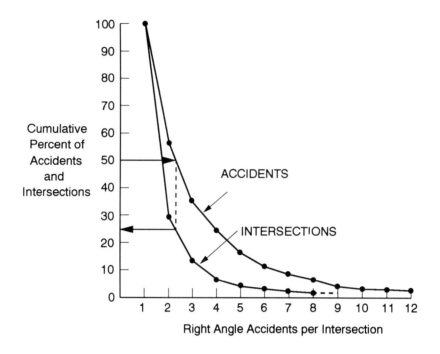

**Figure 5.1    Clustering of accidents**

Source: Andreassen (1989) p 6.

**Chance variations**

The procedures described above for identification of hazardous sites involve analysis of data in the mass accident data base. Like any data analysis, these results can be subjected to statistical analysis in order to distinguish between significant factors and those occurring through chance variation.

In particular, it is important to assess whether an 'abnormally' high number of accidents in a time period (e.g. one year) should be taken as evidence that the site has become 'hazardous' or whether the fluctuation can be taken as mere chance variation. If we assume that the number of accidents at a site varies randomly from year to year, then we may use the Poisson distribution:

$$P(x) = \frac{m^x e^{-m}}{x!}$$

where P(x) = the probability of x occurrences of an event for which the expected number of occurrences is m.

For example, if the accident history at a site for the last five years is 2, 1, 0, 2 and 5, we have reason to be concerned that there may have been a hazardous situation develop which has caused the apparently high number of accidents in the most recent year. But how likely is it that this result may have occurred by chance?

Assuming that the best estimate of m is the accident history at the site, we have 10 accidents in 5 years, so m=2. Using the above formula we can calculate the following probabilities:

P(0) = 0.135
P(1) = 0.271
P(2) = 0.271
P(3) = 0.180
P(4) = 0.090
P(5) = 0.036

That is, the probability of five accidents occurring in a year at a site where the expected value is two accidents per annum is 3.6 per cent, or about one in 28.

More generally, the probability of more than four accidents is 1-{P(0)+P(1)+P(2)+P(3)+P(4)} = 0.053. That is, there is a 5.3 per cent probability of having more than four accidents in a year at a site where the expected accident rate is two accidents per year.

This test is an important one to use when deciding whether to designate a site (or route or area) as one worthy of further investigation, as it will give an indication as to whether an apparently high accident occurrence is due to random variation. Of course, in reality, we must also be mindful of real world changes that might affect the 'expected' accident frequency, such as changes in traffic flow, and as well we should satisfy ourselves that the accident data collection or coding criteria have not changed (see Chapter 4).

115

In Chapter 17, we discuss a number of other statistical tests, particularly for use in evaluating whether a measure has had a significant effect upon accidents, for example in a before-and-after situation. We also discuss methodological issues including regression to the mean, accident migration, risk compensation, and sample size determination.

## Application of hazardous road location criteria

The Institution of Highways and Transportation (1990a, p 25) outline four stages in the *identification* phase of the HRL process:

.   search the data bank for initial identification of accident locations,

.   apply statistical and numerical techniques to produce a preliminary ranking of sites for further study,

.   verify accident locations (with reference to the original police accident report form if necessary) and carry out a preliminary study of accident data, and

.   carry out preliminary on-site observations to relate the accident study to site features and traffic conditions.

These stages are a reminder that the HRL exercise is a process, which is ongoing and inter-related. The previous discussion in this chapter has referred, by implication, to the first two stages here, but in a real-life application, the other stages must follow. Site observations are discussed further in Chapter 6.

The output thus far is a list of candidate sites, i.e. sites which are potential candidates for being selected for remedial treatment. Other influences may come into play at any time and produce other candidate sites - a sudden unexpected increase in accidents at a site, political pressure to 'do something' at a site, or media attention to a particular accident. The response to all of these situations should be to attempt to be objective, and to ensure that all candidate sites are treated on an equitable and consistent basis. Resources are limited and it is important that the process concentrate on sites with the greatest potential for cost-effective treatment. In other words, the process is as much about exclusion of sites from consideration as it is about inclusion.

Having determined, on an on-going basis, which sites are hazardous, the next stage involves determining whether the accident pattern at a site is amenable to treatment with road and traffic engineering remedial measures. This leads us to consideration of the *diagnosis* of accident problems, which is discussed in Chapter 6.

**Notes**

1.    There is an extensive literature on the criteria for identification of a hazardous road location. See for example Organisation for Economic Cooperation and Development (1976), Deacon, Zegeer and Deen (1976), Zegeer (1982), Zegeer (1986), Turner and Hall (1994), Department of Transport (UK) (1986), McGuigan (1981, 1982), National Association of Australian State Road Authorities (1988a), Sanderson and Cameron (1986), Walsh and Dileo (1992). A useful summary is presented by Khisty (1990, Chapter 16).

—

# 6 Diagnosis of road accident problems

*Having identified those high risk sites, routes, areas, or mass action programs which are candidates for inclusion in the Hazardous Road Location (HRL) program (Chapter 5), it is then necessary to carefully examine the nature of the safety problem at the site or sites, with a view to identifying whether those problems can be dealt with through road or traffic remedial measures, and if so, how.*

## Process of diagnosis

The *Highway Safety Guidelines* published by the UK Institution of Highways and Transportation (1990a, p 25) suggest that there are six steps in the diagnosis phase:

.   study detailed accident reports,

.   data sorting to determine groups of accident types and the locations at which they occur,

.   data amplification by detailed on-site investigation (perhaps including conflict studies),

.   detailed analysis of all data,

.   identification of dominant factors and/or road features, and

.   determine the nature of the accident problem.

Therefore, most accident investigations involve two aspects which are related to diagnosis of road safety problems. The first involves an *in-office analysis* to identify predominant vehicle manoeuvres and the accident types which are occurring. It aims to reveal the type of countermeasure needed (e.g. a disproportionate incidence of night time accidents implies a need for delineation, lighting, etc). The second aspect is an *on-site analysis* involving observation of road features and driver behaviour. This may be supplemented by extra studies, such as speed studies, traffic counts, turning manoeuvres, conflict analysis, etc.

## Data analysis and presentation

The source of data for accident investigation work is the mass accident data base outlined in Chapter 4. In the sequence of events in a hazardous road location (HRL) program (Figure 2.3), this data will have already been used in the *identification* phase described in Chapter 5. The output of this phase is a set of candidate sites (or routes, areas, or sites for mass action), i.e. sites where the recorded level of accidents points to the need for some further investigation.

The next step, that of *diagnosis*, involves further analysis of the data with the aim of achieving an appropriate level of familiarity with the site(s) concerned, such that countermeasures can be developed in a systematic way, without jumping to premature conclusions. Having said that, it will nevertheless be the case that countermeasure selection will always involve a balance of formalized procedures and engineering judgement.

*Accident history*

In Chapter 2, we noted that HRL investigations could be directed at four types of program - sites, routes, areas, or mass action programs.

*Site and route studies.* These studies relate to specific locations, and thus it is necessary to examine the accident records for such sites or routes. In these analyses, the aim is not so much to consider every single accident which has occurred at the site, but rather to search for patterns in accident occurrence which will lead to identification of underlying problems.

A key step is to examine the patterns of *accident types*. These may be coded into the data base according to standard classifications (see Figures 4.1 and 4.2 for examples), or may need to be inferred from the data base and/or narratives and sketches on the accident report form (see Chapter 4). In many cases, there will be a relatively small number of accident types at any given site. Dominant accident types provide the most reliable guide to the remedial action required, since they are likely to be indicative of the future accident patterns at the site if it is not treated. For most accident types there are one or more specific countermeasures which are applicable (see Chapter 7), and thus identification of accident type often leads directly to potential treatments. Typical accident types might include (Andreassen, 1989, p 3):

. collisions between vehicles entering from adjacent streets,
. collisions involving vehicles turning from the opposite direction,
. rear end collisions,
. collisions between vehicles and pedestrians,
. collisions between vehicles travelling in the same direction (e.g. sideswiping),
. vehicles running off the road,
. collisions with fixed objects off the road, and
. collisions with parked vehicles.

If there is not a dominant accident type, development of a remedial treatment can be very difficult. One of the tenets of the HRL approach is that accident problems must be capable of resolution through road and traffic engineering measures. If there is no dominant accident type, it may be that no engineering measure is applicable to the problems at that site. Alternatively, it may be that there are two or more major accident types, but that the engineering treatment for each is different and possibly even in conflict. (For example, if there is a signalized intersection with a history of both pedestrian accidents and collisions between turning and oncoming vehicles, the latter can be tackled with fully controlled turn phasing of the signals, but this may make the pedestrian situation more complex, and perhaps even exacerbate it if the pedestrians do not obey WALK/DON'T WALK signals.)

A frequency histogram showing the distribution of accident types is a useful way of representing this data; this may be simply a bar chart showing the dominant accident type codes.

Supplementary analyses at this stage include investigation of the frequency with which accidents occur according to a range of environmental or other characteristics, such as:

. light condition (day, dusk, dawn, dark): to see if there are particular visibility situations which are causing problems,

. road condition (wet, dry): to see if there is evidence of a skidding problem - may be indicative of a low skid resistance pavement, drainage problems, etc),

. time of day: to see if the problem is associated with morning peak, afternoon peak, or off-peak traffic and manoeuvres, or

. day of week: to see if there are problems associated with particular user groups, e.g. party-goers on Saturday night, tourists on Sunday afternoon, etc.

*Mass action studies.* Here, the approach is a little different because the focus is not a particular site. Nevertheless, the basis of the investigation is again an interrogation of the mass accident data base. Accidents may be sorted by *accident type* (as described above) to identify the locations where a particular type of accident, amenable to a standard treatment, is occurring. Examples, with possible countermeasures, might include intersection accidents involving skidding (skid resistant pavements), accidents involving collisions with a bridge or structure (guard fencing and delineation), rural single vehicle run-off-road accidents (sealed shoulders), and accidents with utility poles on a bend (removal of poles, or making them frangible).

Alternatively accidents may be sorted by *road user*, to identify where accidents involving those users are occurring. Examples might include accidents involving elderly pedestrians, accidents involving child pedestrians, accidents involving pedal cyclists, or accidents involving heavy trucks. To the extent that there is any clustering of accidents revealed by such studies, this could form the basis of a mass action program. If there is no clustering, it is unlikely that engineering remedies are available or cost-effective.

*Area studies.* The context of accident diagnosis on an area-wide basis is that a particular area (say a residential precinct up to 5 square km (2 square miles) or a shopping/commercial district) has been identified (Chapter 5) as having an accident problem. In diagnosing that problem the task is to plot, using either manual or digital mapping techniques, the location of all recorded accidents, together with a code indicating the accident type. Since a particular focus of such studies may be the vulnerable road user (pedestrian, cyclist, child), an analysis and presentation similar to that described above for site analysis is useful. An explicit road classification scheme is important here (Chapter 13), since often in these types of study a solution involves adaptation of the road and street network to ensure that extraneous traffic is excluded or discouraged.

Area studies will incorporate aspects of both site and route studies, to the extent that accidents cluster at these locations. However, the feature of an area study is to relate the accident problems evident over the area as a whole, including road network and traffic problems which may be contributing to the accident experience within the area (e.g. traffic using residential streets as a 'rat run'). Solutions resulting from area-wide studies should be integrated into a total scheme to ensure that new safety problems are not created elsewhere, and implementation will often require explicit community consultation.

*Collision diagram*

The fundamental tool used in site-specific accident diagnosis is the collision diagram. This is prepared by interrogating the accident data base, perhaps supplemented by examination of the original accident report form (and in particular the sketch and narrative description) for individual accidents which have occurred at that site.

A collision diagram is a schematic representation of all accidents occurring at a given location over a specified period, typically 1-5 years. Each collision at the site is represented by a set of arrows, one for each vehicle or pedestrian involved, which indicates the type of accident and directions of travel. Arrows may be labelled with codes for date, time, day/night, weather, vehicle type, etc (McShane and Roess, 1990, p 162).

An example of a collision diagram is shown in Figure 6.1. It summarizes the accident history of the site by superimposing on a plan all of the reported accidents at the site being investigated. This summary of vehicle and other road user movements highlights the predominant accident types and the vehicle (or other road user) manoeuvres in such accidents. The exact spot of the accident need not be shown precisely, but it is important to show the directions of the conflicting vehicles and pedestrians (e.g. if the dominant accident type at an intersection involves a collision between a through vehicle and a turning vehicle, it is important to know which leg of the intersection the turning vehicles are approaching from, as this may indicate, say, a visibility problem or an intersection configuration which makes it difficult for drivers to judge gaps in the oncoming traffic). In the collision diagram, the path of each vehicle can be represented by a solid line, and that of each pedestrian by a dotted line.

Data for each accident which may be shown on the collision diagram may include:

. accident type
. severity of accidents
. date and time of accidents
. condition of road
. light condition
. geometry of the site
. locational information
. summary of accidents (table)

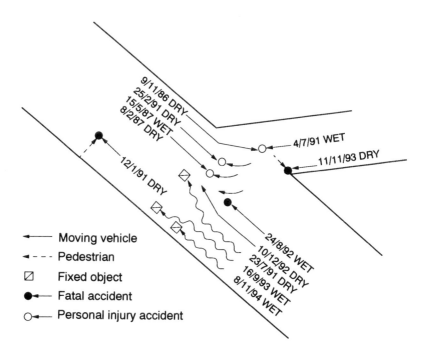

**Figure 6.1**  **Collision diagram**, in which each accident at the site is displayed, with arrows and annotations which summarize details of each accident.

124

It can be useful to include a tabular presentation of these data, in the form of an 'accident factor grid', sometimes known colloquially as a 'stick diagram'. This summarises not only the accident type, but also other pertinent information as shown in the list above in a pictorial or tabular form (Chira-Chivala and Mak, 1986). In this way, a pattern will often be evident to the analyst viewing the diagram. For example in Figure 6.2, the significance of accidents involving vehicles from adjacent approaches, associated with eastbound vehicles in wet weather and obscured vision for westbound vehicles is apparent. Commercial software packages are available in many countries which will produce accident factor grids from information coded in the mass accident data base.

| Accident Number | 1 | 2 | 3 | 4 | 5 | 6 | 7 | 8 | 9 | 10 |
|---|---|---|---|---|---|---|---|---|---|---|
| Date | 1/3/92 | 2/5/92 | 8/11/92 | 12/1/93 | 21/7/93 | 11/9/93 | 9/4/94 | 12/5/94 | 4/7/94 | 11/9/94 |
| Day of Week | SU | SA | SU | TU | WE | TH | SA | TH | MO | SU |
| Time of Day | 2115 | 2010 | 1925 | 0750 | 1310 | 0950 | 1115 | 1500 | 1710 | 2220 |
| Severity | A | A | B | B | K | K | B | B | A | B |
| Accident Type | 110 | 110 | 130 | 111 | 110 | 121 | 113 | 121 | 110 | 110 |
| Road Condition | WET | DRY | DRY | DRY | WET | DRY | DRY | DRY | WET | WET |
| Light Condition | DARK | DARK | DARK | DUSK | LIGHT | LIGHT | LIGHT | LIGHT | DUSK | DARK |
| Direction | N | N | S | W | S | W | N | S | N | N |
| Alcohol (BAC) | .05 | .08 | 0 | .05 | 0 | 0 | .07 | 0 | 0 | .15 |

**Figure 6.2**   **Accident factor grid**, which summarises, in tabular form, information about each accident.

*Summary report and presentation*

Based upon the analyses of accident histories and the collision diagram, an accident summary report is then prepared. This would summarise the information available about the site, including, for example:

.  location (e.g. street name, municipality, highway km post or mile post, map reference)
.  site description, e.g. road geometry
.  photographs of the site
.  roadworks (if any)
.  accident listing (showing details of each accident)
.  accident summary by:
    .  severity
    .  accident type
    .  cost of accidents
    .  road condition
    .  light condition
    .  time of day
    .  month
    .  day of week
    .  year
    .  factors identified (alcohol, fatigue, roadside objects, etc)
    .  objects hit
    .  types of vehicle
    .  age of drivers
    .  traffic volumes
    .  turning volumes
.  the problem(s) evident at the site
.  the recommended solution
.  economic evaluation of the recommended solution

## Site investigations

While the original road accident reports may contain some road and site data, it will inevitably be necessary to carry out a site inspection to accurately assess the road conditions and other site factors which may be relevant.

### Road features

The on-site observations should attempt to identify any adverse features of road design and the road traffic environment. This should include night time investigation, and perhaps investigation under adverse weather conditions. The investigator should walk around the site, and drive through it executing the specific manoeuvres which have been shown to be problematical. This can offer valuable insights into identifying and understanding factors which are contributing to accident occurrence. Particular attention should be given to whether various topographical features such as the sky, colour of buildings, foliage and road alignment may combine to create confusion or uncertainty in the mind of the driver. It may be important to check that the layout, signing, pavement markings, lighting, etc conform with the applicable current standards or guidelines, but it should not be assumed that adherence to such standards will necessarily eliminate or solve the problem (UK Department of Transport, 1986, p 6.4). Indeed, since such standards and guidelines are being continually changed, it is more likely than not that most sites will contain design elements or features which are out of date in one way or another.

Photographs of the site, its problem areas and its approaches can be a valuable tool in accident investigation. It may be appropriate to make a video-recording of the site in order to analyse road user behaviour, and perhaps to form the basis of a before-and-after study.

An illustrative check list for detailing road characteristics is presented in Table 6.1, based upon Landles (1980), National Association of Australian State Road Authorities (1988a, Figure 5.3) and UK Department of Transport (1986, Appendix 6E). This list may be a useful memory jogger, each item to be interpreted freely depending upon the particular site in question. It may be indicative of whether particular items are present, and their condition, appropriateness, conformity with current standards or practice, the need for maintenance or removal or restoration, etc. If the item is not present, should it be? In other cases, the item may provide a clue about accident patterns or a warning about accident potential. The basic point is that this list is indicative of the sorts of items which the investigator may seek on a site visit, not that it is an exhaustive checklist.

*Traffic data*

Data on traffic volumes (including turning volumes), pedestrian flows, and vehicle speeds may be helpful, depending upon the particular circumstances and problems at the site. In some cases these will be available, but in other cases they may need to be collected as a special case (See Chapter 4).

**Table 6.1**
**Illustrative check list for site inspection**

| Road | Signs and markings |
|---|---|
| width | inventory of signs |
| divided/undivided | legibility |
| number of lanes | conspicuity |
| crossfall | comprehensibility |
| gradient | credibility |
| shoulder | centre, lane and edge lines |
| verge | pavement markings |
| median and openings | pavement markers |
| footpath/sidewalk | post-mounted delineators |
| kerbs, ramps | chevrons, alignment markers |
| drainage | |
| combination of factors | Traffic signals |
| | primary/secondary/tertiary |
| Road surface | intensity |
| type | location |
| roughness | turn control |
| friction | pedestrian display |
| service access | detector type |
| | controller type |
| Road geometry | part of linked system |
| curve | cycle times and green splits |
| gradient | |
| superelevation | Pedestrians/bicyclists |
| crest | crossing facilities |
| sag: foot of hill | number and character |
| | pedestrian barriers |
| Intersection | pedestrian refuge |
| type | |
| number of legs | Lighting |
| channelization | type |
| turn lanes | height |
| turning radius | intensity |
| | obstruction |

**Table 6.1 (continued)**

| | |
|---|---|
| *Parked vehicles* | *Roadside* |
| on-street parking | poles, posts, etc |
| off-street parking and access | horizontal railings |
| visibility | rocks, trees, other hazards |
| clearway hours | safety barriers/fences |
| parking control | side slopes |
| loading facilities | culverts |
| bus stops | bridge abutments, railings |
| taxi rank | |
| | *Visibility* |
| *Speed* | of intersection approach |
| safe speed | of side road |
| speed limit | of traffic control devices |
| vehicle speed | of pedestrians |
| | of parked vehicles |
| *Environment* | of bus stops |
| land uses | over crest |
| school children | subliminal delineation |
| heavy vehicles | |
| ambient noise | *Evidence of problems, e.g.* |
| access/egress problems | broken glass, debris |
| | skid marks |
| | damaged road furniture |

*Driver behaviour and conflict studies*

In almost all road accidents, there are human factors derived from the physical and mental condition, experience, and age of the driver(s) which may contribute to a particular accident. In most cases, these human factors will be reflected in the data compiled in the accident reports.

In some cases, it may be helpful to have additional information on driver behaviour at the site. Examples include late braking on entry to a sharp curve, evasive actions at an intersection, behaviour resulting from inadequate or misleading visual information, etc. These actions may be codified in a conflict study. As discussed in Chapter 4, these involve direct observation of the site, or the use of video recording, in order to examine near-accidents as a means of gaining insight into accident problems at a site. The information gained in this way can be valuable in understanding traffic operation and the interactions which occur between traffic streams at the site.


**Problem analysis**

On the basis of the information contained in the accident summary report, the site visit, and perhaps using supplementary data sources as described in Chapter 4, the nature of the accident situation at the site can be investigated. The following questions are relevant (Andreassend, 1983):

. Are accidents associated with a physical condition of the road, and can this situation be eliminated or corrected?

. Is visibility adequate, and can this be corrected, or if not is there adequate warning?

. Are the existing signs, signals, and pavement markings doing the job for which they were intended? Are replacements needed?

. Is traffic properly channelled to minimize the occurrence of conflicts?

. Would accidents be prevented by prohibition of a specific movement (e.g. a right or left turn), or by giving it priority (e.g. exclusive turn phase at a traffic signal)?

. Can some of the traffic be diverted to other streets where the accident potential is not as great?

. Are night time accidents out of proportion to daytime accidents - indicating the need for special night time protection (lighting, delineation, etc)?

. Do conditions show the need for additional traffic law enforcement?

# 7 Development of countermeasures

*The preceding stages of the Hazardous Road Location process have identified locations having an accident problem which is amenable to treatment with road or traffic engineering measures. The next stage is to develop location-specific remedial treatments. In this chapter, the principles of countermeasure development are discussed, and generic treatments applicable to a range of accident types and situations are reviewed. Chapters 8 through 14 then discuss specific countermeasures in more detail.*

**Principles of countermeasure development**

The process of countermeasure development should aim to (Institution of Highways and Transportation, 1990a, p 25; National Association of Australian State Road Authorities, 1988a, p 26):

.   determine the range of measures likely to influence the dominant accident types and road features,

.   select countermeasures which, on the basis of professional judgement and experience, can be expected to reduce the number or severity of accidents of the type dominant at the location,

.   check that adopted countermeasures do not have undesirable consequences, either in safety terms (e.g. lead to an increase in the number or severity of another accident type) or in traffic efficiency or environmental terms,

. be cost-effective, that is, maximize the benefits from the HRL program, and

. be efficient, that is produce benefits which outweigh the costs.

A safe road is one which recognises the realities and limitations of human decision making, as outlined in Chapter 3. This means that the design and management of the road and its environment must ensure that the many characteristics of the road environment (including road geometry, road surface, cross section, roadside features, median treatments, delineation, traffic signs, traffic control devices, route guidance, street lighting, access provisions, etc) individually and in combination provide an environment through which the driver can travel safely. In other words, the road environment must not place demands upon the driver that are beyond the driver's ability to manage, or which are outside normal road user expectations (Rumar, 1982). A safe road may therefore be defined as one which is designed and managed so that it:

. warns the driver of any substandard or unusual features,
. informs the driver of conditions to be encountered,
. guides the driver through unusual sections,
. controls the driver's passage through conflict points and road links, and
. forgives a driver's errant or inappropriate behaviour.

Analogous considerations are equally applicable to other road users, such as pedal cyclists and pedestrians.

In keeping with these determinants, there are a number of principles which should be considered in the development of countermeasures for specific locations. In general, the road safety engineer should attempt to satisfy these principles to an extent determined by the individual needs of significant road user groups and the pattern of accidents at the site.

*Intersections*

The main design principles for intersections are:

. minimize the number of conflict points and hence the opportunities for accidents; both t-intersections and roundabouts have fewer conflict points than a cross-intersection (see Figure 7.1), which is one of the main reasons for their superior safety performance,

132

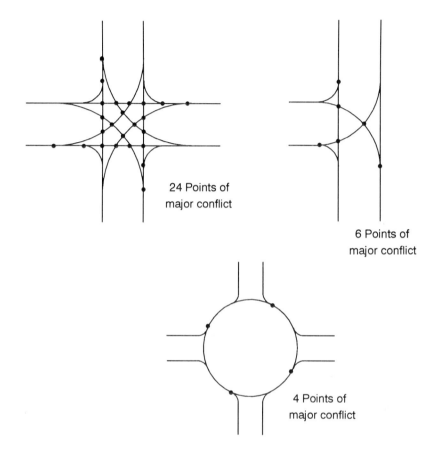

24 Points of
major conflict

6 Points of
major conflict

4 Points of
major conflict

**Figure 7.1    Conflict points at intersections**

. give precedence to major movements through alignment, delineation, and traffic control,

. separate conflicts in space or time,

. control the angle of conflict; crossing streams of traffic should intersect at a right angle or close to it while merging streams should intersect at small angles to ensure low relative speed,

.    define and minimize conflict areas,

.    define vehicle paths,

.    ensure adequate sight distances,

.    control approach speeds using alignment, lane width, traffic control or speed limits,

.    provide clear indications of right-of-way requirements,

.    minimize roadside hazards,

.    provide for all vehicular and non-vehicular traffic likely to use the intersection, including where necessary special provisions for heavy vehicles, public transport vehicles, and pedestrians and other vulnerable road users,

.    simplify the driving task, and

.    minimize road user delay.

Many of the more commonly used intersection traffic control devices combine several of these principles, although additional refinements to the standard treatment are often needed. Roundabouts, for example, usually include to some degree all of the above principles. Similarly, traffic signals also incorporate many of these principles but some, such as ensuring adequate sight distance, minimizing conflict angles and minimizing the number of conflict points, are of lesser importance because of the ability for time-separation of conflicting movements.

Perhaps the most challenging aspect in designing solutions at hazardous road locations is to achieve the safety objective(s) for significant user groups, while at the same time striking an appropriate balance between other competing objectives related to traffic (e.g. road capacity, delay) and the environment (e.g. noise, aesthetics).

*Mid-block locations*

For non-intersection locations (variously called mid-blocks, road links or road sections), the principles for safe design and operation include:

.   ensure appropriate and consistent standards of horizontal and vertical alignment,

.   develop roadway cross sections to suit road function and traffic volumes,

.   delineate roadway and vehicle paths,

.   ensure appropriate standards of access control from abutting land use, and

.   ensure that the roadside environment is clear or forgiving.

Overlaying all of these principles is a vital need to consider the particular needs of all road user groups. Proper consideration of these needs is a major determinant in the quality of the final treatment. In particular, pedestrians have special needs that should be separately considered when investigating safety problems and developing countermeasures (see Chapter 14).

Other examples can be found in the special requirements of heavy vehicles, for example in negotiating low-radius turns or travelling through horizontal curves with adverse super-elevation (Ogden, 1992; Sweatman, et al, 1990). Other user groups, such as general vehicular traffic, cyclists, motorcyclists and public transport vehicles, may all justify explicit attention at particular sites or in relation to particular accident types.

## Countermeasure selection

*Matching solutions to problems*

As mentioned previously, the key to the selection of countermeasures at a particular site, route, area, or for mass application, is to concentrate on the particular accident types which have been identified in the diagnosis phase (Chapter 6) as amenable to treatment with road or traffic engineering measures. However, there will often be a number of remedial treatments which could be applied individually or in combination. The final choice will generally be based upon judgement and experience, utilizing countermeasures which have been successful in similar circumstances elsewhere.

Tables 7.1 through 7.7 at the end of this chapter summarize the treatments which have been found to be effective in relation to the particular accident types which typically occur at (respectively):

. intersections with high speed traffic,
. intersections with low speed traffic,
. mid blocks with high speed traffic,
. mid blocks with low speed traffic,
. roads with high design speed,
. pedestrian facilities, and
. railway crossings.

These tables present a composite review of the more detailed findings outlined in Chapters 8 through 14, but draw more specifically upon similar summaries presented in such sources as Ross Silcock Partnership (1991, p 143), UK Department of Transport (1986, Section 7); Royal Society for the Prevention of Accidents (1994), Travers Morgan (1991, 1992), Khisty (1990, p 640 ff), Garber and Hoel (1988, p 146 ff), Cantilli (1982), Andreassen (1989), Roads and Traffic Authority of NSW (1995), Queensland Transport (1993), Bureau of Transportation and Communications Economics (1995) and National Association of Australian State Road Authorities (1988a).

These tables identify accident types likely to be found in each of these locations or environments, and indicate the potential effects (both positive and negative, the latter being shown in parentheses) of a range of countermeasures. It is important to note that these countermeasures will only be effective if accident data indicate that accidents of the type indicated are in fact a problem at the site in question. This underlines the point emphasized in preceding chapters that the HRL process must identify whether the accident problem at a site is amenable to treatment, as well as determining what that treatment should be. The accident type categorization used in these tables is based upon that presented in Figures 4.1 and 4.2; this same categorization is used later in Chapter 16 in our discussion of the economic appraisal of projects, since each of these specific accident types can have associated with it an average accident cost which means that the economic benefits of a proposed treatment may be calculated.

*Criteria for countermeasure development*

There are a number of criteria for countermeasure selection, including:

. *technical feasibility*: can the countermeasure provide an answer to the accident problems which have been diagnosed, and does it have a technical basis for success?

. *economic efficiency*: is the countermeasure likely to be cost effective and will it produce benefits to exceed its costs?

. *affordability*: can it be accommodated within the program budget; if not, should it be deferred, or should a cheaper, perhaps interim solution be adopted?

. *acceptability*: does the countermeasure clearly target the identified problem, and will it be readily understandable by the community?

. *practicable*: is there likely to be a problem of non-compliance, and can the measure work without unreasonable enforcement effort?

. *political and institutional acceptability*: is the countermeasure likely to attract political support, and will it be supported by the organisation responsible for its installation and on-going management?

. *legal*: is the countermeasure a legal device, and will users be breaking any law by using it in the way intended?

. *compatibility*: is the countermeasure compatible and consistent with other strategies, either in the same locality or which have been applied in similar situations elsewhere?

It can be seen that the decision to adopt a particular countermeasure may involve more than a simple matching of a solution to a problem. The development of countermeasures requires a clearly-understood technical and institutional framework to provide the guiding principles and motivation for action.

Subsequent chapters of this book address in detail the technical or engineering aspects of road safety engineering[1], and the evaluation of road safety engineering programs. However, it is important to remember that all of this technical work takes place within a broader institutional, political, legal and social framework.

## Effectiveness and cost-effectiveness

Tables 7.1 through 7.7 have summarized the accumulated experience of road safety engineers in relation to the types of countermeasure which are likely to be effective in particular situations. However, as has been stressed elsewhere in this book, treatments must be *cost-effective* as well as *effective*.

Economic appraisal of road safety treatments is discussed in Chapter 16. However, at this point it is useful to present, for comparison with the above tables, the findings of a study which used a Delphi method to seek expert opinion on which countermeasures were likely to be cost-effective. More specifically, the study (Travers Morgan, 1991) conducted a major survey of international experts in road safety, asking them to grade, on the basis of their experience, a wide range of 'road features' in terms of their effectiveness ('ability to reduce accidents') and cost-effectiveness ('benefit:cost ratio'). Twenty-one experts from the United States, Canada, United Kingdom, Sweden, Japan, New Zealand and Australia responded. Their results, for urban roads and rural roads respectively, are shown in Tables 7.8 and 7.9.

These show that certain treatments, while perhaps being highly effective, are not cost-effective because of their high initial cost or on-going operational costs. On the other hand, as we move towards the bottom right-hand corner of the tables, we can see that there are a number of projects which as well as being effective are also considered to be highly cost-effective. These types of countermeasure are clearly desirable, and where the accident pattern is such that these types of treatment are suitable, they are likely to be very appropriate.

## Note

1. In Chapters 8 through 14, we review a wide range of road and traffic factors and discuss their effects on road safety. Preparation of this material involved an extensive review of the literature. Of particular value in the literature review were previous reviews of aspects of road and traffic safety, both for what they concluded and also for their links

to the literature. These included Roy Jorgensen and Associates (1978), Federal Highway Administration (1982), Lay (1986), Nairn and Partners (1987), Carney (1986), Smith and Mason (1988), Transportation Research Board (1987a,b), Hoque and Sanderson (1988), National Association of Australian State Road Authorities (1988a), Pak-Poy and Kneebone (1988), Institute of Transportation Engineers (1993a); Travers Morgan (1991); Travers Morgan (1992), UK Department of Transport (1986), Roads and Traffic Authority of NSW (1991b, 1995), Queensland Transport (1993), County Surveyors Society (1989, 1991), Walker and Lines (1991), Hedman (1990) and Ward (1992).

**Table 7.1**
**Countermeasures: high speed intersections**

| Treatment | Accidents Affected (type*) | Reduction (%) |
|---|---|---|
| Channelization | Adjacent approaches (101-109) | 20-40 |
| | opposing vehs, turning (202-206) | 20-40 |
| | U-turn (207, 304) | 20-40 |
| | rear end (301-303) | 20-40 |
| | parallel lanes, turning (308-309) | 20-40 |
| Median, with turn protection | adj approaches (101-109) | 20-30 |
| | opposing vehs, turning (202-206) | 20-30 |
| | U-turn (207, 304) | 20-30 |
| | rear end (301-303) | 20-30 |
| | parallel lanes, turning (308-309) | 20-30 |
| | hit pedestrian (001-003) | 20-30 |
| Roundabout | adj approaches (101-109) | 60-80 |
| | head on (201) | 60-80 |
| | opposing vehs, turning (202-206) | 60-80 |
| | rear end (301-303) | (-20)-0 |
| | U-turn (207, 304) | 40-80 |
| | hit pedestrian (001-003) | (-20)-0 |
| Lighting | adj approaches (101-109) | 20-30 |
| | head on (201) | 20-30 |
| | opposing vehs, turning (202-206) | 20-30 |
| | U-turn (207, 304) | 20-30 |
| | rear end (301-303) | 20-30 |
| | parallel lanes, turning (308-309) | 20-30 |
| | hit pedestrian (001-003) | 20-30 |
| | permanent obstruction (605) | 20-30 |
| Resurfacing, reseal | rear end (301-303) | 30-40 |
| STOP sign | adj approaches (101-109) | 40-60 |
| | rear end (301-303) | (-40)-(-60) |
| YIELD/ GIVE WAY sign | adjacent approaches (101-109) | 10-20 |

**Table 7.1 (continued)**

| Treatment | Accidents Affected (type*) | Reduction (%) |
|---|---|---|
| Delineation, signing | adj approaches (101-109)<br>opposing vehs, turning (202-206)<br>parallel lanes, turning (308-309)<br>lane change (305-307)<br>permanent obstruction (605) | 20-30<br>20-30<br>20-30<br>20-30<br>20-30 |
| Street closure (cross intersection) | adj approaches (101-109)<br>head on (201)<br>opposing vehs, turning (202-206)<br>hit pedestrian (001-003) | 50-80<br>50-80<br>50-80<br>50-80 |
| Realignment, reconstruction | adj approaches (101-109)<br>head on (201)<br>opposing vehs, turning (202-206)<br>parallel lanes, turning (308-309) | 30-50<br>30-50<br>30-50<br>20-40 |
| Staggered intersection | adj approaches (101-109)<br>head on (201)<br>opposing vehs, turning (202-206)<br>hit pedestrian (001-003)<br>rear end (301-303) | 40-80<br>40-80<br>40-60<br>40-60<br>60-80 |
| New traffic signals | adj approaches (101-109)<br>opposing vehs, turning (202-206)<br>rear end (301-303)<br>U-turn (207, 304)<br>hit pedestrian (001-003) | 30-80<br>(-20)-(-100)<br>(-40)-(-70)<br>50-80<br>30-70 |
| Modified traffic signals | opposing vehs, turning (202-206)<br>U-turn (207, 304)<br>hit pedestrian (001-003)<br>adj approaches (101-109)<br>rear end (301-303) | 30-80<br>40-60<br>20-40<br>40-60<br>(-50)-(-70) |
| acceleration/ deceleration lanes | rear end (301-303)<br>lane change (305-307)<br>overtaking (503, 506) | 50-80<br>40-60<br>20-40 |

* accident type codes: refer Figures 4.1 and 4.2.

**Table 7.2**
**Countermeasures: low speed intersections**

| Treatment | Accidents Affected (type*) | Reduction (%) |
|---|---|---|
| Roundabout | adj approaches (101-109) | 60-80 |
| | head on (201) | 50-80 |
| | opposing vehs, turning (202- 206) | 50-80 |
| | rear end (301-303) | (-30)-0 |
| | U-turn (207, 304) | 50-80 |
| | hit pedestrian (001-003) | (-30)-(-10) |
| Lighting | adj approaches (101-109) | 15-25 |
| | head on (201) | 15-25 |
| | opposing vehs, turning (202-206) | 15-25 |
| | rear end (301-303) | 15-25 |
| | lane change (305-307) | 15-25 |
| | parallel lanes, turning (308-309) | 15-25 |
| | hit pedestrian (001-003) | 15-25 |
| | permanent obstruction (605) | 15-25 |
| Resurfacing | rear end (301-303) | 30-40 |
| STOP sign | adj approaches (101-109) | 40-60 |
| | rear end (301-303) | (-40)-(-60) |
| Delineation, signing | adj approaches (101-109) | 10-20 |
| | opposing vehs, turning (202-206) | 10-20 |
| | parallel lanes, turning (308-309) | 10-20 |
| | rear end (301-303) | 10-20 |
| | lane change (305-307) | 10-20 |
| | permanent obstruction (605) | 10-20 |
| Street closure (cross intersection) | adj approaches (101-109) | 50-80 |
| | head on (201) | 50-80 |
| | opposing vehs, turning (202-206) | 50-80 |
| | hit pedestrian (001-003) | 10-50 |

**Table 7.2 (continued)**

| Treatment | Accidents Affected (Type*) | Reduction (%) |
|---|---|---|
| Realignment, reconstruction | adj approaches (101-109)<br>head on (201)<br>opposing vehs, turning (202-206)<br>lane change (305-307)<br>hit pedestrian (001-003)<br>rear end (301-303) | 30-50<br>40-60<br>40-60<br>30-40<br>40-60<br>10-20 |
| Improved sight distance | adj approaches (101-109)<br>opposing vehs, turning (202-206)<br>rear end (301-303)<br>U-turn (207, 304)<br>lane change (305-307)<br>parallel lanes, turning (308-309)<br>hit pedestrian (001-003) | 30-50<br>30-50<br>30-50<br>30-50<br>30-50<br>30-50<br>30-50 |
| New traffic signals | adj approaches (101-109)<br>opposing vehs, turning (202-206)<br>rear end (301-303)<br>U-turn (207, 304)<br>hit pedestrian (001-003) | 30-60<br>(-10)-(-30)<br>(-30)-(-50)<br>50-80<br>30-60 |
| Modified traffic signals | opposing vehs, turning (202-206)<br>U-turn (207, 304)<br>hit pedestrian (001-003)<br>adj approaches (101-109)<br>rear end (301-303) | 30-80<br>40-60<br>10-30<br>10-30<br>(-20)-(-70) |
| Channelization | adj approaches (101-109)<br>opposing vehs, turning (202-206)<br>rear end (301-303)<br>parallel lanes, turning (308-309)<br>U-turn (207, 304) | 20-40<br>20-40<br>20-40<br>20-40<br>20-40 |
| Red light camera | adj approaches (101-109)<br>opposing vehs, turning (202-206)<br>rear end (301-303) | 30-40<br>20-30<br>(-20)-(-30) |

* accident type codes: refer Figures 4.1 and 4.2.

## Table 7.3
## Countermeasures: high speed mid-block locations

| Treatment | Accidents Affected (type*) | Reduction (%) |
|---|---|---|
| Removal of roadside hazards | permanent obstruction (605) | 60-80 |
| | off road, on straight (701-704) | 60-80 |
| | off road, on curve (801-804) | 60-80 |
| Clear zone, frangible posts, safety barrier | permanent obstruction (605) | 30-40 |
| | off road, on straight (701-704) | 30-40 |
| | off road, on curve (801-804) | 30-40 |
| Route lighting | rear end (301-303) | 20-30 |
| | hit pedestrian (001-003) | 20-30 |
| | permanent obstruction (605) | 25-50 |
| | off road, on straight (701-704) | 25-50 |
| | off road, on curve (801-804) | 25-50 |
| | out of control on curve (805) | 25-50 |
| Resurfacing, reseal | rear end (301-303) | 20-40 |
| | off road, on straight (701-704) | 10-20 |
| | off road, on curve (801-804) | 20-30 |
| | out of control (705, 805) | 20-30 |
| Barrier line | head on (201) | 50-60 |
| | overtaking (503, 506) | 40-60 |
| Seal shoulder | head on (201) | 20-60 |
| | off road, on straight (701-704) | 20-60 |
| | off road, on curve (801-804) | 20-60 |
| | out of control (705, 805) | 20-60 |
| Advisory speed sign | U-turn (207, 304) | 10-20 |
| | rear end (301-303) | 10-20 |
| | off road, on curve (801-804) | 20-40 |
| | out of control on curve (805) | 30-40 |

**Table 7.3 (continued)**

| Treatment | Accidents Affected (Type*) | Reduction (%) |
|---|---|---|
| Delineation | head on (201) | 30-40 |
| | overtaking (503, 506) | 30-40 |
| | rear end (301-303) | 10-20 |
| | lane change (305-307) | 10-20 |
| | hit pedestrian (001-003) | 10-20 |
| | permanent obstruction (605) | 10-20 |
| | off road, on straight (701-704) | 10-20 |
| | off road, on curve (801-804) | 10-30 |
| | out of control (705, 805) | 10-20 |
| Widen or replace bridge or culvert | head on (201) | 30-50 |
| | overtaking (503, 506) | 30-50 |
| | hit pedestrian (001-003) | 30-50 |
| | permanent obstruction (605) | 30-50 |
| | off road, on straight (701-704) | 30-50 |
| | off road, on curve (801-804) | 30-50 |
| | out of control (705, 805) | 30-50 |
| Widen shoulder | head on (201) | 20-30 |
| | off road, on straight (701-704) | 20-30 |
| | off road, on curve (801-804) | 20-30 |
| | out of control (705, 805) | 20-30 |
| Profiled edge line | permanent obstruction (605) | 20-40 |
| | off road, on straight (701-704) | 30-60 |
| | off road, on curve (801-804) | 30-60 |
| Overtaking lane | overtaking (503,506) | 30-50 |
| | off road, on straight (701-704) | 30-50 |
| | off road, on curve (801-804) | 20-30 |
| | head on (201) | 20-30 |
| Guide posts | off road, on curve (801-804) | 30-40 |
| | out of control on curve (805) | 30-40 |

* accident type codes: refer Figures 4.1 and 4.2.

## Table 7.4
## Countermeasures: low speed mid-block locations

| Treatment | Accidents Affected (type*) | Reduction (%) |
|---|---|---|
| Removal of roadside hazards | permanent obstruction (605)<br>off road, on straight (701-704)<br>off road, on curve (801-804) | 60-80<br>60-80<br>60-80 |
| Clear zone, frangible posts, safety barrier | permanent obstruction (605)<br>off road, on straight (701-704)<br>off road, on curve (801-804) | 30-50<br>30-50<br>30-50 |
| Route lighting | hit pedestrian (001-003)<br>rear end (301-303)<br>permanent obstruction (605)<br>off road, on straight (701-704)<br>off road, on curve (801-804)<br>out of control on curve (805) | 20-30<br>20-30<br>25-40<br>25-40<br>25-40<br>25-40 |
| Resurfacing, reseal | rear end (301-303)<br>off road, on curve (801-804)<br>out of control (705, 805) | 20-40<br>10-20<br>10-20 |
| Clearway, parking restrictions | lane change (305-307)<br>rear end (301-303)<br>veh leaving driveway (407)<br>hit parked veh (601)<br>hit pedestrian (001-003) | 20-30<br>20-30<br>20-30<br>50-60<br>30-40 |
| Skid resistant pavement | rear end (301-303)<br>off road, on curve (801-804)<br>out of control (705, 805) | 40-60<br>10-20<br>10-20 |
| Speed zoning | veh leaving driveway (407)<br>hit pedestrian (001-003)<br>off road, on straight (701-704)<br>off road, on curve (801-804)<br>out of control (705, 805) | 10-25<br>15-30<br>10-25<br>10-25<br>10-25 |

**Table 7.4 (continued)**

| Treatment | Accidents Affected (Type*) | Reduction (%) |
|---|---|---|
| Delineation | lane change (305-307) | 15-25 |
| | rear end (301-303) | 15-25 |
| | hit pedestrian (001-003) | 15-25 |
| | permanent obstruction (605) | 15-25 |
| | off road, on straight (701-704) | 15-25 |
| | off road, on curve (801-804) | 15-25 |
| | out of control (705, (805) | 15-25 |
| Access control (service roads) | adj approaches (101-109) | 50-60 |
| | rear end (301-303) | 50-60 |
| | lane change (305-307) | 10-30 |
| | veh leaving driveway (407) | 50-60 |
| | hit parked veh (601) | 50-60 |
| | hit pedestrian (001-003) | 10-30 |
| Duplicate road (dual carriageway) | adj approaches (101-109) | 30-50 |
| | head on (201) | 90-100 |
| | rear end (301-303) | 30-40 |
| | veh leaving driveway (407) | 40-50 |
| | overtaking (503, 506) | 50-100 |
| | hit parked veh (601) | 10-20 |
| | hit pedestrian (001-003) | 50-60 |

* accident type codes: refer Figures 4.1 and 4.2.

**Table 7.5**
**Countermeasures: high speed road design**

| Treatment | Accidents Affected (type*) | Reduction (%) |
|---|---|---|
| Improve horizontal alignment | head on (201) | 30-45 |
| | rear end (301-303) | 30-45 |
| | overtaking (503, 506) | 30-45 |
| | hit pedestrian (001-003) | 30-45 |
| | off road, on curve (801-804) | 30-45 |
| | out of control on curve (805) | 30-45 |
| Improve vertical alignment | head on (201) | 40-50 |
| | rear end (301-303) | 40-50 |
| | overtaking (503, 506) | 40-50 |
| | hit pedestrian (001-003) | 40-50 |
| | off road, on straight (701-704) | 40-50 |
| | off road, on curve (801-804) | 40-50 |
| | out of control (705, 805) | 40-50 |
| Improve horizontal and vertical alignment | head on (201) | 60-80 |
| | rear end (301-303) | 60-80 |
| | overtaking (503, 506) | 60-80 |
| | hit pedestrian (001-003) | 60-80 |
| | permanent obstruction (605) | 60-80 |
| | off road, on straight (701-704) | 40-60 |
| | off road, on curve (801-804) | 60-80 |
| | out of control on straight (705) | 40-60 |
| | out of control on curve (805) | 60-80 |
| Provide correct superelevation | head on (201) | 40-60 |
| | overtaking (503, 506) | 40-60 |
| | off road, on curve (801-804) | 40-60 |
| | out of control on curve (805) | 40-60 |
| Duplicate road (dual carriageway) | adj approaches (101-109) | 30-50 |
| | head on (201) | 90-100 |
| | rear end (301-303) | 30-50 |
| | overtaking (503, 506) | 50-80 |
| | hit pedestrian (001-003) | 30-50 |

* accident type codes: refer Figures 4.1 and 4.2.

**Table 7.6**
**Countermeasures: pedestrian treatments**

| Treatment | Accidents Affected (type*) | Reduction (%) |
|---|---|---|
| Lighting, ped crossing | hit pedestrian (001-003)<br>rear end (301-303) | 20-30<br>10-20 |
| Pedestrian refuge | head on (201)<br>veh leaving driveway (407)<br>overtaking (503, 506)<br>hit pedestrian (001-003) | 80-90<br>40-50<br>80-90<br>20-60 |
| Pedestrian fencing | hit pedestrian (001-003) | 30-50 |
| Pedestrian crossing | hit pedestrian (001-003) | 10-50 |
| Kerb extensions | hit pedestrian (001-003) | 30-50 |
| Pedestrian signals | rear end (301-303)<br>hit pedestrian (001-003) | (-10)-0<br>10-70 |
| Ped grade separation | hit pedestrian (001-003) | 70-90 |

* accident type codes: refer Figures 4.1 and 4.2.

**Table 7.7**
**Countermeasures: railway crossings**

| Treatment | Accidents Affected (type*) | Reduction (%) |
|---|---|---|
| Overpass or underpass | hit train (903)<br>hit crossing furniture (904) | 100<br>40-60 |
| Barriers, gates | hit train (903)<br>hit crossing furniture (904) | 70-90<br>(-10)-(-40) |
| Flashing lights | hit train (903)<br>hit crossing furniture (904) | 50-80<br>(-10)-(-40) |
| Improve horizontal alignment | hit train (903)<br>hit crossing furniture (904) | 30-40<br>30-40 |
| Improve vertical alignment | hit train (903)<br>hit crossing furniture (904) | 40-50<br>30-40 |
| Improve horizontal and vertical alignment | hit train (903)<br>hit crossing furniture (904) | 50-70<br>60-80 |
| Improve delineation | hit train (903)<br>hit crossing furniture (904) | 20-30<br>20-30 |
| Lighting | hit train (903)<br>hit crossing furniture (904) | 10-20<br>20-30 |
| Warning signs | hit train (903)<br>hit crossing furniture (904) | 10-20<br>10-20 |

* accident type codes: refer Figures 4.1 and 4.2.

**Table 7.8**
**Effectiveness and cost-effectiveness of urban treatments**

| Cost Effect-iveness | Safety Effectiveness | | |
|---|---|---|---|
| | Low | Medium | High |
| Low | Widen traffic lanes<br>Bus transit lanes<br>Warning signs<br>Resurfacing less frequently | Widen sealed area<br>Raised pavt markers (edge)<br>Widen squeeze points<br>Bus bays<br>Lighting<br>Widen for parking/ breakdown<br>Cycle paths | Boom gates/ bells/ lights<br>Concrete median barrier |
| Medium | Relocate waste containers<br>Reflectorized guide posts | Speed zoning<br>Electronic guidance<br>Flashing lights<br>Safety barrier<br>Resurfacing more frequently<br>Guardrail<br>Edge line marking<br>Raised pavt markers (centre)<br>Advance direction/ reassurance signs | Concrete raised median<br>Roundabouts<br>Relocate poles |
| High | | Painted median<br>Warning/ advisory signs<br>Chevron signs | Turn lanes<br>Resurfacing at accident spots<br>Frangible poles<br>Painted channelization |

Source: Travers Morgan (1991)

**Table 7.9**
**Effectiveness and cost-effectiveness of rural treatments**

| Cost Effect-iveness | Safety Effectiveness | | |
|---|---|---|---|
| | Low | Medium | High |
| Low | Resurfacing less frequently | 3 Lane sections<br>Short 4 lane sections<br>Widen traffic lanes | Concrete median<br>Major realignment<br>Boom gates/ bells/ lights |
| Medium | Warning signs | Widen sealed area<br>Resurfacing more frequently<br>Flatten batters<br>Remove trees<br>Widen shoulder<br>Overtaking lanes<br>Flashing lights<br>Raised pavt markers (edges)<br>Passing bays | Concrete raised median<br>Roundabouts<br>Relocate poles<br>Staggered t-intersection<br>Widen narrow squeeze-points<br>Guard fence (median) |
| High | | Speed zoning<br>Painted median<br>Warning/ advisory signs<br>Advance direction/ reassurance signs<br>Minor realignment | Turn lanes<br>Reflectorized guide posts<br>Edge lines<br>Resurfacing at accident spots<br>Raised pavt marker (centre)<br>Guard fencing<br>Chevron signs<br>Painted channelization<br>Seal shoulder |

Source: Travers Morgan (1991)

# 8 Road design

*In the design of new roads, particular attention must be given to safety as a prime design criterion. The reconstruction of existing roads should similarly have a safety component, and indeed such reconstruction is often an important means of progressively upgrading the safety of the road network. In this chapter, we review safety aspects of road design, drawing upon the results of previous work, and presenting a succinct summary of the key safety aspects of a range of road design elements[1].*

## Design standard

Design standard refers to strategic decisions concerning the geometric standard to which the road is built. Such decisions are usually made at the planning stage and are primarily affected by considerations of capacity and economic efficiency, but safety should be a consideration also.

### Road standard

As traffic flow increases, it often becomes necessary or economical to design and build roads to higher geometric standards. In general, the higher the geometric standard, the safer the road. Indeed one of the economic factors which should be taken into account in deciding the appropriate design standard is the safety benefits of higher geometric standards (Lay, 1986, p 52). For example, Walker and Lines (1991) investigating the safety benefits of road improvements in the UK, examined 85 per cent of British non-motorway construction between 1982 and 1984. They found the following accident reductions (significant at the 10 per cent level or better) for various types of project:

.   rural town bypasses: 32 per cent reduction
.   rural road duplication: 29 per cent reduction
.   urban intersection grade separation: 57 per cent reduction
.   other rural projects: 28 per cent reduction.

Non-significant accident reductions were also noted for urban bypasses, rural grade separations, and 'other' urban projects.

The highest geometric standard of road is one with a high design speed, full control of access from abutting property, forgiving roadsides, entry and exit at grade-separated interchanges, and opposing directions of traffic separated by a median. This type of road is variously referred to as a freeway, motorway, autobahn, autostrada, autoroute, and sometimes an expressway. It is the safest form of road, because many of the opportunities for collisions between vehicles are designed out (Figure 8.1).

**Figure 8.1**    **A freeway (motorway) is the safest form of road.** It has most of the potential sources of conflict designed out of it, with high geometric standards, access control, forgiving roadsides, median, etc.

Typical accident rates in terms of casualty accidents per hundred million vehicle kilometres (vehicle miles, rounded to nearest significant digit) are (Australian Road Research Board, 1988):

| | | |
|---|---|---|
| . one-lane road | 800-1200 | (1300-1900) |
| . narrow two-lane road | 100-200 | (160-320) |
| . wide two-lane road | 20-100 | (30-160) |
| . undivided arterial road | 20-100 | (30-160) |
| . divided arterial road | 10-100 | (15-160) |
| . all freeways/motorways | 10 | (16) |
| . new freeways/motorways | 5 | (8) |
| . all roads | 200-800 | (320-1300) |

*In summary, safety improves dramatically with design standard, and freeways/motorways are much safer per kilometre (mile) of travel than other roads. The precise safety advantage cannot be explicitly given because there is wide variation within road types, but freeways/motorways are at least 4 times as safe as other roads, and can be as much as 20 times as safe as other arterial roads. New freeways/motorways, built to contemporary standards, are the safest form of road, and may be twice as safe as older freeways/motorways built to lower standards.*

*Access control*

Access in this context refers to the entry to a roadway of traffic from other roads, including intersections, business driveways, private driveways, and median crossovers (Cirillo, 1992). Access control therefore reduces or eliminates the variety and spacing of events to which the driver must respond. It has been described as 'the most important single design factor ever developed for accident reduction' (Federal Highway Administration, 1982, p 4-2).

Part of the safety advantage of freeways/motorways stems from the control of access from abutting property through the elimination of unexpected events and the separation of decision points (Cirillo, 1992). However, a measure of access control can be achieved without the other design features of freeways/motorways (e.g. grade-separated interchanges).

Controlling access on existing roads through the use of frontage roads can be an effective safety device (Figure 8.2). Federal Highway Administration (1982, p 4-1 ff) and Cirillo (1992) quote several American studies from the 1960s and 1970s which show that the accident rate increases rapidly with the density of access driveways. For example, in one study, the difference between a low level of development (fewer than about 20 driveways per km (30 per mile)) and a high level of development was to more than double the number of driveway accidents. Interestingly, several studies were quoted which indicated that this is a rural problem as well as an urban problem in the US. Other studies quoted in these same sources indicate that accidents increase with the density of other forms of access, including intersections and median crossovers.

In most roads of course, it is not possible or meaningful to eliminate access, but the effects of access can be moderated by reducing the conflict at access points. Glennon and Azzeh (1976) divide these into treatments which:

. reduce the number of accesses (e.g. eliminating median openings, providing frontage roads, and providing access via frontage roads rather than the main roadway), and

. separate through vehicles from vehicles using the access (e.g. turning lanes, acceleration and deceleration lanes).

**Figure 8.2    Access control using frontage roads**. These reduce the frequency of access conflicts and separate decision points.

Cirillo (1992) succinctly summarized the situation by saying that 'on those facilities which carry the most traffic, connect major activity centres, and/or are major regional arterials, access should be controlled wherever possible'.

*Control of access (i.e. reducing the frequency of intersections and median openings and preventing direct access from abutting property onto a through roadway/carriageway), and the use of devices such as frontage roads, turning lanes, and access limitation from abutting property all have safety benefits.*

## Medians

Medians, or central reservations, are used to separate opposing directions of traffic. They are of several types, including:

. wide medians without a physical barrier which provide space for the driver of an errant vehicle to regain control and/or provide room for turning lanes (see Figure 8.1 above),

. narrow medians with a physical barrier (such as a steel guard fence or shaped concrete barrier) designed to deflect an errant vehicle back into its own traffic stream; these also have the effect of discouraging inappropriate crossing of the road by pedestrians (Figure 8.3), and

. narrow medians without a physical barrier, which may do little for errant vehicles, but clearly separate opposing directions of traffic and provide an opportunity for pedestrians to cross the road in two stages (Figure 8.4).

Because of the separation of opposing traffic, medians have a beneficial effect on safety, and in addition provide some benefit to pedestrians. Walker and Lines (1991) in a British study reported that dual carriageways (i.e. roads with a median) had an accident rate on a vehicle-kilometre basis two-thirds that of single carriageway (undivided) roads. A study in Adelaide, Australia, (National Association of Australian State Road Authorities, 1988a, p 29) compared accident rates for 4-lane roads having wide medians, narrow medians, and painted narrow medians, with 4-lane roads without medians. Compared with the undivided roads, the others reduced the accident rate by:

. narrow painted median     30 per cent
. narrow raised median     48 per cent
. wide median                   54 per cent

In urban areas, medians should, where possible, be wide enough to protect a turning or crossing vehicle. 'Wide medians' in the above study were those which met this criterion.

In rural areas, wide medians should be provided to allow space for the driver of an errant vehicle to regain control. American studies in the 1970s (Federal Highway Administration, 1982, p 1-7 ff; Zegeer and Council, 1992) found that with a median width of 9 m (30 ft), between 70 and 90 per cent of vehicles encroaching on the median do not reach the other roadway/carriageway (see Chapter 12).

**Figure 8.3    Narrow median with a physical barrier.** Opposing traffic streams are separated by a physical barrier to reduce head-on conflicts.

**Figure 8.4    Narrow median with no physical barrier**. These separate opposing traffic streams and in urban areas provide a refuge for pedestrians.

Narrower medians with a physical barrier typically have a higher overall accident frequency, but a lower accident severity since the more severe opposite-direction accidents are reduced or eliminated (Zegeer and Council, 1992). For example, a British study (Johnson, 1980) found that installing a steel guard fence in the median of divided rural roads led to a reduction of 15 per cent in fatalities, but an increase in non-injury accidents of 14 per cent. A later British study (Simpson and Brown, 1988) however found that while the fatal accident rate for accidents involving the median on the fenced roads was only 43 per cent of that on roads in an unfenced control group, the total accident rate for such accidents was also lower, at 71 per cent of that found for the control group.

The median slope on wide medians can also influence accidents, and Zegeer and Council (1992) suggest that a maximum slope of 6:1 is desirable on wide medians and that slopes of 4:1 or steeper are associated with rollovers.

For maximum safety effectiveness, the number of median openings should be minimized, although this is of course at the expense of convenient access. Homburger, et al (1989, p 95) state that while the provision of a median improves the safety of a 'major street', such improvement is 'inversely proportional to the number of openings provided in the median'.

*The separation of opposing traffic streams by a median leads to significant safety benefits. In urban areas, medians should ideally be wide enough to protect turning or crossing vehicles, while a minimum width of about 9 m (30 ft), with a cross slope no greater than 6:1, is appropriate for rural areas. Medians can provide benefits to pedestrians by allowing them to cross the road in stages.*

## Cross section elements

The road cross section includes the carriageway or roadway, shoulders, kerbs, drainage features, and cut and fill batters. Over the years, a number of studies have been conducted to investigate the safety effects of elements like lane and shoulder width, shoulder type, pavement cross slope, etc. However, few of them have been able to control for other factors such as alignment and roadside clear zone, nor to distinguish between accident types and their logical relationship to cross section elements (Zegeer and Council, 1992). Nevertheless, there appears to be general consensus about some aspects, and these are reported below.

*Lane width*

Lane widths of 3.4-3.7 m (11-12 ft) have been shown to have the lowest accident rate on rural roads (Zegeer, Deen and Mayes, 1981; Zegeer and Council, 1993, p 22; McLean, 1985), and also represent the 'most appropriate balance between safety and traffic flow' (Cirillo and Council, 1986).

Lane widths of less than 3 m (10 ft) have been shown to contribute to multi-vehicle accidents (Lay, 1986, p 563; Zegeer, Deen and Mayes, 1981, p 41; Hedman, 1990).

A number of studies have shown the safety advantages of widening narrow lanes. For example, Transportation Research Board (1987a) quote an American study where 2.7 m (9 ft) lanes on rural roads were widened to 3.4 m (11 ft) and 3 m (10 ft) lanes were widened to 3.7 m (12 ft), with a serious injury accident rate reduction of 22 per cent. Zegeer and Council

(1992) quote a 1987 US study which, after control for such aspects as road and traffic features, terrain, traffic volumes, accident type, etc, developed an accident prediction model which aimed to isolate the effects of lane and shoulder width. For lane width, the amount of widening, as distinct from the ultimate lane width, was the prime factor affecting the reduction in the accident rate for *related* accident types only (i.e. the types of accident that logically should be affected by lane width, such as opposite direction and run-off-road accidents). The percent reductions were:

. for 0.3 m (1 ft) of lane widening:      12 per cent reduction
. for 0.6 m (2 ft) of lane widening:      23 per cent reduction
. for 0.9 m (3 ft) of lane widening:      32 per cent reduction
. for 1.2 m (4 ft) of lane widening:      40 per cent reduction

Just as lane widths of less than 3 m (10 ft) have been shown to contribute to multi-vehicle accidents, there is little if any benefit in increasing lane width beyond about 3.7 m (12 ft), except where there is a large volume of trucks, where lanes of about 4.0 m (13 ft) may be appropriate (Zegeer, Deen and Mayes, 1981, p 41). Indeed wider lanes may be counter-productive, since they encourage unsafe and indecisive manoeuvres such as overtaking along the centre line, perhaps in the face of oncoming traffic. Very rarely, a very wide undivided roadway/ carriageway is provided, sufficient to allow three lanes of traffic but only striped for two (Figure 8.5). This invites vehicles from either direction to overtake in the face of oncoming traffic. This is a serious abrogation of responsibility on the part of the road authority by not providing clear guidance to the motorist as to how the road is to be used, and a dereliction of its duty to deter unexpected and unsafe manoeuvres. It would be much better, from both safety and user service viewpoints, to stripe the road with three lanes, with a clearly defined overtaking lane in one direction. It would also be much cheaper to do this, as the overtaking lanes need not be provided over the full length of road, but over perhaps 10 per cent of the road, as described later in this chapter.

*Shoulder width*

Information concerning the effect of shoulder width on accidents is less conclusive. The more important feature of shoulders appears to be whether they are sealed or unsealed (see Chapter 12). However, there is some evidence that accident rates reduce as shoulder width increases up to about

3 m (10 ft). For example, an American study (Zegeer, Deen and Mayes, 1981, p 40) produced results which showed a 21 per cent reduction in total accidents when a road with no shoulders had shoulders of 0.9-2.7 m (3-9 ft) provided. The study went on to suggest (op cit, p 41) that for roads currently without shoulders, the optimum shoulder width to be provided was 1.5 m (5 ft). Hedman (1990) using Swedish data has also found a decrease in accidents with increases in shoulder width from 0 m to 2 m (about 7 ft), and that little additional benefit was obtained for shoulder widths above 2.5 m (about 8 ft).

*Lane and shoulder width*

Lane and shoulder widths are not independent, and the above results should not be regarded as conclusive. In 1982, the US Congress requested the National Research Council's Transportation Research Board to study the safety cost-effectiveness of design standards and recommend minimum geometric standards. The results of this study were published by Transportation Research Board (1987a), and supported by critical reviews of current knowledge (Transportation Research Board (1987b).

**Figure 8.5** **Very wide lanes encourage overtaking in the face of oncoming traffic.** A preferable treatment would be to provide clearly marked overtaking lanes.

One of the key areas examined was that of lane and shoulder width. Zegeer and Deacon (1987), as part of this study, produced relationships showing the expected accident rate (for run off road and opposite direction accidents) as a function of lane and shoulder width. These showed clearly that increasing lane width (up to 3.7 m (12 ft)) and increasing shoulder width (up to 3.0 m (10 ft)) had a beneficial effect, but that the two effects were not independent.

The Transportation Research Board (1987a, p 81) used these and other findings to examine these relationships. It's conclusions were that widening lanes on rural roads from 2.7 m (9 ft) to 3.7 m (12 ft) without shoulder improvement can be expected to reduce accidents by 32 per cent. Widening shoulders is less effective than widening lanes; adding a 0.9 m (3 ft) unsealed shoulder where none existed reduced accidents by 19 per cent. If the 0.9 m (3 ft) shoulder addition were paved, the expected reduction would be about 22 per cent.

The greatest gains came from a combination of improvements. For example, widening a highway with 2.7 m (9 ft) lanes and no shoulders to 3.7 m (12 ft) lanes and 1.8 m (6 ft) shoulders reduced accidents by about 60 per cent. However, the accident reduction as a result of improving a specific feature will be less if other features are also improved.

Based upon these analyses and calculations of the cost-effectiveness of various combinations, Transportation Research Board (1987a, p 144) then prepared recommendations for lane and shoulder widths. Their recommendations are shown in Table 8.1.

*Surface cross slope*

Drainage is an essential part of any road. This involves three aspects: drainage of the road surface, roadside drains, and bridges/culverts. We deal here with the first of these; the others are discussed elsewhere, in Chapters 12 and 8 respectively.

Lay (1986, p 542) has pointed out the necessity for good road surface drainage, as a 6 mm film of water can cause hydroplaning which reduces the friction coefficient to near zero, thus making both braking and turning virtually impossible. Roy Jorgensen and Associates (1978) has shown that most wet weather accidents occur on low skid resistant pavements. Dunlap, et al (1978) found that the thickness of a water film on large radius curves can be almost twice that on a crowned straight section of road with the same cross slope.

**Table 8.1**
**Recommended lane and shoulder widths**

| Traffic Flow (ADT) | Speed (km/h) (mph) | > 10 % trucks | | < 10 % trucks | |
|---|---|---|---|---|---|
| | | lane width (m) (ft) | lane + shoulder (m) (ft) | lane (m) (ft) | lane + shoulder (m) (ft) |
| 1 - 750 | < 36 (50) | 3.0 (10) | 3.7 (12) | 2.7 (9) | 3.3 (11) |
| | > 36 (50) | 3.0 (10) | 3.7 (12) | 3.0 (10) | 3.7 (12) |
| 751 - 2000 | < 36 (50) | 3.3 (11) | 4.0 (13) | 3.0 (10) | 3.7 (12) |
| | > 36 (50) | 3.7 (12) | 4.6 (15) | 3.3 (11) | 4.3 (14) |
| > 2000 | all | 3.7 (12) | 5.5 (18) | 3.3 (11) | 5.2 (17) |

Source: Transportation Research Board (1987a), p 144.


This is an important factor to consider in road design, especially where drainage distance is longer than one lane width (Zegeer, Twomey, Heckman and Hayward, 1992; Ivey and Mounce, 1984).

*Lane and shoulder widths as set out in the Table 8.1 represent the state of current knowledge. Lane widths in excess of 3.7 m (12 ft) are unnecessary except where truck volumes are very high, while those less than 3.0 m (10 ft) are less safe. Shoulder width needs to be considered in the light of lane width, as in the table. The standard of the shoulder (sealed or unsealed), and if unsealed, its condition, are also important considerations; see Chapter 12 below. Moreover, in the design of roadway elements, careful attention needs to be paid to drainage considerations, to avoid the incidence of hydroplaning.*


## Sight distance

A driver needs to be able to see the roadway ahead in order to navigate, guide and control the vehicle. This forward sight distance on a roadway (as distinct from sight distance at intersections, which we discuss in

Chapter 9) should be not less than the distance required to stop, referred to as stopping sight distance (SSD). Hence, there is a need for the road designer to ensure that the driver can travel safely at the speed appropriate to the road, making allowance for forward sight distance.

*General sight distance*

A Swedish study (reported in Hedman, 1990) found that in most cases accident rates decrease with increasing average sight distance, especially single vehicle accidents at night. McBean (1982) found that on rural roads in Britain, sight distances shorter than 200 m (about 700 ft) were relatively more likely to be found at accident sites through their association with horizontal curves.

*Sight distance at crest vertical curves*

Transportation Research Board (1987a, p 93) reported a study which found accident frequencies to be 52 per cent higher at sites with sight distance restrictions due to *vertical* curvature than at control sites. This study (op cit, p 171) went on to develop a model to assist in determining when it is cost-effective to lengthen a vertical curve to increase sight distance over a crest. It concluded that reconstructing such crests was likely to be cost effective when the design speed is more than 33 km/h (20 mph) below operating speeds in the area, traffic flows exceed 1500 veh/d, and/or there is a major hazard (such as a high volume intersection, sharp curve, steep downgrade or lane drop).

Glennon (1987c) however concluded that it was cost-effective to improve stopping sight distance on crest vertical curves only when very short sight distances were improved to provide very long sight distances, and even then only when traffic volumes were sufficiently high to justify the expense. He also warned against improving extremely sub-standard crest vertical curves to a standard which is still less than the minimum; this may actually lead to a deterioration in safety, as the length of road with poor sight distance will necessarily increase.

*Sight distance on horizontal curves*

Improving sight distance on *horizontal* curves has been found to be highly cost effective by Glennon (1987c). He suggested that 'low-cost treatments such as clearing vegetation or other minor obstructions on the inside of horizontal curves may be cost-effective on almost all highways.' In earlier work (Neuman and Glennon, 1983), the cost-effectiveness of improving sight distance during major rehabilitation or reconstruction of the road was noted, since 'only the incremental costs of treating the sight distance are attributable to cost-effectiveness analysis.'

Sight distance is particularly important for trucks, since in general they have poorer braking performance and this must be compensated, in part, by greater sight distance (Jarvis, 1994). Federal Highway Administration (1986, p 14-9) concluded that increased eye height compensates for inferior braking for the average of all truck sizes, but does not hold true for larger and heavier trucks having longer braking distances. The study also concluded that sight distance requirements in sag vertical curves, determined by headlight sight distance, is satisfactory for trucks. However, Fancher (1986) has suggested that sight distances around horizontal curves were also a problem for trucks, as the extra driver's eye height is of little advantage.

*Poor sight distance is associated with accidents. The degree of hazard varies with the road feature, but some features and combinations of features are more hazardous than others. Reconstruction of vertical curves to increase sight distance is however unlikely to be cost effective except in extreme cases. On the other hand, improving sight distance on horizontal curves is very likely to be cost-effective if it involves relatively low-cost treatments like clearing of vegetation or other minor obstructions. This is particularly so if there are significant truck volumes present.*

**Horizontal and vertical alignment**

Horizontal curvature is the main factor affecting vehicle speed on rural roads, especially at speeds below 100 km/h (60 mph) (Lay, 1986, p 371), and so horizontal curves should be designed so that they can be negotiated safely. Vertical curves and gradients also affect safety, but the designer should principally be aware of the need for integration of the horizontal and vertical alignment details, and also the need for consistency of design standard along a length of road.

*Horizontal alignment*

All else being equal, accidents are more likely to occur on highway curves than on tangents (straight sections of road). Glennon (1987b, p 50) quotes results which suggest that the average accident rate for curved road segments is three times that of tangents, and the average single vehicle, run off road accident rate is four times higher. Moreover, curved road segments have higher proportions of severe, wet road, and icy road accidents.

Numerous studies have attempted to investigate the relationship between horizontal curve design and accidents. These studies have identified a number of traffic, roadway, and geometric features related to the safety of horizontal curves, including curve radius, length of curve, traffic volume, lane and shoulder width, roadside hazards, stopping sight distance, vertical alignment at the horizontal curve, distance to adjacent curves, distance to a nearby intersection, presence of traffic control devices, etc. (Zegeer, Twomey, Heckman, and Hayward, 1992, p 1-2).

However, Neuman, Glennon and Saag (1983) determined that curve radius was the main factor affecting safety at curves, but that shoulder width, width of the travelled way, and length of the curve (in that order) were also important. Numerous other studies have attempted to quantify this relationship. For example:

.   McBean (1982) in the UK found that curve radii of greater than about 500 m (about 1700 ft) did not produce safety problems, but 'curves sharper than this are associated with a fairly abrupt increases in risk',

.   Johnston (1982) using Australian data found that curves with a radius of less than 600 m (2000 ft) were associated with a higher accident rate,

.   The Organisation for Economic Cooperation and Development (1976, p 26) suggested that the critical radius is about 430 m (about 1400 ft),

.   Hedman (1990) using data for Swedish two lane rural roads indicated that accident rates increase on curves below about 1000 m (3300 ft) radius, and again if the radius exceeds about 3300 m (10,000 ft); the reason for this latter finding is perhaps that at large radii, curves can be very long, leading to dangerous overtaking manoeuvres.

The Transportation Research Board (1987a, p 91) in its major study commissioned by the US Congress reviewed many of these studies and set out to perform a definitive analysis. They suggested that the relationship between accidents and road geometry was more related to the consistency of the road feature within the overall context of the road segment. Based upon this, they went on to develop guidelines for the cost-effectiveness of 'curve-flattening' (i.e. reconstructing existing curves to have a larger radius) (op cit, p 148 ff); the results suggested that this was likely to be worthwhile if traffic flow exceeded 750 veh/d and the design speed of the existing curve was more than about 25 km/h (15 mph) below the 85 percentile of the speeds of vehicles approaching the curve. Benefits to travellers in terms of travel time and vehicle operating costs were noted, and that 'taking these savings into account strengthens the case for curve flattening'. However, it also concluded that universal guidelines were inappropriate because of the high degree of site to site variations in the cost effectiveness of curve upgrading. The benefits of curve flattening have also been implied by Wong and Nicholson (1992) in a New Zealand study, which calculated the levels of side friction generated by each driver as they negotiated a bend, before and after realignment. They found that while vehicle speeds increased, side friction demands generally fell, and that 'the margin of safety was increased for all curves, and this is supported by the accident data.'

As with other aspects of alignment, of greater importance from a safety viewpoint than curve radius alone is the consideration of this factor in a consistent fashion with other design parameters along a stretch of road; this is considered below.

Curve flattening is expensive, and is only cost-effective under certain conditions. Other treatments for safety problems at horizontal curves include (Krammes, 1993):

. physical rehabilitation and/or partial reconstruction, including removal of roadside hazards (such as trees or utility poles), flattening the side slopes, resurfacing the roadway to improve skid resistance, increasing the superelevation, paving the shoulders, and eliminating pavement edge drops; or

. low cost treatments such as upgrading the pavement edge lines and centre lines, adding raised reflective pavement markers, providing curve alignment markers, or upgrading the advance warning; these devices are discussed further in Chapter 10.

*Vertical alignment*

Vertical alignment includes both grades and vertical curves. Sag vertical curves are rarely a problem (except where they are in the vicinity of a horizontal curve - see below), while the issue with crest vertical curves is principally a problem of sight distance, as discussed above (Federal Highway Administration, 1982, p 1-15).

Steeper grades are generally associated with higher accident rates. For example, Roy Jorgensen and Associates (1978, p 7) and Organisation for Economic Cooperation and Development (1976, p 26) have suggested that accident rate and severity increase with gradient, both upgrade and downgrade. Some studies (e.g. Hillier and Wardrop (1966) in Britain and Zegeer, Twomey, Heckman and Hayward (1992) quoting US studies) have found that downgrades are a greater problem. However, this result is largely due to truck accidents, and arise from studies which are now dated; the improvement of truck performance and truck braking in particular (Jarvis, 1994) could mean that this observation is no longer as valid as once it may have been.

Hoban (1988) concluded that steep grades above about 6 per cent are associated with a higher accident rate. However, Hedman suggests that in Sweden any grade is potentially a problem, with grades of 2.5 per cent and 4.0 percent having accidents rates greater by 10 per cent and 20 per cent respectively than adjacent horizontal road sections; this result may be a reflection of Swedish weather conditions.

On the other hand, Pak Poy and Kneebone (1988, p 101) suggested that the evidence that gradients alone are a contributing cause to increased accident rates on rural roads is weak; they suggested that grades and curves need to be considered together.

*Combinations of horizontal and vertical alignment*

As noted above, of greater significance than either horizontal or vertical alignment individually is the way in which they are provided and/or combined along a length of road. Horizontal and vertical alignments should not be considered either independently of each other, or independently of the design standards applicable to the rest of the road in question. Transportation Research Board (1987a, p 104) summarized this as follows:

'unfortunately, (individual) safety relationships ... fail to capture situational influences present in the roadway environment that contribute greatly to road way hazards. Illustrative of these particular hazards are high-volume intersections in isolated rural settings, sharp horizontal curves following long segments of generally straight alignment, and compound curves - contiguous horizontal curves turning the same way - in which a flat curve precedes a sharper one. Common to such situations is the violation of driver expectancy ...'

This question of driver expectancy has been confirmed in a number of studies. For example, Kihlberg and Tharp (1968) in a US study found that simultaneous presence of two or more factors (gradients, curves, intersections, structures) typically produced 2 or 3 times as many accidents as highway segments free of such factors, and that 'the presence of combinations of the geometric elements generated higher accident rates than the presence of the individual elements. Combinations gave accident rates as high as six times the rates on pure segments.' Lay (1986, p 563) has quantified this, recommending that horizontal curves under 450 m (1500 ft) and gradients of over 4 per cent should be avoided, particularly in combination. A particularly hazardous situation occurs where a horizontal curve is placed just over a crest vertical curve (Figure 8.6).

Consistency along a road is critically important. In other words, the effect of a geometric design feature depends upon its context (Oglesby, 1985, Chatfield, 1987). Hence, for example, an isolated sharp curve on a road which generally features long straight sections and large radius curves is likely to have a safety problem, but the same curve on a road which is generally of lower geometric standard may not have such a problem. For the same reason, the first curve in a series of curves may have more accidents than similar or even more severe curves a little further along. Hoban (1988) observed that 'curves present a hazard to drivers when their design speed is more than 10-15 km/h (6-10 mph) below the 85 percentile traffic speed on the approach.' It is important to remember that from the driver's viewpoint, it is all one road, and that, as we noted in Chapter 3, continuity is critical to driver expectations and behaviour.

The implication of this is that consistency is very important, and when driver expectations are violated, it is necessary to take serious steps to alert the driver, e.g. with extensive use of warning signs or other delineation devices, including those which affect drivers' visual perceptions (see Chapter 10). It also implies that any reconstruction work done on a road should be at a consistent standard; unless there is a conscious policy to upgrade the whole length of a road which currently has a lower design standard, any work done on that road should probably be at the lower standard, again in the interests of consistency.

The Transportation Research Board (1987a, p 105) suggested the following guidelines for dealing with situations of varying geometric standards or unexpected features:

. provision of gradual geometric transitions appropriate to the anticipated vehicle operating speed,

. improvement of sight distance for early detection of the presence of the critical feature,

. provision of gentle side slopes with few roadside obstacles at critical locations, and

. installation of traffic control devices appropriate for the situation.

**Figure 8.6 Driver expectancy and consistency of design standard.** A horizontal curve just beyond a crest vertical curve is hazardous, and where it occurs, strong delineation and warning devices are necessary.

*Transition curves*

Horizontal curves are almost always designed as circular arcs. A vehicle cannot move instantly from travelling in a straight line to travelling on a circular path, but will take some distance to change its trajectory. Sometimes, a short length of roadway is inserted between the straight section and the circular curve to facilitate this change; such a curve has a constantly changing radius of curvature, a property which is termed a spiral.

Similarly, the cross slope on the road may change as the alignment changes from a tangent to a circular arc, particularly on the outer lane where the cross slope may change from a downwards slope from the centre line on the straight (for drainage) to an upward slope on the curve (so that gravity may provide some of the centripetal force necessary to change the vehicle's direction). This curve cross slope is called superelevation, and it too must be introduced over a length of roadway. There are thus at least two transition lengths which may be required - a plan transition, or spiral, and a superelevation transition.

Zegeer, Stewart, Council and Reinfurt (1991) quote US studies which show that the provision of spiral transitions has a positive effect on safety; the transition reduces the friction demands of critical vehicle movements through the curve. They then quantify the safety effectiveness of spiral transitions on high speed horizontal alignments, demonstrating that the provision of spiral transitions reduces curve accidents by 2 to 9 per cent, depending upon curve radius and central angle. An accident reduction of 5 per cent of total curve accidents was representative of the effect of adding spiral transitions to both ends of a curve on a 2-lane 2-way rural road.

This study also examined the effect of having an incorrect amount of superelevation, and concluded that sites with incorrect superelevation had a significantly worse accident record than sites with the correct amount of superelevation. They concluded that for a superelevation deficiency (i.e. the difference between the amount as recommended in the US guidelines and the amount as measured in the field) of 0.2, a 10 per cent reduction, on average, in accidents at that site could be expected by correction; if the deficiency was between 0.1 and 0.2, a 5 per cent reduction could be expected.

The problems with an absence of transition curves are particularly critical with articulated trucks. Donaldson (1986, p 12) for example has noted that the absence of a plan transition affects the friction developed between tyre and road, the path through the curve, and the likelihood of encroachment into the other lane or the shoulder. Similarly, Hutchinson (1988) has suggested that the conventional engineering approach to the design of horizontal curves, based upon generation of centripetal forces by a combination of gravity (superelevation) and friction is satisfactory for passenger cars, but 'there is some concern about the stability and control of high centre of gravity and less torsionally rigid vehicles such as trucks'. Finally, the Federal Highway Administration (1986) has noted in relation to freeway/motorway ramps that the short section of circular curve without full superelevation (which is a design consequence of having no spiral transition curve) 'seems to be a critical point adversely affecting trucks.'

> *On new rural roads, horizontal curves rural roads should not be less than about 600 m (2000 ft) radius; below about 450 m (1500 ft) a significantly higher accident rate can often be expected. Grades should ideally not exceed 6 per cent, with a lower value (4 per cent) when there is a high proportion of trucks using the road.*
>
> *In treating existing roads, particular attention should be paid to isolated or unexpected sub-standard features, including sharp curves and steep grades, and other road features such as intersections. The worst situation occurs when two or more such features occur simultaneously or in close proximity to each other; this can produce a situation several times worse than one where there is only a straight, flat, road segment.*
>
> *However, consistency in design standard along a length of road is more important than the standard of an individual element, since driver expectations largely determine behaviour.*
>
> *Horizontal curves should utilize plan transitions to connect the straight with the circular arc, particularly on roads with a high proportion of articulated trucks. Provision of the correct amount of superelevation also contributes to safety.*

## Bridges, structures and culverts

Bridges and culverts can be significant in terms of their involvement in run-off-road accidents, and therefore may need to feature in roadside hazard management programs. Strategies for dealing with this problem are discussed in Chapter 12.

For new bridges, Mak (1987) has recommended that the bridge should be 1.8 m (6 ft) wider than the travelled way (i.e. 0.9 m (3 ft) shoulders should be carried across the bridge). On roads with high traffic flows, full width shoulders may be carried across the bridge.

Overpasses should have bridge piers which are designed for impact loading. Abutments should be well clear of the roadway, and ideally there should be no pier at the edge of the roadway; if the abutment is located at the top of the batter slope it is well clear of the traffic. Depending upon the span, a central pier may be needed in the median (Figure 8.7).

Bridge railings are a longitudinal barrier designed to prevent an errant vehicle running off the side of the bridge. As such they are designed to have little or no deflection. However, if there is guard fencing alongside the road on the bridge approaches, this will likely be designed to yield on impact. There is thus a need for a transition in the stiffness of the guard fencing adjacent to the bridge end post, and the guard fence should be rigidly attached to the end post (see Chapter 12).

*Safety is one of the important considerations in the design of new bridges. Adherence to current standards related to bridge width, shoulders, bridge railings and posts, and the location of bridge piers and columns is important to ensure that new bridges are safe as well as functional.*

### Overtaking

Restricted overtaking opportunities on two-lane two-way roads, combined with the presence of slower vehicles, can result in substantial congestion, and thence to accidents through overtaking. Armour (1984) for example found that overtaking is involved in about 10 per cent of rural casualty accidents in Australia.

On a two-lane road, overtaking vehicles must overtake slower vehicles by entering the opposing lane. Therefore an overtaking opportunity requires a sufficiently large gap in the on-coming traffic for the overtaking manoeuvre, plus the distance travelled by that vehicle, plus a safety margin (Hoban, 1982). The road alignment (vertical and horizontal) must allow sight distances of this magnitude if overtaking is to occur. On high volume roads, opposing traffic will limit overtaking opportunities, while on hilly terrain, sight distance may not be sufficient to allow overtaking.

**Figure 8.7  Bridge abutments and piers clear of the roadway**

In these circumstances, overtaking lanes can be very effective in improving traffic operations by breaking up bunches and reducing delays caused by inadequate overtaking opportunities over substantial lengths of road. In moderate traffic, judiciously placed overtaking lanes comprising around 10 per cent of the length of a road can provide much of the benefit of full duplication (Hoban, 1982, 1988).

Several studies have assessed the safety effects of overtaking lanes. Hoban (1982) reported a 25 per cent reduction in accidents when overtaking lanes were provided on rural roads in Australia. Harwood, St John and Warren (1985) in the US performed a matched comparison of 13 pairs of sites, and found that those with overtaking lanes had a 38 per cent better record for all accidents and 29 per cent for fatal and injury accidents. Hedman (1990) has noted a Swedish study which showed a 10-20 per cent reduction when provided on 3-4 per cent upgrades, and a 20-40 per reduction when provided on steeper grades. Importantly, these studies show that the accident reduction extends downstream of the overtaking section, indicating that the pressure to overtake slower vehicles has been relieved. This effect can be also extended upstream of the overtaking section, through the provision of advance signing 2-5 km (about 1-3 miles) upstream of the start of the overtaking section (Figure 8.8).

175

**Figure 8.8  Advance signing of overtaking lane**. This assists in carrying the benefits of the overtaking lane upstream since drivers are less likely to commence a risky overtaking manoeuvre knowing that an overtaking opportunity is imminent.

It should also be noted that other studies have reported no statistically significant effect of overtaking lanes. This indicates partly the difficulty of conducting a controlled experiment to test the effects (e.g. how far upstream and downstream of the site might an effect be expected?), but also indicates that their effectiveness is greater in some situations than others, as would be expected (Harwood, St John and Warren, 1985).

In an authoritative study, Harwood and Hoban (1987) combined the results of several studies to demonstrate a statistically significant reduction of 25 per cent for roads in flat to rolling terrain. They also discussed the effect of short 4-lane sections of highway, which provide overtaking opportunities in both directions; such a feature may be part of a stage construction of an eventual full duplication of a substantial length of the highway. They found a 35 per cent reduction in all accidents and a 40 per cent reduction in fatal and injury accidents.

Design details of overtaking lanes vary, and their location may be determined by the use of simulation models (e.g. TRARR; McLean 1989, p 204). This generally points to the desirability of providing a number of relatively short overtaking lanes frequently along a highway, rather than isolated sections of longer overtaking lanes. In Australia for example, the recommendation for a two-lane rural road with a design speed of 100 km/h (60 mph) is to have a minimum length of overtaking lane (including start and end tapers) of 600 m (about 2000 ft), and a maximum length of 1200 m (about 4000 ft); the total taper length in this case is 250 m (about 800 ft) (National Association of Australian State Road Authorities, 1989).

The model also suggests that overtaking lanes on a 2-lane, 2-way road are typically worth considering when the opportunity to overtake occurs less than 30 per cent of the time. Optimum spacing also varies with overtaking opportunities, which is principally determined by alignment and traffic flow. Typical spacings of 10-15 km (6-9 miles) are suggested for roads with moderate traffic volumes.

Suitable locations for overtaking lanes include bottlenecks (e.g. steep grades, sites with traffic generators near the foot of a hill), sites which exhibit a high incidence of overtaking accidents, locations where construction is of low cost (e.g. avoid deep cut or fill sections, bridges, etc), and sites where appropriate sight distance at merge and diverge tapers can be generated. Locations to be avoided include sites close to towns, sites which include significant intersections, or sites with a large number of access points.

Attention to detail in the signing and line marking of overtaking lanes is also important to maximize their effectiveness. As mentioned, an advance sign upstream of the start of the overtaking section reduces the pressures on drivers to perform overtaking manoeuvres since they know that there will be an opportunity very soon. Australian practice is to lead all vehicles into the nearside lane (i.e. the left lane, remembering that vehicles travel on the left in Australia) (Figure 8.9). This means that drivers must make a deliberate manoeuvre to overtake, rather than drift into the overtaking lane. At the terminus of the overtaking section, vehicles in the overtaking lane have right of way (Figure 8.10). This is because those in the left lane have a better view of the road and traffic situation (especially those in trucks or vehicles with limited visibility), and if there is a conflict which requires one vehicle to perform an evasive manoeuvre at the merge point, it is better that the vehicle on the left heads for the shoulder than to have the vehicle on the right swerving into a lane of oncoming traffic.

177

**Figure 8.9  Start of overtaking lane.** Vehicles are led into the nearside lane, requiring a positive decision to overtake.

*Overtaking is associated with accidents on rural roads, and overtaking lanes provide significant operational and safety benefits. Their specific effect depends upon the location, and the effectiveness of overtaking lanes is greater if they are installed as part of a strategy for the road as a whole, in terms of the intervals between overtaking lanes and the number provided in relation to the traffic flow and terrain.*

**Truck escape ramps**

One of the few safety treatments specifically designed for trucks involves the installation of an escape ramp to reduce the hazard of a runaway truck on a downgrade. The US Federal Highway Administration (1982, p 14-12) has indicated that the following factors are associated with such incidents:

**Figure 8.10**    **Terminus of overtaking lane**. Vehicles in the nearside lane must yield right of way to overtaking vehicles.

.    gradient,
.    driver error such as failure to downshift,
.    equipment failure such as defective brakes,
.    inexperience with mountain driving,
.    inexperience with the vehicle,
.    unfamiliarity with the actual location,
.    driver impairment due to fatigue or alcohol, and
.    inadequate signing for downgrade.

There are six different types of general design of truck escape ramp (Ballard, 1983; Wambold, 1988):

.    sand pile,
.    gravity ramp,
.    ascending-grade arrester bed,
.    horizontal-grade arrester bed,

. descending grade arrester bed, or
. roadside arrester bed.

These function according to at least one of two basic methods of vehicle deceleration: by gravity, or by the use of some form of arresting material which increases the rolling resistance on the truck wheels.

Federal Highway Administration (1982, p 3-9) quote a study in Colorado, USA, involving a before and after study of the effectiveness of the construction of six truck escape ramps. The most successful ramp showed a 400 per cent reduction in accidents and a benefit:cost ratio of 10:1. However, elsewhere Federal Highway Administration (1982, p 14-12) say that 'what is not available from the research is the effectiveness of truck escape ramps in reducing the severity of truck runaway accidents. Studies ... provide data to substantiate that truck escape ramps are indeed used. This implies an accident severity reduction. The studies did report accidents which occurred because drivers of runaway trucks unsuccessfully attempted to 'ride it out' rather than use escape ramps.'

A related technique is the use of weight-specific advisory speed signs. These are based on the notion of a grade severity rating model. Braking capability has been found to correlate with brake temperature, which in turn depends upon the length and gradient of the grade, the truck weight, and the speed of the vehicle (Stein and Johnson, 1984). Hence an advisory speed applicable to a grade for trucks of different gross vehicle mass (GVM) can be estimated. A weight-specific advisory speed sign may then be installed at the top of the grade to advise drivers of its safe speed (Federal Highway Administration, 1982, p 14-12; Bowman and Coleman, 1990).

*Truck escape ramps, when properly designed, are effective in stopping runaway trucks which use them. However, the scope of application is limited to long, steep grades, and they can only be installed when the road geometry allows. Ramps are only effective after a truck has already run away. An alternative measure which aims to prevent runaways is the use of weight-specific advisory signs based upon a grade severity rating system. These are a relatively recent innovation, not yet in general use.*

## Notes

1.  In this chapter, we present a summary of road safety and its relation to a range of road design elements. This attempts to represent a 'state of the art' review, but any such review needs to be qualified to the extent that the original source material is in some cases is getting quite old. There has not been a great deal of research in this field since the 1970s, and as road systems mature and improve, it would be reasonable to suppose that we reach a point of diminishing returns, so that perhaps the safety benefits of current projects will be smaller. Also, some sources have methodological deficiencies, such as poor statistical controls, or failure take adequate account of other factors apart from the road design element under consideration. In some cases, the research has produced inconsistent or even conflicting results. It is also important to note that the results may not readily translate from one place to another because of such things as climate, driver behaviour, regulations, enforcement, etc.

# 9 Intersections

*Intersections are critical locations in the road network from both a safety and efficiency (capacity) viewpoint. Intersections have a range of control strategies, ranging from being uncontrolled, having priority control, or using roundabouts or traffic signals. Safety is one the important considerations in selection of control strategy, and these aspects are discussed in this chapter. The chapter also examines sight distance requirements at intersections, and discusses the application of channelization. Grade separation and safety at railway crossing are also examined.*

## Intersection safety

From a safety viewpoint, intersections are the most critical element of the road network. By their very nature, at-grade intersections are risky because different road users (vehicles, pedestrians, cyclists) are required to use the same *space*, and a collision is only avoided if they are separated in *time*. In America, over one-half of reported urban accidents and over one-third of reported rural accidents are at intersections (Kuciemba and Cirillo, 1992). Corresponding figures in Australia are 43 per cent and 11 per cent (Howie and Oulton, 1989).

Interestingly, Kuciemba and Cirillo (1992) note that intersections are associated with a deceasing proportion of fatal accidents in America, and that the severity of accidents at intersections has also fallen over time. They attribute this to improved road safety engineering at intersections, improved vehicle design, and increased use of passenger restraints, especially seat belts.

However, intersections will always be a major focus of the work of the road safety engineer, since, as noted above, this is where a large number of accidents occur. A detailed study of the safety benefits of road improvements in the 1980s in Britain (Walker and Lines, 1991) reported that 'treatments at junctions, where the majority of conflicts occur, produced the most significant savings. Accident remedial junction treatments produced net savings of the order of 50 per cent, significant at the 5 per cent level.'

In a major review of road safety measures, Transportation Research Board (1987a, p 286 ff) reviewed the factors affecting safety at intersections. The main factors include:

. number of legs,
. angle of intersection,
. sight distance,
. alignment,
. auxiliary lanes,
. channelization,
. friction,
. turning radii,
. lighting,
. lane and shoulder widths,
. driveways,
. right of way (rules, signs, signals), and
. approach speed.

Guidelines for the design and of intersections generally incorporate these considerations. The basic principles of good intersection design have been reviewed in Chapter 7. The intersection should allow vehicles and other road users to progress straight ahead or to turn into another roadway with minimum delay and maximum safety. The layout and operation of the intersection should therefore be obvious and unambiguous, with good visibility of traffic control devices, and of other road users as necessary.

Different intersection types will be appropriate under different circumstances, but in general, as traffic flows and the ratio of minor to major road flow increases, more control is necessary, for both safety and capacity reasons. A British guideline on appropriate intersection treatments classified by approach traffic volumes is shown in Figure 9.1.

184

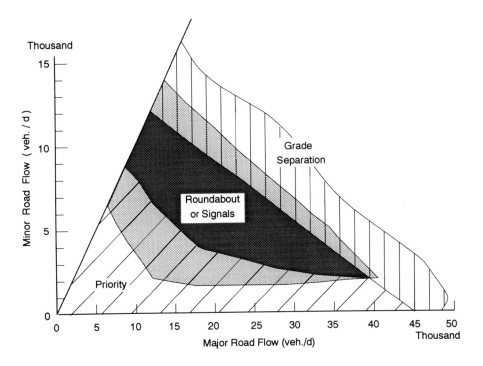

**Figure 9.1** **Type of intersection appropriate for different traffic flows**

Source: Institution of Highways and Transportation (1987, p 328). Crown copyright is reproduced with the permission of the Controller of HMSO.

In increasing degree of standard and control, intersections are:

.   uncontrolled, relying on a priority rule to indicate right of way,
.   priority road designated by GIVE WAY (YIELD) or STOP signs,
.   roundabout,
.   signal controlled, with turning traffic filtering through on-coming traffic,
.   signal controlled, with control of some or all turning movements, or
.   grade separations.

185

*Intersection type*

Table 9.1 (Barton, 1989) shows one example of how the accident rate (in terms of casualty accidents per $10^7$ entering vehicle) varies with the type of intersection and degree of control. It can be seen that different configurations (cross intersections, t-intersections), different forms of control (signals, roundabouts), and different road functions (primary arterial, secondary arterial, collector, etc) all influence the safety performance.

Table 9.1 indicates that certain intersection configurations tend to be safer than others. However, intersections must also satisfy other efficiency and environmental objectives, particularly road capacity on arterial roads. It is common to combine these safety, environmental, and capacity considerations to develop guidelines as to which type of intersection is appropriate to particular situations in the road network. Table 9.2 shows a typical outcome, indicating the appropriate intersection type in relation to the role of the intersecting roads in a road functional hierarchy.

## Uncontrolled intersections

The simplest form of intersection is one where there is no physical control or device at the intersection to indicate that one road user has priority over another. Priority is allocated by rule, e.g.:

.   offside priority rule (give way to the right if vehicles drive on the left, and give way to the left if vehicles drive on the right);

.   nearside priority rule (give way to the left if vehicles drive on the left, and give way to the right if vehicles drive on the right);

.   terminating road rule (applicable at t-intersections: traffic on the stem of the 't' (which has to slow down anyway) gives way to through traffic on the top of the 't'; or

.   vehicles have priority in the order in which they arrive.

**Table 9.1**
**Typical intersection accident rates (Australia)**

| Intersection Type | Number of sites | Mean casualty accident rate* |
|---|---|---|
| **Intersection configuration** | | |
| | | |
| Cross intersections | | |
|    urban: signalized | 138 | 1.7 |
|    urban: unsignalized | 31 | 2.4 |
|    high speed: signalized | 35 | 2.5 |
|    rural: unsignalized | 128 | 5.2 |
| | | |
| t-intersections | | |
|    urban: signalized | 32 | 1.4 |
|    unsignalized | 58 | 1.5 |
|    high speed: signalized | 15 | 2.1 |
|    rural: unsignalized | 210 | 3.3 |
| | | |
| Multi-leg intersections | | |
|    urban: signalized | 13 | 3.2 |
| | | |
| Roundabouts | 68 | 1.6 |
| | | |
| Staggered-t: rural | 28 | 2.9 |
| **Road hierarchy (urban)** | | |
| | | |
| primary arterial/primary arterial | 49 | 2.4 |
| primary arterial/secondary arterial | 63 | 1.8 |
| primary arterial/collector street | 77 | 1.4 |
| primary arterial/local street | 586 | 0.8 |

* Rate in casualty accidents per $10^7$ entering vehicles.

Source: Barton (1989).

**Table 9.2**
**Intersection control in a functional road hierarchy**

| Control | Primary arterial | Secondary arterial | Collector road | Local street |
|---|---|---|---|---|
| **Traffic signals** | | | | |
| primary arterial | A | A | O | X |
| secondary arterial | | A | O | X |
| collector road | | | X | X |
| local street | | | | X |
| **Roundabouts** | | | | |
| primary arterial | O | O | X | X |
| secondary arterial | | O | O | X |
| collector road | | | A | O |
| local street | | | | A |
| **STOP or GIVE WAY signs** | | | | |
| primary arterial | X | X | A | A |
| secondary arterial | | X | A | A |
| collector road | | | A | A |
| local street | | | | A |
| Legend: A Most likely to be an appropriate treatment O May be an appropriate treatment X Usually an inappropriate treatment | | | | |

Source: National Association of Australian State Road Authorities (1988e).

One or other of these rules applies in most countries, in particular at low-volume intersections in both urban and rural areas. Usually, the priority rule will apply as a fallback control if the main control (sign, signal) is inoperative, e.g. through vandalism or signal failure.

Apart from sight distance considerations (see below), there is little information on safety at uncontrolled intersections. This is perhaps not surprising, as inevitably such intersections involve very light traffic flows, and therefore the probability of an accident is small. The problem readily translates therefore into one requiring an area-wide treatment, such as local area traffic management (see Chapter 13), or a mass action program of installation of traffic control devices (e.g. GIVE WAY (YIELD) or STOP signs). Interestingly, no information could be found on the relative safety of the various priority rules outlined above.

*An uncontrolled intersection is the most basic form of intersection control, relying on a regulatory rule to resolve priority between conflicting users. It is only applicable in very low volume situations, and requires the establishment and maintenance of a sight triangle to enable vehicles on conflicting paths to see each other.*

## Priority controlled intersections

These are intersections which comprise a major or priority road, usually running straight across the intersection, and one or more minor roads which intersect it, with traffic on the minor roads being controlled with STOP or GIVE WAY (YIELD) signs. Normally, there is no restriction on the major road traffic, apart from an intersection warning sign to alert drivers that traffic may be exiting from the minor road, or that other vehicles in the major road may be turning to the left or right.

A network of main or priority roads will normally be defined as part of an area-wide road hierarchy (see Chapter 13), and thus designation of the major/minor legs is not usually difficult.

### STOP versus GIVE WAY (YIELD) control

The decision as to whether to install a STOP sign or a GIVE WAY (YIELD) sign is primarily based upon sight distance considerations. However, implementation varies considerably from country to country. For example, in the United States, the YIELD (GIVE WAY) sign is routinely used where sight distances at the intersection of two minor streets permit traffic on the controlled street to approach safely at 10-15 mph (15-25 km/h) or higher (Homburger, et al, 1989, p 88), otherwise a STOP sign is used. A different approach is used in Australia. Table 9.3 summarizes the practice adopted; if the sight distances outlined in the table cannot be obtained, then a STOP sign should be provided (all distances taken from a height of 1.15 m above the ground). In Britain, STOP signs are much more rarely used.

**Table 9.3**

**Sight distance restrictions requiring the use of STOP signs, Australia**

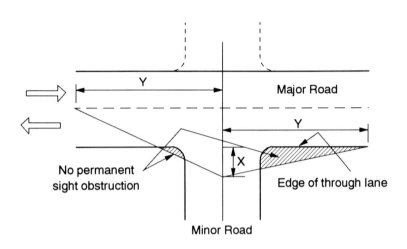

| Major road speed (km/h) (mph) | Distance along minor road: X* (m) (ft) | Distance along major road: Y (m) (ft) |
|:---:|:---:|:---:|
| 40 (25) | 3 (10) | 20 (67) |
| 50 (31) | 3 (10) | 30 (100) |
| 60 (37) | 3 (10) | 40 (133) |
| 70 (43) | 3 (10) | 55 (183) |
| 80 (50) | 3 (10) | 65 (216) |
| 90 (56) | 3 (10) | 80 (267) |
| 100 (62) | 3 (10) | 95 (317) |
| 110 (43) | 3 (10) | 115 (383) |
| 120 (75) | 3 (10) | 140 (467) |

* Where the minor road approach is an arterial road, use X = 4.5 m (15 ft)

Source: Standards Australia (1994). Copyright 1994 by Standards Australia. Reprinted with permission.

Where sight distance is the criterion used to decide between a STOP and a GIVE WAY (YIELD) sign, it is generally agreed that STOP signs should only be used in circumstances where it really is necessary for traffic on the minor road to come to a complete standstill before proceeding. Experience indicates that if the STOP sign is over-used, it is likely to be disregarded and treated as equivalent to a GIVE WAY (YIELD) sign (Rosenbaum, 1983), with the result that more hazardous sites, where drivers should come to a stop, are not perceived as having a higher risk.

Perhaps as a consequence, research on the relative safety benefits of STOP and GIVE WAY (YIELD) does not support the argument that the former are inherently safer in situations where sight distance considerations indicate that the latter is appropriate. For example, Polus (1985) found that STOP signs were not inherently safer than GIVE WAY (YIELD) signs. He studied a number of sites in Israel where control was changed from GIVE WAY to STOP because of the accident history, but found that there was no statistically significant change in the number of accidents. Polus noted non-significant decreases in pedestrian accidents and increases in vehicle accidents. Lum and Stockton (1982) analysed accident data for low-volume intersections in Texas, New York and Florida, and concluded that STOP signs do not improve safety at such locations, relative to the use of YIELD signs. In later work, Lum and Parker (1982) examined almost 900 rural intersections in Michigan, and reached a similar conclusion. They warned however that this does not necessarily mean that STOP signs can be removed, but that 'the decision to use STOP signs should be based upon sound engineering practice', as reflected in consideration of approach speeds, visibility, and accident experience.

These studies showing the perhaps counter-intuitive effects of STOP signs are explained by the realisation that such signs do not necessarily address the accident types which are occurring. For example, accidents where a vehicle on the side road overshoots the intersection and collides with a main road vehicle may be better addressed by relocating or repainting the holding line, relocating the GIVE WAY (YIELD) sign, using a GIVE WAY AHEAD sign, or building a central splitter island to give the driver a stronger cue as to the location of the holding line. Conversely, if the accident type involves a 're-start' (i.e. the collision occurs after the side traffic has stopped or yielded right of way), the problem is more likely to relate to visibility.

191

Moreover, use of STOP signs rather than GIVE WAY (YIELD) signs can increase vehicle emissions, delay, noise and energy use (Chadda and Carter, 1983; Upchurch, 1983).

Some jurisdictions are now reviewing their use of STOP signs. For example, in Victoria, Australia, there was a major program in the early 1990s to replace STOP signs with GIVE WAY signs if a STOP sign was not necessary for sight distance purposes, as indicated in Table 9.3. In the US, McGee and Blakenship (1989) have developed guidelines for converting STOP to YIELD signs and recommended changes to US warrants for such signs.

STOP and GIVE WAY (YIELD) signs must be of standard design, for both legal reasons and to aid recognition; the red octagon common in many countries (Figure 9.2) is instantly recognisable from its unique colour-shape combination. On sealed roads, the sign may be reinforced by pavement markings, in the form of a transverse line painted on the road, referred to as the holding line. Ross Silcock Partnership (1991, p 156) argue strongly that different holding line markings should be used at STOP and GIVE WAY (YIELD) signs, as in Figures 9.2 and 9.3, since drivers generally will not come to a full stop if there is no apparent need, and if the marking at STOP and GIVE WAY (YIELD) signs are the same 'drivers lose confidence in the markings, begin to ignore them on occasions, and possibly expose themselves to unnecessary danger as a result. Using a single type of marking in all circumstances leaves little flexibility to the road engineer to convey appropriate information.'

Irrespective of the type of control, accidents will occur at priority controlled intersections because they require the minor road traffic to yield right of way, and this requires judgement on the part of the motorist. However, in general, installation of STOP or GIVE WAY (YIELD) signs can be effective, particularly at low volume sites with low approach speeds (e.g. suburban intersections) (Cairney, 1986; Homburger, et al, 1989, p 88). Improving sight distance so that the driver has more warning of the presence of the intersection, and indicating clearly the presence of the location of the holding line can assist the driver to control his/her vehicle on the approach to the intersection. It is helpful to recognise that accidents at priority intersections may involve a vehicle overshooting the holding line, which implies a problem upstream of the intersection, or a vehicle being involved in a collision with another vehicle or a pedestrian/cyclist after commencing the manoeuvre into the intersection, which may imply a visibility or perception problem at the holding line itself. Careful examination of the accident data may be necessary to determine which type of problem exists.

**Figure 9.2    STOP sign and associated pavement markings.** The unique shape/colour combination assists recognition, and the pavement markings reinforce the message.

*Rural intersections*

Most intersections in rural areas are likely to be priority intersections. Various measures can be taken to improve safety at rural intersections, many of which involve some form of channelization (see below). However, one treatment particularly worthy of note is the conversion of a cross intersection to a pair of staggered t-intersections. This is often very effective in reducing both accident frequency and accident severity. Hedman (1990) for example in Sweden has reported that paired t-intersections are 1.5 to 2.0 times as safe as cross intersections for the same traffic flow (a figure comparable to that found in US studies - see

Kuciemba and Cirillo, 1992), and that the 'injury consequence' is 1.5 times greater at cross intersections. Hedman therefore concluded that 'it is often advantageous to replace 4-way junctions by staggered 3-way junctions'. In Australia, Nairn (1987, p 41) reports a study which showed a 47 per cent reduction in accidents from this type of treatment, while another study showed an 80 per cent reduction (Hoque and Sanderson, 1988, p 18).

It is generally preferable to orient the stagger such that drivers cross the nearest traffic lane at nearly a right angle and then have unimpeded exit from the far lane. (Ross Silcock Partnership, 1991, p 87). That is, for traffic driving on the left, a right-left stagger is preferable, as shown in Figure 9.4a. If a left-right stagger is provided, there should desirably be a protected right turning area in the centre of the major road (Figure 9.4b). These directions will of course be transposed if traffic drives on the right.

**Figure 9.3    GIVE  WAY  (YIELD)  sign  and  associated  pavement markings.** The unique shape/colour combination aids recognition, and the pavement markings assist in reinforcing the message, especially if the sign is faded or vandalized, as in this example.

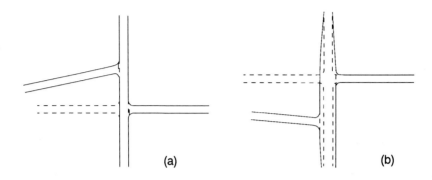

**Figure 9.4** **Staggered t-intersection.** A right-left stagger (a) is preferable to a left-right stagger (b) (for traffic driving on the left, and vice versa for traffic driving on the right). The photograph illustrates the situation depicted in (a).

195

*Priority controlled intersections, involving the use of STOP or GIVE WAY (YIELD) signs to indicate major and minor roads, are very common, and are effective at low volume sites with low approach speeds. If sight distance, rather than general policy, is the criterion for the decision as to which sign to use, the STOP sign should not be over-utilized as this will likely lead to disrespect. In rural areas, conversion of a cross intersection to two t-intersections can be a highly effective treatment. Sight distance considerations and use of channelization, both of which are discussed later in this chapter, are relevant to the design of priority controlled intersections.*

## Roundabouts

A roundabout is a traffic control device involving a one-way circulating roadway around a central island. Priority within the roundabout is controlled by GIVE WAY (YIELD) signs, although occasionally signal control may be used. It is usual to give priority to traffic already on the roundabout, to ensure that traffic keeps moving. Roundabouts are common in the UK and many British Commonwealth countries, and are becoming more common in Europe. They are comparatively rare in the US, principally because of the use of an onside rather than an offside priority rule (Todd, 1988, 1991).

Roundabouts in one form or another have been used on every type of road intersection ranging from motorway/freeway interchanges and major arterial roads (where multi-lane operation is required) through to minor local streets where essentially only one vehicle at a time uses the intersection; in this latter configuration they are particularly useful as a 'traffic calming' device for resolving priority at local intersections and reducing traffic speeds (see Chapter 13).

From an operational viewpoint, roundabouts may be applicable (Austroads, 1993a; Ross Silcock Partnership, 1991, p 149):

.   at intersections where traffic volumes would lead to unacceptable delays to traffic on the minor road with STOP or GIVE WAY (YIELD) control, or where traffic signals would lead to increased delay for all approaches,

. at intersections where there are high right-turning volumes (for traffic driving on the left) or high left turning volumes (for traffic driving on the right),

. at intersections with more than four approaches, where priority control may not resolve the situation and where signals may be less efficient due to the large number of phases which may be required,

. at intersections between collector streets, or between a collector and a local street (Figure 9.5), where a disproportionally high number of accidents occur (see Chapter 13); experience in the UK and Australia indicates that roundabouts are superior to STOP or GIVE WAY (YIELD) control in these instances (Austroads, 1993a, Appendix A),

. on local streets (Figure 9.6) as part of a traffic management strategy to control speeds (see Chapter 13),

. at rural cross intersections (Figure 9.7) where there is an accident problem involving vehicles on adjacent approaches or turning vehicles,

. at intersections where the main traffic flow turns through a right angle, e.g. where a main road passes through a rural town,

. where major roads intersect at 'Y' or 't' intersections, as these usually involve a high proportion of turning traffic.

On the other hand, they are less likely to be suitable where:

. where a satisfactory geometric design cannot be provided due to space or topography,

. where traffic flows are unbalanced with high volumes on one or more approaches which would dominate use of the roundabout,

. where a major road intersects a minor road, and a roundabout would cause unacceptable delay to the minor road traffic,

. where there is considerable pedestrian activity, and high vehicle speeds or heavy flows would make it difficult for pedestrians to cross (unless pedestrian crossing facilities are provided),

197

. at an isolated intersection in a network of linked signals; in this case it is usually preferable to provide a signalized intersection and incorporate it in the linked system to minimize delay, energy consumption, and emissions,

. where peak period reversible lanes are used,

. where traffic flows leaving the intersection are interrupted by a traffic control device (e.g. a pedestrian crossing) which could result in traffic queues blocking the intersection.

**Figure 9.5    Roundabout at the intersection of collector streets, or of a local and a collector street**

**Figure 9.6    Roundabout at the intersection of local streets**

**Figure 9.7    Roundabout at a rural cross intersection**

The good safety record of roundabouts (Table 9.1) results from the control that they exercise on approach speeds, the smaller number and spatial separation of conflict points (Figure 7.1), the low relative speeds at these conflict points, the simplicity of decision-making required of the driver, and the positive response which is required of a driver in order to pass through a roundabout (unlike other intersections where the driver may not even notice the intersection). These attributes can be enhanced by the provision of splitter islands on the approaches which provide additional advance warning to the driver and give a good visual cue of the location of the intersecting traffic flows, as well as providing refuges for pedestrians to allow them to cross the road in stages. However, safety problems can occur if (Ross Silcock Partnership, 1991):

.   the merging angle is too sharp,
.   the roundabout is of unusual shape,
.   signing is inadequate or confusing,
.   there are steep approach gradients,
.   there is adverse crossfall on the circulating roadway,
.   there are slow-moving vehicles such as bicyclists or animal-drawn vehicles,
.   the deflection on approach is insufficient to slow vehicles to a safe speed; Maycock and Hall (1984) noted that 'for safety, roundabouts with heavily flared entries should have as much entry path deflection as possible'.

Of these, most can be removed through good design, and to this end, design guidelines such as those produced by the UK Department of Transport (1993d) or Austroads (1993a) should be followed.

*Pedestrian and bicyclist safety*

Perhaps the major safety problem at roundabouts is with bicyclists, and to a lesser extent, pedestrians. One British study (Lawson, 1989) found that 22 per cent of accidents at roundabouts involved a bicyclist, compared with only 8 per cent of accidents at signalized intersections. Allot and Lomax (1991) found that accident rates involving bicyclists at roundabouts in the UK were up to 15 times greater than that of cars at roundabouts, and 2-3 times greater than bicycle accident rates at signalized intersections. The problem is primarily one of a bicyclist circulating within the roundabout being struck by an entering vehicle (i.e. failing to give way)

(Jordan, 1985; Layfield and Maycock, 1986; Crampton, Hass-Clau and Thrush, 1990).

Austroads (1993a) in its roundabout design guide notes that 'concern about the increased risk to cyclists ... needs to be seriously considered when weighing up the benefits and disbenefits of adopting a roundabout treatment at a particular location. The choice will often depend on the proportion of cyclists and other non-motorized road users expected to use the intersection.' At least one English county with a large bicyclist population has a policy of not providing roundabouts as a result of this experience. However, Dutch research (van Minnen, 1990), has found that in some cases, bicyclist safety has improved following the replacement of a signal-controlled intersection by a roundabout; this was attributed to lower vehicle speeds.

Measures to improve bicyclist safety at roundabouts include (Austroads, 1993a, 1993c; Harrison, Hall and Harland, 1989; Institution of Highways and Transportation, 1987; Burden, 1993):

.   avoid squeeze points on the approach,

.   ensure adequate deflection and speed control; vehicle speeds should not exceed about 50 km/h (30 mph),

.   avoid large roundabouts, to discourage high speed circulating traffic,

.   avoid excessive width of the circulating roadway,

.   ensure that sight lines are not obstructed,

.   consider the provision of paths and ramps to allow bicyclists (and pedestrians) to bypass the roundabout by moving from island to island, and

.   provide adequate lighting.

Pedestrians are as safe at roundabouts as at other intersections, provided that they are adequately considered in the design (Austroads, 1993a). This is due to such factors as the provision of splitter islands which allow the pedestrian to cross the road in stages, and the slower speed of vehicles. The facilities required for pedestrians depend upon the amount and intensity of pedestrian activity. It may be necessary, for example, to provide a signal-controlled pedestrian crossing adjacent to the roundabout. If this is done, as noted above, it needs to be some distance away from the roundabout to ensure that traffic does not queue back and block the circulating roadway. For this reason, it may also be necessary to provide a pedestrian fence to prevent pedestrians crossing the road away from the pedestrian crossing.

Mutual visibility of pedestrians and motorists is important to maximize pedestrian safety. Visibility can be enhanced by prohibiting parking on the approach to the roundabout, by providing a higher level of street lighting, and by ensuring that signs and vegetation do not obscure the view of pedestrians, particularly children.

*Safety effectiveness and cost-effectiveness*

A number of studies have shown that, except in situations involving significant numbers of bicyclists, roundabouts are highly cost-effective in safety terms as replacements for STOP or GIVE WAY (YIELD) controlled intersections. For example:

. An Australian study (Teale, 1984) found a 78 per cent reduction in casualty accidents when roundabouts were installed at low volume sites.

. Another Australian study (Corben, Ambrose and Foong, 1990) found that the installation of roundabouts at nine sites led to an 81 per cent reduction in casualty accidents.

. Walker and Pittam (1989) found that the accident rate at mini-roundabouts (Figure 9.8) was comparable to that at rural t-intersections, and superior to that of signalized intersections.

. The County Surveyors' Society (1987) in the UK found that the installation of small or mini-roundabouts at existing priority controlled intersections can reduce accidents by 30-40 per cent, and at existing signalized intersections they can reduce fatal and serious accidents by 40-60 per cent.

. The UK Department of Transport (1986) indicates that roundabouts have the potential to achieve a 50-60 per cent reduction in injury accidents, compared with a 40 per cent potential for traffic signals.

. On the other hand, Hedman (1990) using Swedish data suggested that the installation of roundabouts led to little change in accident frequency, but a 50 per cent reduction in severity.

**Figure 9.8 Mini-roundabout (UK)**

The cost-effectiveness of the Australian installations was also impressive; the aforementioned study of Corben, Ambrose and Foong (1990) indicated a benefit:cost ratio of 7.5 for accident savings alone, over a project life of ten years. Another study, comprising a detailed evaluation of accident remedial programs conducted by the Australian Bureau of Transport and Communication Economics (1993) determined a benefit:cost ratio of between 3.1 and 6.0 for roundabout construction at accident sites.

*Replacement of traffic signals*

While the installation of roundabouts is usually seen as a replacement for STOP or GIVE WAY (YIELD) control, under certain circumstances they have been used as replacements for traffic signal installations on road safety grounds in both the UK and Australia. In the UK, the County Surveyors' Society (1989a) in a study of six urban and three rural sites which were converted on safety grounds, found an average reduction in accidents of 80 per cent and 50 per cent respectively. However, at other sites where the conversion was not undertaken for safety reasons, there was a non-significant increase in accidents. This indicates the importance of selecting sites which are suited for conversion. In Australia, Corben (1989) suggested that candidate sites were those that were:

. not part of a coordinated signal route,
. not along a tram (light rail) route,
. not where active priority is provided for buses,
. not at an intersection of an arterial and a non-arterial road,
. not part of a designated on-road bicycle route, or
. not requiring special timing, directional control, or monitoring to achieve specific traffic management objectives.

*Signalized roundabouts*

As noted above, some heavily trafficked roundabouts in the UK are signalized, i.e. there is a succession of signal controlled intersections around the central island, at all or some of the entering roadways. The County Surveyors' Society (1993a) has reviewed the safety of this treatment, and concluded that there is little influence on total accidents, but that there is a decrease in accidents involving bicyclists and motor cycles, and an increase in rear-end accidents, and possibly also an increase in pedestrian accidents.

*Roundabouts can be a very effective and cost-effective safety measure if installed at sites where they are a suitable device. These sites include local areas, to resolve priorities at intersections and reduce the speed of traffic, and at some sites on the arterial road network where traffic signals are not preferred for operational reasons. There is some evidence that accident severity as well as accident frequency is reduced by roundabouts.*

204

## Traffic signals

Traffic signals are widely used as an intersection control device in urban areas, and occasionally in rural areas, where they meet capacity and safety objectives. By separating in time the use of road space across major traffic flows, they have the potential to significantly reduce conflicts. They also have the scope for providing for pedestrians and cyclists. In their simplest form, they operate under a fixed time sequence, but more commonly are vehicle actuated (i.e. respond to traffic demands) and increasingly are linked and coordinated to provide control of the network as a whole.

### *Effects of signalization*

It is apparent that, under the right circumstances, the installation of traffic signals will reduce the number and severity of accidents. These circumstances are that there is a significant number of accidents currently occurring, and that these are of a type that can be reduced through signalization. Howie and Oulton (1989) suggest that it is 'not clear' whether road safety benefits will result if the site has fewer than three casualty accidents per year prior to signalization.

In general therefore, if signals are installed where the site satisfies a safety warrant, there will likely be a statistically significant reduction in the number of accidents. Some specific results can be quoted:

. A UK study (Hakkert and Malalel, 1978) based on 34 intersections found that sites with more than 4.7 casualty accidents per year in the 'before' period experienced a statistically significant reduction of 48 per cent, while those with fewer than this experienced a non-significant increase of 5.3 per cent; the parallels with Howie and Oulton's (1989) aforementioned figure of 3 accidents in the before period is noteworthy.

. Corben, Ambrose and Foong (1990) in a study using Australian data found a statistically significant (at the 5 per cent level) reduction of 53 per cent for new intersection signals.

. A US study in the State of Michigan, based upon 102 intersections, found a 15.5 per cent reduction in 'total accidents' (Datta and Dutta, 1990).

While these results clearly indicate the potential for signals to reduce the overall incidence of accidents, it is also important to note that they change the pattern of accidents at an intersection, and can lead to an increase in the incidence of some types of accident. For example, Nguyen, Hodge and Hall (1987) found an 84 per cent reduction in right angle accidents (significant at the 1 per cent level), a 31 per cent reduction in rear-end accidents (significant at the 5 per cent level), and a 52 per cent *increase* in accidents involving vehicles turning from the opposite direction. An Australia study (Willett, 1979) of 52 intersections found a reduction of 36 per cent in the total number of accidents, despite a 139 per cent *increase* in the number of accidents involving vehicles turning from the opposing direction. In an American study, Datta and Dutta (1990) reported a 52 per cent reduction in right angle accidents, a 65 per cent *increase* in rear end accidents, and a 75 per cent increase in accidents involving vehicles turning from the opposite direction.

These results indicate that (subject to the earlier qualification that signals are installed where warranted) they will likely produce a reduction in the more severe category of right angle accidents, albeit probably at the expense of an increase in accidents involving vehicles turning from the opposite direction and (possibly) rear end accidents.

*Cost-effectiveness of new signal installations*

The previous section has discussed the effects of signalization. The cost-effectiveness of new signal installations - i.e. whether the benefits outweigh the costs - has been examined by the Australian Bureau of Transport and Communications Economics (1993) in a recent study of the cost-effectiveness of a range of road safety engineering measures. The Bureau found a benefit:cost ratio of between 2.4 and 6.0 (depending upon the calculation of benefits) for new traffic signal installations. Corben, Ambrose and Foong (1990) in their Victorian study found a benefit:cost ratio of 8.2:1 for new signal installations, for a project life of 10 years and including safety benefits only, but allowing for capital and operating costs. In the US, Tignor (1993) has reported the results of analyses of the cost-effectiveness of various traffic control devices, and indicated that, considering safety benefits and installation costs only, new traffic signals had a benefit:cost ratio of 4.0:1.

*Controlled turns*

The previous section highlighted the problem with accidents at signalized intersections involving vehicles turning from the opposite direction. In response to these and other safety problems at existing signal-controlled intersections, there is an increased tendency to use separate signal phases to fully or partially control turning manoeuvres, especially right turns (in countries where traffic drives on the left) and left turns (for those which drive on the right). *To avoid the need for verbal gymnastics, the following discussion will be based on the former, i.e. for traffic driving on the left.*

A fully controlled right turn is one which allows vehicles to turn right only with a green arrow (or equivalent), with filtering being prevented by a red arrow, or equivalent (Figure 9.9a). This is sometimes known as protected-only phasing (Parsonson, 1993). A partially controlled right turn allows vehicles to turn right in two stages during the cycle, with signal control (green arrow) and without signal control (filtering) (Figure 9.9b). This is sometimes known as protected/permissive phasing (Parsonson, 1993).

These measures are effective, with the fully controlled turn having much greater safety benefits. Some examples from Britain and Australia, where traffic drives on the left, can be quoted:

. Corben and Foong (1990) found a 33 per cent reduction in casualty accidents from intersection remodelling works in Victoria, Australia (primarily the installation of right turn phases); this led to an estimated benefit:cost ratio of 22:1, with an average net present value of $0.85 million per intersection (10 year analysis period, 4 per cent real discount rate).

. In the first part of a comprehensive and detailed study of the safety and operational effects of turn control, Bui, Cameron and Foong (1991) examined 217 intersections approaches in Australia at which right turn phases had been installed. They found that the installation of *fully controlled* right turns led to a statistically significant reduction in all casualty accidents (45 per cent) including a reduction of 82 per cent in accidents involving vehicles turning from the opposite direction, 48 per cent in right angle accidents and 35 per cent in pedestrian accidents. However, rear end casualty accidents increased by 72 per cent. On the other hand, the study concluded that partially controlled right turn phases have no apparent safety benefits.

207

**Figure 9.9** **Fully and partially controlled turn signal.** The top (a) allows turns only on a green arrow, while the bottom (b) also allows vehicles to filter through oncoming traffic.

. In the second part of this study, Taylor (1991) examined the effects of the right turn phase on intersection capacity. He concluded that full control of right turns yields poorer intersection performance than partial control under virtually all conditions. However, the differences in performance is slight, and 'unlikely to negate the safety advantages.'

. The UK County Surveyors' Society (1989a) in a study of 13 urban sites found that the right turn facility was very effective, and suggested that it was justified where right turn accidents accounted for more than two-thirds of the accidents at the site.

. Simmonds (1987) in a study of 28 sites in London, found that right turn control produced accident reductions ranging from 33 per cent to 73 cent.

The safety benefits of fully controlled turns which have been indicated in several of these studies are probably due in substantial part to the clear and unambiguous direction which they present to drivers. Hummer, Montgomery and Sinha (1990) for example found that drivers had difficulty in understanding what was required of them with partial, or protected/permissive control, but conversely the use of full control was well understood by drivers.

Overall then, it is clear that there are definite safety benefits to be gained from the provision of fully controlled turns where there is a safety problem with vehicles turning from the opposite direction. The costs, in terms of additional delay, somewhat negate these benefits, but with modern fully actuated signal controllers and linked signal systems, these costs may be small in comparison with the safety benefits.

Controlled turns should ideally use a leading turn phase (i.e. the turn phase should be introduced before the through movement phase). This reduces the potential for collisions resulting from the through vehicle driver failing to see the turning vehicle. Also, the queue of turning vehicles is cleared from the intersection before through vehicles begin moving. In addition, in the event of a collision, the approach speeds are likely to be lower with a leading turn (Triggs, 1981; Parsonson, 1993).

*Inter-green times*

Signal phase design includes a yellow period, followed by an all-red interval; the sum of these is referred to as the inter-green time, and is the time in which the stream of vehicles approaching from one direction is brought to a standstill so that another phase can commence. The law usually allows drivers to enter the intersection during the yellow period if they are unable to stop; entry to the intersection on the red phase is prohibited.

Since the signal phases are nothing more than an indication to individual drivers as to what is expected or required of them, driver response to signals is critical to intersection performance. A key aspect is the so-called dilemma zone, whereby a driver may be in a position of neither being able to clear the intersection before the commencement of the red phase, nor stop before reaching the stop line (Gazis, Herman and Marududin, 1960; Triggs, 1981). This is the reason for the all-red period, and driver braking behaviour and reaction times determine the length of the green period (Stein, 1986).

However, one of the problems with introducing the all-red period (thereby lengthening the inter-green time) is that some drivers will choose to 'run the red'. This has been documented as a significant safety problem. For example, Croft (1980) found that red-running accidents accounted for 19 per cent of reported accidents at signalized intersections in Australia. This finding led to a major study, in which the yellow phase at a sample of intersections was increased from a uniform 3 seconds to a longer period, typically 4.0 - 4.5 seconds. Red light running was reduced substantially, from 9 per thousand entering vehicles to 3.4, although there was little change in the number or frequency of accidents. Although there was some regression to red-running behaviour over the following two years (Hulsher, 1984), this study led to a revised signal practice, using longer all-red and/or yellow periods.

Triggs (1981) has noted that there is a second type of dilemma zone in addition to the one described above (the behaviour of one's own vehicle). The second concerns the behaviour of other vehicles, involving the perception of the turning driver as to whether the approaching driver will attempt to stop given the change to yellow. He notes that this could be important given the incidence of accidents at signalized intersections involving vehicles turning from the opposite direction.

Stein (1986) has claimed that there is clear evidence from US studies that drivers will continue to enter an intersection if they are required to decelerate at a rate greater than 0.37g - 0.46g. He points out that current US practice is based on a deceleration rate of 0.31g. He suggested that an additional time of 1-2 seconds would cater for the 'late entering' vehicle, and would not significantly reduce traffic operational efficiency.

Ogden, et al (1994b) have found an association between approach grade and accidents at signalized intersections, and suggested that inter-green times might need to be somewhat longer at sites where one or more approaches is on a gradient.

Another specific response to red-running involves enforcement, including red-light cameras; this is discussed below.

*Linked signal systems*

It appears that signal coordination has a modest effect upon accidents. An Australian study (Moore and Lowrie, 1976) showed a reduction of 23 per cent in all accidents. However, more detailed analysis revealed that there was a significant difference between previously signalized intersections which were incorporated into the scheme, and intersections at which new signals were added. In the former, total accidents reduced by 16 per cent, and in the latter, they reduced by 34 per cent. Commenting on this result, Cairney (1988) noted that 'although the scheme as a whole provided considerable benefits, much more than coordination of signals was involved. Gains at already-signalized intersections were more modest, and possibly attributable to in part to the installation of additional signals upstream.' Another Australian study (Hodge, Daley and Nguyen, 1986) found a 6 per cent reduction in casualty accidents along 10 routes which had been linked. However, much of the reduction in accidents involving vehicles turning from the opposite direction occurred at sites where right turn phases had been incorporated as part of the scheme. Thus again, the benefits can not be entirely attributable to coordination.

*Advance warning*

One means of alerting drivers to the presence of a signalized intersection and in particular to an impending change from a green to a yellow/red phase is to provide a form of advance warning. These are particularly relevant where there is a high speed approach, where there is poor visibility of the intersection (e.g. if it is just over a crest vertical curve) or where it is the first signal after a long period of uninterrupted flow conditions, such as where a rural highway enters a city.

Eck and Sabra (1985) undertook a review of then-current practice in the US concerning active advance warning devices for use at high speed approaches. They considered three devices, a flashing strobe light, a flashing RED SIGNAL AHEAD sign, and a PREPARE TO STOP WHEN

FLASHING sign. Each of these were 'active' in the sense that they were activated at a predetermined time in the signal cycle, usually at a certain time before the commencement of the red phase. They concluded that the flashing RED SIGNAL AHEAD was the most effective device. Importantly, they concluded that active devices should be used selectively so that their effectiveness is not diminished by overuse.

An alternative to active warning signs is to actively detect vehicles which are travelling at a speed such that they are in the dilemma zone, and extend the inter-green time to allow such a vehicle to clear. Zegeer and Deen (1978) have reported on one study at three US sites which found that such arrangements halved the rear-end accident rate.

*Enforcement*

Howie and Oulton (1989) report two studies of the effect of police enforcement on driver behaviour at signalized intersections. The first, found that 'the presence of surveillance, whether continuously by mechanical means or sporadic but frequent by patrols, reduces the incidence of unsafe behaviour of drivers. They found no evidence that the duration of stay of a patrol, longer than 30 minutes in any one location, is of any additional benefit, but as long as surveillance remains evident, its effect on the driver's behaviour continues.'

The second study was a Swedish investigation, which showed that 'the average approach speeds and percentage of traffic signal violations dropped significantly with visible police supervision of the site.'

Automated enforcement, using cameras to photograph vehicles entering an intersection on the red (red light cameras), is a more recent innovation. An Australian study of the effectiveness of these cameras was undertaken by South, et al (1988). Accident data from 46 treated sites and 46 control sites were analysed. The results indicated that there was a 7 per cent reduction in total accidents and a 32 per cent reduction in right angle accidents at the treated sites; this was significant at the 5 per cent level. There was no statistically significant effect on any other accident type.

Lawson (1992) extrapolated these findings to the situation in Britain and suggested that 'it is likely that there will be sites with red-light running accidents amenable to treatment in all urban areas.' He recommended that the police accident form be modified to include additional data to assist in the identification of red-light running accidents.

Rolls, et al (1991) suggested that red light cameras might be particularly useful if used to influence 'those drivers, especially the young, who possess the necessary skills to drive safely but choose not to do so', since this the behaviour of this group is affected by an increase in the probability of detection (see Chapter 2).

On the other hand, Bui, Corben, Leeming and Brierley (1991), based upon interviews with drivers who had been involved in collisions at signalized intersections, questioned the efficacy of red light cameras, on the grounds that most drivers who ran red lights did so because of inattention or distraction.

*Signal design and operation*

While signals may be and are installed at new sites, a major effort in many countries is being devoted to making existing signals safer. In a UK study of signals at cross-intersections on undivided urban roads, Hall (1986) found the following geometric and control characteristics to have an effect on safety, remembering that Britain drives on the left side of the road:

. wider approaches and multiple lanes were both associated with higher accident rates for right angle accidents,

. increasing the number of lanes at the holding line was associated with higher pedestrian accident rates,

. longer approach sight distances were associated with lower accident rates for both left turning vehicles, and pedestrians,

. displacement of opposing legs of the intersection to either the left or the right was associated with lower right turning and right angle accidents,

. longer inter-green times were associated with higher accident rates for right turning vehicles,

. shorter cycle times were associated with higher accident rates for right-turning vehicles and total vehicle accidents, and

. the presence of yellow box markings (Figure 9.10) contributed to a substantially lower accident rate for right turning vehicles.

213

**Figure 9.10 Yellow box markings.** These may be used to indicate a no-standing area within the intersection.

There are a number of aspects of signal design and operation which have been analysed with respect to their effect on safety. Some of these are briefly reviewed here.

*Flashing green.* This approach aims to warn drivers of the impending end of the green period by introducing a flashing green phase in the last 2 or 3 seconds of the green period. It has been used extensively in Israel. However, this arrangement has been found to lead to a significant increase in rear end collisions (Mahalel and Zaidel, 1985). Triggs (1981) suggests that is due to there being two possible responses to a flashing green - one being to stop and the other being to accelerate.

*Starting yellow.* In some countries, there is a short yellow period before the start of the green. Triggs (1981) presented an extensive review of the effect of starting yellow on driver response, and concluded that there may

214

be a slight benefit in terms of reaction times, and hence potentially on capacity. No studies of its effects on safety have been found.

*Off-peak operation.* In off-peak periods (especially at night) the practice in some places is to have the signals operate in a flashing yellow mode (or flashing red in one direction and flashing yellow in another). This has been done mainly for mobility and energy reasons - not bringing a vehicle to a full stop unnecessarily. However, it appears that there are safety disbenefits; a US study (Gaberty and Barbaresso, 1987) found that right angle accidents were significantly over-represented (at the 0.1 level of significance) at '4-legged arterial intersections when signals are in a flashing mode during night-time hours'. There was no significant change in rear end collisions.

*Mast-mounted signal heads.* There are various arrangements of signals. In some places, the practice is to use primary signals (on the upstream approach), secondary signals (on the downstream side, in the median or on the far side of the road, e.g. on the downstream right hand side for countries where vehicles drive on the left) and tertiary (also downstream, but on the kerb side, e.g. left side for countries where vehicles drive on the left). Often, there are also overhead primary signals (Figure 9.11), the purpose of which is to provide adequate advance warning of the approach of the intersection itself, and then to give earlier indication of the signal aspect. A recent US study (Bhesania, 1991) has confirmed the safety benefits of mast-mounted signal heads, reporting a statistically significant reduction of 63 per cent in right angle accidents and 25 per cent in total accidents when a number of installations were modified in this way.

In some countries, particularly in Europe, it is common to provide only the primary set of signals, and to have a small repeater set mounted on the signal post at driver's eye level, since the first driver in the queue cannot see the primary signals (Figure 9.12).

*Demographic factors*

There is evidence that different groups of drivers behave differently, and perhaps inconsistently, in their approach to driving through signalized intersections. For example:

**Figure 9.11  Traffic signal mounted on a mast arm**. Signals mounted on a mast arm enhance visibility by an approaching motorist.

. women are more likely to be involved in accidents as a result of misjudgment or lapse of attention than men, while men are more likely to be involved in accidents as a result of driving too fast (Storie, 1977),

. in accidents involving vehicles turning from the opposite direction, women are more likely to be the turning driver and men more likely to be the through driver (Cairney, 1983),

. higher risk-taking is associated with drivers with prior accidents or violations, drivers with no passengers, young drivers, males, and drivers not wearing seat belts (Evans and Wasielewski, 1983),

. women drivers have a greater tendency to stop at a yellow signal, while males tend to continue through the intersection after the start of the yellow phase (Konecni, Ebbeson and Konecni, 1976),

**Figure 9.12 Repeater signal at eye height.** In some European countries, a repeater signal is necessary at drivers' eye height since practice does not provide for departure side signals.

. elderly drivers take significantly longer to respond, or to make the correct decision, when confronted with complex signals such as multiple signal displays (Staplin and Fisk, 1991), and

217

. elderly drivers have more difficulty in correctly handling left turns (for drivers travelling on the right); they are also over-involved in right angle and rear end accidents and accidents involving vehicles turning from the opposite direction, all of which are consistent with deterioration of visual capabilities (Stamatiadis, Taylor and McKelvey, 1991).

*Driver decision-making*

Bui, Corben, Leeming and Brierley (1991) interviewed drivers who had been involved in collisions at signalized intersections. They concluded that human performance and behaviourial factors were responsible for 79 per cent of the investigated accidents. These factors were in two groups: human error (e.g. misjudgment of the speed or position of the other vehicle), and driver inattention or distraction.

This study drew particular attention to the right turn (for drivers travelling on the left) manoeuvre performed without a green arrow, saying that it was 'perhaps the most difficult task for a driver at a signalized intersection', and supported the introduction of more fully-controlled right turns.

Cairney and Catchpole (1991) examined police accident reports to 'reconstruct' intersection accidents and driver behaviours within them. They concluded that failure to see the other road user was a common feature of many of the accident studies, and concluded that if vehicles and pedestrians were more conspicuous, safety would be enhanced. They also concluded that in intersection accidents, single and multiple road user accidents result from quite different sequences of events and behaviours.

Carsten, et al (1989) in a study of causal factors in road accidents in the UK identified 'perceptual error' as a significant factor, especially for pedestrians, with females making somewhat more such errors. Although not specifically related to signalized intersections, their conclusion is relevant: 'this seems to indicate an inability on the part of these road users to cope with the present highly complex traffic system and hence underlines the need for changes to be made to the road environment to make it safer for such road users.'

*The installation, modification or replacement of traffic signals is an effective and cost-effective safety measure, only when specific problems identified at high risk locations are amenable to treatment with signalization. Fully controlled right turns are particularly beneficial at* sites where there is a right turn problem (for countries where traffic drives on the left, and vice versa for countries which drive on the right). Operational and design features, such as the use of mast arms and yellow box markings have safety benefits. Enhanced enforcement, especially the use of red light cameras, contribute to safety at sites where there is problem of red light running. Area traffic control (signal linking), does not appear to contribute significantly to safety, though of course it has other benefits.

## Intersection sight distance

A key factor in all intersections, but particularly at uncontrolled intersection, is sight distance. Three situations are applicable (Glennon, 1993), the first of which applies to uncontrolled intersections (as defined above), and the other two to controlled intersections (Figure 9.13).

### Uncontrolled intersections

The first situation is that which requires vehicle to vehicle visibility. In Figure 9.13, drivers of vehicles A and B must be able to see each other, and therefore there must be a clear area, or sight triangle ABX in each quadrant of the intersection. Keeping this sight triangle clear of undergrowth and other obstructions is essential if the intersection is to operate safely as an uncontrolled intersection.

The size of the sight triangle ABX must obviously increase with increasing vehicle speeds, since it requires one or both vehicles to slow and perhaps even stop before reaching the intersection, having sighted the other vehicle. Sight triangles which allow for this situation are very large (Glennon, 1993) - e.g. American guidelines indicate that for an approach speed of 100 km/h (60 mph), traffic on the conflicting approaches must be mutually visible at least 87 m (260 ft) before the vehicles reach the intersection. A sight triangle must therefore be cleared and be maintained with this dimension along both legs of the intersection.

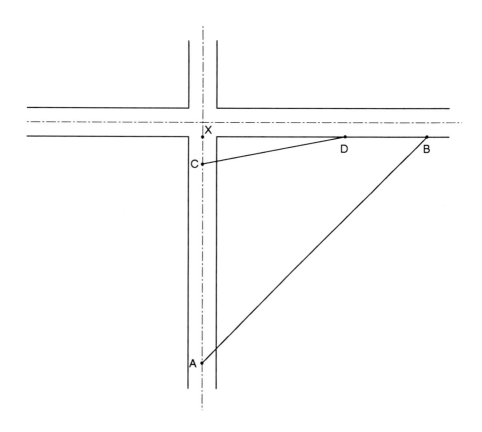

**Figure 9.13  Intersection sight distance**

*Controlled intersections*

The second situation applies to controlled intersections, and requires that drivers approaching on the minor leg of a controlled intersection must have a clear view of the intersection and/or its control devices (including GIVE WAY (YIELD) or STOP signs, or traffic control signals) in sufficient time to react and stop if necessary before encroaching into the intersection. In Figure 9.13, the distance AX must be equal to at least the stopping sight distance corresponding to the speed of traffic on that leg. This is referred to as the *approach sight distance*.

Because any vehicle which overshoots the intersection approach and enters the intersecting road is potentially at risk, it is very important that a driver facing any traffic control device (and therefore having to yield right of way if another vehicle is present) not only has adequate approach sight distance, but also has a clear indication of where the main road is located (e.g. with a splitter island or a holding line on the outside edge of the major road (Figures 9.2 and 9.3). Intersections where a minor road intersects a priority road on the outside of a horizontal curve can be a particular problem here, since the superelevation on the priority road can mean that drivers approaching from the minor road cannot see the priority road until very late. This often calls for special delineation and signing to alert the side road driver of the need to stop and/or be prepared to give way (Figure 9.14).

**Figure 9.14 Intersection on the outside of a horizontal curve.** Where a minor road intersects a priority road on the outside of a horizontal curve, the latter may not be visible to an approaching motorist, so extra warning and control signs may be required.

The third situation is visibility at the holding line itself. In urban areas in particular, traffic on the side road may be quite close to the main road before it is clear of buildings etc which inhibit sight distance, and therefore, the point C, at which drivers are able to see main road traffic, defines a second sight triangle CDX. In this situation, a driver on the minor road (whether stopped at a stop sign, approaching a GIVE WAY (YIELD) sign, or approaching on the stem of an intersection controlled by the terminating road rule) must, at or near the intersection, have visibility along each approach on the major road to allow time to scan both directions and make a decision to proceed. Two further possibilities occur here. The desirable situation is that the minor road driver can accelerate into the intersection, and complete the crossing or turning manoeuvre without colliding with another motor vehicle, pedestrian or cyclist. If this sight distance is not available, safe operation requires major road traffic taking some evasive action if a minor road vehicle (which commenced its manoeuvre before the major road vehicle was present) occupies part of the intersection. These two distances are referred to as the *entering sight distance* and the *safe intersection sight distance* respectively (National Association of Australian State Road Authorities, 1988b).

Table 9.4 shows the approach, entering and safe intersection sight distances based upon observed deceleration rates, and for a reaction time of 2.0 seconds (typical of an unalerted driver state).

It can be seen that there are two sight triangles, each of which is critical to the safe operation of the situations for which they are designated: XBA for uncontrolled intersections, and XDC for controlled intersections (i.e. where the traffic on the minor road has to yield right of way to traffic on the main road). In each case, it is important that the sight triangle be kept clear; indeed Glennon (1993) has gone so far as to assert that 'vigilance to prevent manmade (sic) objects from being placed and vegetation from growing in the necessary sight triangle will probably do more for highway safety at the lowest cost than most other measures.' Several studies (Kuciemba and Cirillo, 1992) have shown that intersections with poor sight distance on one or more approaches tend to have a higher than normal accident rate, particularly with regard to angle accidents at uncontrolled rural intersections. As noted previously, the distances CX and DX are often used as criteria to decide between STOP and GIVE WAY (YIELD) signs.

**Table 9.4**
**Sight distances for controlled intersections**

| Speed* | | Approach Sight Distance | | Entering Sight Distance | | Safe Intersection Sight Distance | |
|---|---|---|---|---|---|---|---|
| km/h | (mph) | m | (ft) | m | (ft) | m | (ft) |
| 40 | (24) | 35 | 115 | 100 | 330 | 70 | 230 |
| 50 | (30) | 45 | 150 | 125 | 415 | 90 | 300 |
| 60 | (36) | 65 | 215 | 160 | 530 | 115 | 380 |
| 70 | (42) | 85 | 280 | 220 | 730 | 140 | 470 |
| 80 | (48) | 105 | 350 | 305 | 1010 | 175 | 580 |
| 90 | (54) | 130 | 430 | 400 | 1330 | 210 | 700 |
| 100 | (60) | 160 | 530 | 500 | 1670 | 250 | 830 |
| 110 | (66) | 190 | 630 | 500 | 1670 | 290 | 970 |

* Speed of minor road traffic for approach sight distance; speed of major road traffic for entering and safe intersection sight distances.

Source: National Association of Australian State Road Authorities (1988b), Page 24.

*The provision of the appropriate sight distance for the type of intersection is essential to allow drivers time to perceive the need for a response, and react. In some cases, such as intersections located on horizontal curves or beyond a crest vertical curve, particular attention to signing or delineation may be needed. The maintenance of sight triangles, whether at uncontrolled intersections or at priority controlled intersections, is an important safety measure.*

**Channelization**

Channelization is the use of painted road markings, raised kerbs, traffic islands or bollards to guide vehicles along a specific path on the approach to and exit from an intersection. It provides positive guidance to the driver, and as a result simplifies the movements and reduces the room for error, reduces confusion, and separates the conflict points. The number of decisions required of a driver at any given instant is reduced, allowing the driver time to make the next decision (see Chapter 3). Traffic islands also have the added benefit that they provide a refuge for pedestrians crossing the road, and they also provide a convenient location for street furniture such as signs, signals, and drainage pits.

Channelization is an inherent component of all but the most simple intersections, but its installation or upgrading can have significant safety benefits. For example:

. a study of the addition or installation of intersection channelization in Australia (Teale, 1984) showed reductions of 26 per cent in casualty accidents for new channelization at signalized intersections and 54 per cent at non-signalized intersections,

. the use of painted channelization at rural intersections in Britain to protect a turning vehicle and discourage overtaking led to a 35 per cent accident reduction (Ward, 1992),

. one US study (quoted in Kuciemba and Cirillo, 1992) suggested that the minimum number of 'passing' accidents per year necessary to justify particular treatments was 1.47 accidents per year for the provision of a separate lane for left turners (equivalent to right turners where traffic drives on the left), and 1.75 accidents per year for the provision of a by-pass lane at t-intersections,

. other US studies, quoted in Neuman (1993) have found that the provision of exclusive (US left) turn lanes at signalized intersections have reduced accidents by 18-40 per cent, and

. in the UK, the County Surveyors' Society (1989) reported that at rural intersections, 'ghost islands' (painted channelization) had the potential to reduce accidents by up to 50 per cent, and if introduced as part of a package involving other treatments such as improved signing, the benefits could be even greater.

Principles of intersection design and layout have been summarized in Chapter 7. Particular guidelines applicable to channelization include (National Association of Australian State Road Authorities, 1988b, p 10; American Association of State Highway and Transportation Officials,

1990, p 788 ff; Neuman, 1985; Institution of Highways and Transportation 1987, p 336):

. reduce the general area of conflict by causing opposing traffic streams to intersect at (or near to) right angles,

. merge traffic streams at small angles to ensure low relative speed between the conflicting streams,

. control the speed of traffic crossing or entering an intersection by alignment,

. control speed by restricting width,

. provide a refuge for turning or crossing vehicles,

. provide a clear and unambiguous path through the intersection,

. avoid sudden and sharp reverse curves,

. reduce the number of islands to the minimum necessary to ensure safe and effective operation,

. provide adequate curve radii and lane width for the prevailing type of vehicle,

. provide explicitly for pedestrians and bicyclists (see Chapter 14),

. improve and clearly define alignment of major movements,

. provide locations for the installation of traffic signals and signs, and

. prohibit certain turns if necessary.

*Channelization is an integral component of all but the simplest intersections. Adherence to design guidelines will contribute to safety. The installation of channelization treatments can be a highly effective safety measure, provided it is aimed at the accident problems identified at the particular site under examination.*

## Grade separated interchanges

An interchange is a system of interconnecting roadways that provides for movement between two or more grade separated highways. They are an integral part of freeway/motorway design, and may be used on other high-standard roads.

Twomey, Heckman and Hayward (1992) have recently reviewed the safety aspects of interchanges, noting that the key issues are configuration, traffic controls and spacing. They found that:

. in general, accidents on ramps and connecting roadways increase with traffic volume and with decreasing curve radius,

. uphill off-ramps have lower accident rates, so from a safety viewpoint, where possible it is preferable for the connecting road to pass over the freeway/motorway,

. particular attention needs to be given to the needs of trucks on ramps, as these have a greater potential for both rollovers and skidding (jackknifing),

. cloverleaf ramps, scissor ramps, and ramps leaving from the median edge of the carriageway all have lower safety performance,

. collector-distributor roads in high volume interchanges contribute to safety, especially where loop and cloverleaf ramps are used,

. it is safer to merge (or diverge) a given number of entering vehicles at two or more on-ramps (or off ramps) than at a single high volume ramp, and

. modification to older interchanges to bring them up to contemporary standards can be beneficial.

In a major study of the safety benefits of road improvements in Britain, Walker and Lines (1991) found that the provision of urban grade separations led to a significant 57 per cent reduction in accidents; this was the greatest reduction of any scheme which they analysed, although it was based upon a small sample of sites.

Grade separating an existing at-grade intersection may be justified more on capacity than on safety grounds, but the safety benefits are likely to be considerable. Hedman (1990) for example indicates that in Sweden, grade separations have led to a 50 per cent reduction in accidents at a cross intersection, and a 10 per cent reduction at a t-intersection. Accident severity was also reduced.

Principles and design details for grade separated interchanges are contained in the relevant design guides, such as American Association of State Highway and Transportation Officials (1990, Chapter 10), Institution of Highways and Transportation (1987, Chapter 42); and National Association of Australian State Road Authorities (1984). Safety aspects of these guides relate to layout (e.g. type of interchange and facilities for right and left turning traffic), operational aspects (e.g. merge and diverge areas), and the design of structures to ensure that they do not constitute a hazard.

*Grade separated interchanges are the safest form of intersection. Adherence to contemporary design guidelines will ensure that interchange merges, diverges, and ramps operate safely and efficiently.*

### Railway crossings

A special form of intersection is where a railway crosses a road at grade. Most such crossings involve 'heavy' rail, that is freight or passenger trains, although some involve 'light' rail systems, in which the train length is typically much shorter.

Although accidents at railway crossings are usually a small proportion of total accidents, they tend to be severe when a train is involved, and often attract a high level of media attention. Responsibility for safety at the crossing is shared between the road agency and the railway, but since trains almost invariably have right of way and usually cannot take any evasive action (apart from last-minute braking, which may often be too late to be effective) the onus is almost always on the road user to stop if a train is approaching. An exception may be a crossing involving a light rail vehicle, in which the intersection may be controlled using conventional means such as traffic signals, albeit perhaps with signals pre-emption by the light rail vehicle. Accidents at railway crossings include:

. collisions in which a train strikes a road vehicle,

227

. collisions in which a road vehicle runs into the side of a train,

. collisions between vehicles on or near the crossing, perhaps associated with a vehicle taking action in response to an approaching train or the activation of a warning system (e.g. a rear-end accident), or

. accidents involving a vehicle colliding with the crossing furniture.

Most accidents at railway crossings do not involve a train, indicating a need for better integration of the design of the crossing with the adjacent road. Of the accidents which do involve a train, more involve a vehicle running into the side of the train than vice versa (Ogden, Patton and Clark, 1973).

*Safety devices*

Accident countermeasures at rail-road crossings may involve devices on the train, elimination of the crossing, active control, active warning devices, passive warning devices, visibility improvements, and special measures aimed at pedestrian protection. Apart from the first category (which includes such things as locomotive mounted strobe lights, daytime use of locomotive headlights, and reflective devices on the side of the train), all of these are within the ambit of road safety engineering. Their application and effectiveness is discussed below.

*Elimination of the crossing.* The at-grade crossing may be eliminated by grade-separation, i.e. construction of an overpass or underpass. While most types of accident involving the railway crossing or trains can be eliminated by grade separation, the railway crossing itself represents a hazard of similar dimensions to the crossing. Schoppert and Hoyt (1968, p 79) commented that 'grade separation may not be the answer, especially when automatic protection provides a 90 per cent reduction in accidents'. Grade separation would therefore usually be justified on the grounds of road capacity and delay, rather than safety.

*Active control devices.* These include gates and boom barriers (Figure 9.15). In most cases they are activated automatically by an approaching train, although hand-operated gates may still be found in some places. Usually they are accompanied by an active warning device of the sort described below.

**Figure 9.15 Active railway crossing control**. Boom barriers and flashing lights are activated by an approaching train.

They contribute to safety in two ways - by physically preventing vehicles from entering the crossing when a train is approaching, and through the movement of the boom or gate, which provides an advance warning and thereby has an effect on vehicle-vehicle collisions. Such devices virtually eliminate risky and illegal behaviour, with substantial safety improvements (Heathington, Fambro and Richards, 1989). They are specially valuable at sites with multiple-tracks, where a second train may approach shortly after a first train has completed a crossing, and at sites with high speed trains. Bayley and Uber (1990) have reported that a program of upgrading urban railway crossings from flashing light installations to boom barriers in Melbourne, Australia reduced the number of train-vehicle fatalities almost to zero.

Shinar and Raz (1982) in a study of driver response to different railway crossing devices found that although drivers slowed down before crossing the tracks under all types of warning and control devices, a significant number were still going too fast to stop if it was necessary to do so unless the crossing was protected with gates or booms.

229

*Active warning devices*. These include both visual and audible devices; in many cases the two operate simultaneously as part of integrated warning system, activated by an approaching train.

Provided that a driver sees and responds to the warning, safety is enhanced. In particular, the problem of a vehicle running into the side of a train at night is reduced, while the incidence of vehicle-vehicle collisions is also reduced since the warning is visible or audible at a distance in advance of the crossing. Accident reductions of the order of 70-90 per cent have been reported following the installation of such devices (Schoppert and Hoyt, 1968).

However, there are problems with active devices. Berg, Knoblauch and Hucke (1982) for example have shown that the credibility of an active warning device is more important than its conspicuity, particularly if the device is activated for a lengthy period and no train appears. Sanders (1976) noted that drivers' decision-making at crossings is related to their knowledge of the crossing control strategy, a point reinforced by Wigglesworth (1978, 1990) who noted that the absence of a flashing signals could mean either that a train was not coming (at a signalized crossing) or that it might be (at an unsignalized crossing). A green signal to indicate that the road vehicle can proceed (as at a regular at-grade road intersection) would convey more positive information, a point emphasized by Fambro, Heathington and Richards (1989) who found that driver response to highway traffic signals was superior to their response to flashing railway crossing signals on several safety and behaviourial measures. Tenkink and van der Horst (1990) suggested that a yellow phase in advance of the red phase at a railway crossing would be beneficial.

A difficulty with active devices is that traditionally, these installations are expensive, since they incorporate complex track circuitry and comprehensive signal heads. While this expense may be justified where train and/or vehicle flows are high, they are difficult to justify in more remote, lightly-trafficked sites, and as a result these sites tend to rely in many cases on passive protection. There may be scope for low-cost active devices, perhaps activated from within the locomotive cab rather than from track circuits, and utilizing simpler warning systems such as rotating beacons.

*Passive warning devices*. There are a range of warning signs in use in different jurisdictions, informing motorists not only of the presence of the crossing, but in some cases providing additional information such as the number of tracks and the crossing geometry (Richards and Heathington,

1988). Typical devices include unique railway crossing warning devices such as crossbucks, advance warning signs, and pavement markings. They are commonly fitted with a GIVE WAY or YIELD sign, or in cases where visibility is very restricted, with a STOP sign.

Passive devices tend to be associated with more lightly trafficked lines, since in many countries the more heavily trafficked lines are by now fitted with active devices, as described above.

*Visibility*. Most railway crossing warning systems depend for their effectiveness upon some type of visual message. There are a range of visibility requirements at railway crossings. The driver must be able to see the crossing and its warning or control devices, and/or an approaching train, in time to take appropriate action. Particular problems occur at night, especially with visibility of the side of a train on or passing through the crossing, and illumination of the crossing may be necessary if there are night time train movements at a crossing with passive protection. It may be necessary to be vigilant in keeping undergrowth cut to maintain a sight triangle. It is common, especially in urban areas, to locate active warning devices on overhead mast arms so that they are more visible.

In some cases, it may be appropriate to provide supplementary warning devices where visibility is poor. For example, Bowman (1987) describes an installation where yellow flashing lights added to a railway warning sign upstream of a crossing, and these caused significant reductions in the speed of approaching vehicles. Bayley and Uber (1990) describe the installation of an illuminated 'keep tracks clear' sign which is activated when traffic is detected queuing back from a signalized intersection downstream of a level crossing.

*Pedestrian devices*. Pedestrian facilities may be part of some of the above treatments, for example with pedestrian booms or gates activated along with those provided for vehicular traffic. In other cases however, special facilities for pedestrians may be appropriate. These arise largely from the need to provide additional warning and/or visibility for pedestrians crossing railway tracks. Pedestrian facilities include the provision of a maze, which faces the pedestrian one way and then the other as they pass through it, pedestrian gates and booms (Figure 9.16), and grade-separated pedestrian facilities.

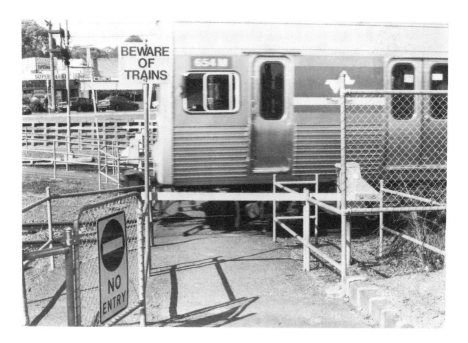

**Figure 9.16 Pedestrian boom barrier at a railway crossing**

*Selection and ranking.* The various countermeasures described above are appropriate to different situations. In general, the following factors affect the selection of the device which is appropriate at a given crossing (American Association of State Highway and Transportation Officials, 1990, p 843):

.   type of highway
.   road traffic volume
.   number of trains
.   speed of trains
.   speed of road traffic
.   number of pedestrians
.   accident record at the site
.   sight distance
.   geometry of the crossing
.   number of rail tracks
.   number of buses using the crossing
.   use of the crossing by trucks carrying hazardous materials.

232

Numerous hazard index formulae have been developed to assess the relative hazard of crossings on the basis of these factors, but no single formulae has universal acceptance (Zegeer, 1986, p 12). The US guide (American Association of State Highway and Transportation Officials, 1990, p 844) notes that 'each has its own values in establishing an index, that when used with sound engineering judgement, provides a basis for a selection of the type of warning devices to be installed at a given crossing.'

*Geometric design of crossings*

Desirably, the road and the railway should intersect at right angles, or close to it. This not only enhances the driver's view of the crossing and assists the driver to look in the correct direction to see any approaching train, but minimizes any instability to the vehicle as it crosses the tracks. Similarly, crossings ideally should not be located on a horizontal curve of either the road or the railway; it is a difficult task for the driver to have to control the vehicle as it travels around the curve and at the same time be on the lookout for trains.

The vertical alignment at the crossing should be as level as possible in the interests of sight distance, rideability, braking, and acceleration. If there are vertical curves on the highway, they should not impede visibility of the crossing or its control devices. At the crossing itself, care should be taken to ensure that long, low vehicles are able to pass through the crossing without become grounded on the tracks.

The road cross section should, as far as possible, be continuous across the crossing (Figure 9.15). Lane and shoulder width, and median provision should be maintained to avoid either a pinch point or the introduction of a roadside hazard (e.g. in the form of any crossing furniture).

Sight distance is a critical consideration at any crossing. If there are active warning devices, these must be visible to approaching motorists in time for them to brake to a standstill when the device is activated. If the crossing has only passive devices, these rely on drivers actively looking for a train, and if one is approaching, to either proceed safely through the crossing in advance of the train, or to stop before reaching the crossing to allow the train to pass. There is evidence that many drivers do not look for an approaching train (Wigglesworth, 1978), and thus the provision of adequate sight distance, although a necessary condition, is not a sufficient condition for safety at level crossings with passive control. American Association of State Highway and Transportation Officials (1990, p 844 ff) present a comprehensive discussion of sight distance at railway crossings.

> *Although accidents at railway crossings are rare, they tend to be severe, especially if a train is involved. However, most accidents do not involve a train, and therefore careful attention to the design and layout of the crossing itself, and its integration with the road approaches is important. Grade separations are rarely justified on safety grounds alone, but active control devices such as gates or booms, or active warning devices such as lights and audible warnings, are appropriate where road traffic is heavy and/or train movements are frequent. On more lightly trafficked crossings, passive warning may be all that is justified. Where pedestrians cross a railway track, some form of protection or control should be considered. In all cases, careful attention must be given to visibility requirements.*

# 10 Delineation, signing and lighting

*Most of the information which the driver requires to guide, operate and control the vehicle is visual. The road system must therefore provide adequate visual information to enable the driver to control and navigate the vehicle, and also to enable the pedestrian to safely walk to the intended destination. These needs are met in a number of ways - roadside and pavement delineation of the route ahead, warning and direction signs, and, to ensure that these devices can be effective at night in conjunction with vehicle head lamps, the provision of street lighting. Safety aspects of these devices are reviewed in this chapter.*

## Delineation

Roadway delineation is used to (Freedman, et al, 1988):

. control the placements and movements of vehicles by supplying visual information to the driver that identifies the safe and legal limits of the travelled way,

. regulate the direction of travel, lane changing and overtaking,

. mark lanes or zones where manoeuvres such as turns or parking are permitted, required or restricted,

. improve lane discipline, particularly during night time driving, and

. aid in identifying potentially hazardous situations such as obstacles and pedestrian crossings.

235

Delineation is of critical importance to the safe and efficient operation of the road system. Most of the information which the driver uses to control a vehicle is visual. Delineation is vital in enabling the driver to locate the vehicle on the roadway and to make navigation and control decisions. Adequate delineation enables the driver to keep the vehicle within the traffic lane (short range delineation), and plan the immediate forward route driving task (long range delineation) (Good and Baxter, 1985).

Long range delineation enables the driver to plan the forward route, and thus it needs to be consistent and continuous. It is not restricted to locations where forward visibility is particularly confusing or critical, but has application to a road as a whole. Lay (1986, p 386) has noted that 'the curve characteristics of direction and curvature may need to be assessed up to 9 seconds ahead (and) even detailed tracking data for actual curve negotiation may be required 3 seconds ahead of the curve'.

Delineation has always been important, but it is likely to become even more critical in the years ahead as the driving population ages; older drivers have a reduced visual capability and hence rely to a greater extent on correct delineation of the road ahead (Transportation Research Board, 1988; Cunard, 1993).

There are numerous delineation devices in use (Tignor, 1993) and in general these fall into two groups - pavement markings and roadside devices.

*Pavement markings*

Pavement markings are usually applied using either paint or a thermoplastic material. Because they are required to operate at day and night, they should be highly reflective, e.g. through the use of glass beads mixed into the paint. They also need to be skid-resistant and durable. The message they convey must be clear and not lead to confusion, and since any given symbol may be visible for only a very short time, the message must be simple and clearly understood. There are three categories of pavement markings:

.   longitudinal lines (centre lines, lane lines, edge lines, barrier lines, etc),

.   transverse lines (stop lines at intersections pedestrian crossing lines), and

. word and symbol markings (e.g. pavement arrows, painted channelization, etc).

Each country will have its own national standards for the use of such devices. These vary in detail, but principally in the extent to which use is made of the third category listed above. For example, in the UK it is common to use a pavement marking to indicate which lane the driver should be in for a particular exit from an intersection (Figure 10.1), zig-zag lines are used to indicate the approach to a pedestrian crossing (Figure 10.2), yellow box markings are used to indicate the extremities of signalized intersections (Figure 9.10), speed limits may be painted on the road surface (Figure 10.3), etc. Generally however, word and symbol markings are used sparingly, mainly because their usefulness is limited in adverse conditions (e.g. at night, in the wet, and under heavy traffic), and because such markings may lead to skidding.

**Figure 10.1 Pavement marking indicating exit lane (UK)**

**Figure 10.2  Zig-zag pavement markings adjacent to pedestrian crossing (UK)**

**Figure 10.3  Speed limit marking on road pavement**

*Lane lines and edge lines*. Traffic flow and safety are almost invariably improved if traffic streams are separated into clearly marked lanes by the use of road markings (Ross Silcock Partnership, 1991, p 156). Lane lines on multi-lane facilities (and their equivalent on two-lane roads, namely centre lines) allow drivers to locate the vehicle laterally on the roadway, and thus assist in avoiding collisions with both roadside objects and opposing vehicles. They are particularly helpful in conditions of poor visibility such as at night or in fog or rain. They are inapplicable of course to unsealed roads.

Edge lines are sometimes provided at the outside edge of the carriageway/roadway. They have been found to give marginal advantages in driving performance (Johnston, 1983). Their main advantage is in short-term lane positioning (Triggs, 1980). Schwab and Capelle (1980) have noted that edge lines are as effective on straight alignments as on curves, and reached the general conclusion that 'delineation of the outside edge of the travel lane is highly desirable, especially for roads wider than 6 m.... there is substantial evidence that delineation provides important guidance information to motorists, especially when visibility decreases due to adverse weather or night time conditions'. Various studies have shown the safety benefits of edge lines. For example:

. Nairn (1987, p 47) suggests that accidents may be reduced by 15 per cent (straight roads) to 45 per cent (curves).

. Jackson (1981) reported reductions in total accidents of between 13 and 30 per cent, and reductions in night-time accidents of between 37 and 42 per cent following the installation of edge lines at sites in Britain.

. Moses (1986) reported that following the installation of wide edge lines on rural highways in Australia, accidents fell by 8 per cent, and out of control single vehicle accidents fell by 34 per cent.

. Tignor (1993) has reported US experience, which suggests a 2 per cent reduction in total accidents, and a 25 per cent reduction in run-off-road accidents. Russell (1993) has extended this to indicate that edge lines can be justified on two-lane rural roads if there is an average of one non-intersection accident annually per 15.5 miles (25 km).

. Miller (1992) reviewed a number of American studies, and found that edge lines had been claimed to reduce accident by between 3 and 60 per cent. No explanation was given for this very wide variation, which suggests that they may possibly be more effective in some locations than others. Miller concluded that overall, the provision of edge lines would generally reduce accidents by about 20 per cent.

On the other hand, some studies have indicated that the usefulness of edge lines as a general policy may be questionable. A study of 600 km (360 miles) of edge-lined rural road in the UK was inconclusive as to whether edgelining was an effective accident prevention measure (Willis, Scott and Barnes, 1984). The UK County Surveyors' Society (1989b) found that edgelining was effective only where it was introduced at a site with a specific problem involving loss of control.

Edge lines are usually either 100 mm (4 inches) or 150 mm (6 inches) wide. Research has shown that 150 mm edge lines are more effective, especially on curves (Nedas, Belcar and Macy, 1982). Recently, even wider edge lines (200 mm - 8 inches) have been used in some parts of the US; Lum and Hughes (1990) found that these could be cost-effective where pavement width exceeds 7.3 m (24 ft), shoulders are unpaved, and traffic volumes exceed 2,000 veh/d.

As noted, edge lines affect the position of vehicles in a lane, and therefore the incidence of vehicles leaving the paved surface is reduced. For this reason, some road agencies have adopted edge lines to reduce shoulder and pavement maintenance costs, as well as to increase road safety (Nairn, 1987, p 47).

*Raised reflective pavement markers.* Raised reflective pavement markers (RRPM) are devices which are attached to the road surface and raised slightly so as present a reflective face to oncoming traffic (Figure 10.4). A variation is to have them recessed into the pavement surface; these are relevant to areas where snow clearing is necessary and raised markers would suffer damage from the clearing machinery.

RRPM's provide better night time delineation than painted centre lines and edge lines, especially under adverse weather conditions. Hoque and Sanderson (1988) quote various studies which show accident reductions of 15 - 18 per cent following their installation. Moses (1985) reported a reduction from 33 to 10 head-on accidents, and 29 to 4 sideswipes following the installation of RRPM's on sections of rural road in Australia. Tignor (1993) quotes US studies which indicate a more modest effect - 5 per cent accident reduction following their installation.

In a review of the use of RRPM's at narrow bridges in the USA, Niessner (1984) determined that such devices were effective in reducing encroachment across the centre line, and appeared to have a beneficial effect on safety.

**Figure 10.4  Raised reflective pavement marker**

*Rumble devices*. Rumble devices are grooves or raised ridges placed on the roadway to provide a sudden audible and tactile warning to the driver. They are of two types (Harwood, 1993):

.   longitudinal installations, which may be used on the shoulder, the edge line, or the centre line of a road, primarily to counter driver fatigue or inattention; and

.   transverse installations, which are placed to alert drivers to an impending feature, such as on the approach to an intersection, a toll plaza, a speed limit change, a horizontal curve, a lane drop, or on the approach to a work zone.

A number of designs have been used for longitudinal installations, but typically the markings are highly reflective and because they are much thicker than paint, the lines are easily visible above road water on wet days, and have a longer life than painted lines. Raised reflective pavement markers give a tactile sensation when a wheel runs over them, and this may contribute towards their safety effectiveness.

Profiled edge lines include thermoplastic material applied either as a continuous extrusion with raised transverse bars or as separate transverse bars laid directly on the pavement, or a series of parallel grooves pressed into the shoulder. They are particularly relevant in situations where the accident information suggests that driver fatigue plays a part, since their main feature is to alert drivers of vehicles which stray from the through lane. For this reason, it is important that there be a width of sealed shoulder outside the profiled edge line to allow time for the necessary correction to be made by the driver.

Profiled edge lines have been shown to be cost-effective on applications on rural highways in the US. For example, an application on a freeway crossing California's Mojave Desert led to a 49 per cent reduction in run-off-the-road accidents and a reduction of 19 per cent in total accidents over a 7-year period (Anon, 1988b). An earlier application of a similar shoulder treatment in Arizona has been reported in Federal Highway Administration (1982, p 1-5). This showed a 61 per cent reduction in run-off-the-road accidents, and an estimated accident reduction over the 16 km (10 mile) section of 13 accidents in 3 years. A similar experiment using painted shoulders did not lower the accident rate. Both the California and Arizona installations were highly cost effective. Harwood (1993, p 40) summarized US experience by stating that shoulder rumble strips installed along extended sections of roadway 'have generally reduced the rate of run-off-road accidents by 20 per cent or more.'

In the UK, the County Surveyors' Society (1989) reported that on a motorway, total accidents fell by a non-significant 37 per cent in the three years following the installation of shoulder rumble strips, but that accidents involving vehicles leaving the outside edge of the road fell by a statistically significant 76 per cent.

Transverse rumble devices may consist of raised bars, grooves, or an exposed aggregate rumble pad. Most research on the effectiveness of such devices has related to rumble devices placed on the approach to STOP sign controlled intersections. In a review of these studies, Harwood (1993, p 10) noted that few reported a reliable research method, and of those that did, only two showed a statistically significant accident reduction. One was a study in Iowa involving 21 sites on the primary highway network. This produced a 51 per cent reduction in the total accident rate at those sites.

The second study was in the UK, which assessed the effect of transverse rumble strips on accidents and speeds on the approach to intersections and rural towns (Sumner and Shippey, 1977). This study showed a significant 50 per cent reduction in accidents of a type which could have been related to the device, and a 39 per cent overall reduction (not significant). However, a more recent UK Department of Transport (1993c) publication casts doubt on the long term influence of these devices for speed modification: 'any speed reduction obtained will tend to be minimal, and will be eroded with the passage of time. It is known that in some locations drivers have learned to accelerate over the devices to lessen the vibratory effect. Reliance should not therefore be placed on using rumble devices alone to reduce speed.' This publication indicated that they could be used to 'alert drivers to take greater care in advance of a hazard such as a bend or junction (and) in combination with a gateway they can indicate the entry to a village or the start of a series of traffic calming measures.' Similar warnings were sounded by Harwood (1993, p 39) who cautioned against over-use of such devices, noting that if they are used at too many locations, 'they may lose their ability to gain the motorist's attention'. He also noted that their use in residential areas may be objectionable to nearby residents.

In a non-intersection application, Emerson and West (1986) reported on the use of rumble strips on the approach to 52 narrow bridges on two highways in Oklahoma. Over a four year period, the number of run-off-the-road accidents per million crossing vehicles at the test sites fell by 35 per cent on one highway and 47 per cent on the other, while fatal and injury accidents fell by 52 per cent and 56 per cent.

*Roadside devices*

Roadside devices include continuous devices such as guide posts, and devices used only at discrete sites such as bends (e.g. chevrons) or objects such as bridges.

*Guide posts and post mounted delineators.* Guide posts are lightweight posts about 0.9-1.2 m (3-4 ft) high, located 0.6-3.0 m (2-10 ft) from the edge of the outside lane (Figure 10.5). They should be low cost, easy to transport, cheap to install and replace, resistant to extreme weather conditions, present no safety hazard to road users, and present no psychological obstacle to road users keeping the vehicle in the correct place on the road. They are available in a number of materials, including timber, fibre glass, aluminium and plastic. They may be provided as isolated devices, for example to mark the presence of a culvert, over a short section of road (e.g. to mark the presence of a curve - Figure 10.6), or continuously along an extended length of road. In the last case, the driver should always be able to see at least two and preferably three pairs of guide posts (National Association of Australian State Road Authorities, 1988f, p 28). Practice varies from place to place, and local practice should be adopted to ensure consistency.

Guide posts usually have a reflective device attached, often referred to as a post-mounted delineator (PMD). These assist long range delineation at night, and are made from reflective sheeting or from moulded plastic using the corner cube principle (Lay, 1986, p 481). They should be designed to ensure a width adequately visible at long distances, especially at night, and be high enough to avoid being soiled by mud (Ross Silcock Partnership, 1991, p 160; Bissell, 1993).

**Figure 10.5 Curve advisory speed sign.** Guide posts are also visible in this photograph.

**Figure 10.6 Guide posts used to delineate horizontal curve**

Triggs, Harris and Fildes (1979) demonstrated that the combination of centre lines and guide posts with PMD's enhanced static direction judgement at night. Increasing the number of posts on the outside of a bend improved these judgements. Good and Baxter (1985) found that PMD's were the best form of long range delineation, and that a combination of PMD's and wide (150 mm - 6 inch) edge lines best catered for drivers' needs for both long and short range delineation.

The safety effectiveness of guide posts with reflective delineators has been demonstrated in a number of studies. For example:

. Bissell (1993) reports a US study which found that PMD's installed on curves on two lane roads reduced accidents by up to 30 per cent,

. The UK County Surveyors' Society (1989) indicated that on undivided roads, the installation of guide posts was associated with a statistically significant 67 per cent accident reduction, and on divided roads, the

245

reduction was of the order of 30 per cent (from a very small sample), and

. In Australia, Vincent (1978) found a 60 per cent decrease in night-time accidents after the installation of PMD's, compared with a 21 per cent decrease for those sections of the same highway where no change was made.

However, a Finnish study (Kahlberg, 1991) cautions against the extension of these results to lower standard roads. On two lane rural roads with an 80 km/h (50 mph) speed limit, it was found that the 'reflector posts' led to an increase in night time average speeds of 5 km/h, and an increase of 20 per cent in accidents. However, on higher standard roads with a speed limit of 100 km/h (60 mph), no statistically significant change in either speeds or accidents was detected. Kahlberg warned that these results may not be transferable to other countries because of 'differences in driving culture and habits', and also noted that such devices are used in Finland only on 'curves and short sections of dangerous road, usually on secondary roads with little traffic'.

*Chevrons.* Delineation is critical on horizontal curves, especially isolated curves with a radius less than 600 m (Johnston, 1982), and chevrons are commonly used to warn drivers of sharp bends and other situations such as medians and islands (Figures 10.7 and 10.8, the latter illustrating an internally illuminated bollard as used in the UK).

Chevrons are often introduced as part of a package of delineation measures, and it is difficult to isolate their effects, but the UK County Surveyors' Society (1989) found statistically significant reductions in accidents at 9 out of 18 sites for which data were available; an accident reduction of up to 70 per cent for applicable accidents was found.

*Curve alignment markers.* A relatively recent innovation is the curve alignment marker (CAM), which is a single post-mounted chevron (Figure 10.9) with highly contrasting colours (e.g. black on yellow or red on yellow) (Bhatnagar, 1994; Jennings and Demetsky, 1985).

**Figure 10.7  Chevron marker at intersection island**

Bhatnagar (1994) has developed relationships between approach speed and curve advisory speed which indicate that CAMs are suited where there is a difference between these two speeds of around 20 km/h (12 mph), with the CAMs spaced at:

0.12R + 4 metres (for V < 80 km/h) or

0.08R + 2 metres (for V > 80 km/h)

where V is the approach speed (km/h) and R is the curve radius (m).

Bhatnagar (1994) also, importantly, recommends that the use of CAMs should be reserved exclusively for curve delineation, and not used for any other purpose such as roundabouts, pedestrian refuges, bullnose of guard rail, etc, since such practices will 'reduce their effectiveness in more critical curve delineation'.

247

**Figure 10.8 Internally illuminated bollard**

CAMs have been shown to improve curve negotiation strategy, especially with impaired drivers (Johnston, 1982, 1983). Jennings and Demetsky (1985) found that drivers react favourably to CAMs on sharp curves, and provide better long-range information on such curves than guide posts. Tignor (1993) reports that in the US, 'reflectorized guide markers at horizontal curves' have an accident reduction potential of 30 per cent.

*Object markers.* Object markers are common throughout the road network, and are applied to hazards such as bridge abutments (Figure 12.18), underpass piers, handrails, culverts, trees, poles, and hazards in the roadway such as bridge piers.

**Figure 10.9  Curve alignment markers**

Bissell (1993) states that 'no known studies have been conducted to determine the effectiveness of specific object markers', but goes on to mention that as part of a package of devices applied at sites such as narrow bridges, accident reductions as high as 40 per cent have been found.

*Variable message signs.* Hoque and Sanderson (1988) mention experimental variable message signs which have been successful in trials in reducing accidents. These include speed-activated 'too fast' signs which have reduced accidents at sharp curves in Canada, and electronic freeway management systems in Holland. King, et al (1978) describes a range of dynamic aids which were tested at bridge sites; these included flashing beacons, actuated flashing strobes, actuated 'narrow bridge' and 'oncoming traffic' signs, etc.

*Novel delineation devices*

A number of illusory devices have been trialed at various places with the intention of emphasizing hazardous locations. These include innovative signs, road markings, irregular post spacing, transverse lines on the pavement lane, width restrictions, curvature enhancement treatments, etc. While these have been found to have had some immediate impact on reducing speed and the incidence of accidents, their effects have dissipated with time (Fildes and Lee, 1993, p 78).

One particular application is yellow bar markings on the approach to intersections; these are common in the UK, and Helliar-Symons (1981) found that speed-related accidents at roundabouts where these were installed were reduced by 57 per cent; they were more effective in daylight than in dark, and also tended to reduce accident severity, presumably because of the slower speeds.

*Good delineation is an essential part of a modern road system, and has demonstrated safety benefits. The various devices listed in this section have all been shown to be effective, if applied in accord with sound guidelines, and installed at sites where there is an accident problem involving relevant accident types. Attention to on-going maintenance is essential, since the devices can only be effective if they are maintained in sound condition, with replacements (due to being struck by vehicles or as a result of vandalism) being rapidly attended to.*

## Road signs

Apart from the delineation devices discussed in the previous section, road signs are of three types (see Chapter 3):

.   regulatory signs, which inform the road user of legal requirements which must be followed, such as speed limits, parking restrictions, direction of traffic flow, turn controls (see Figure 13.5); STOP or GIVE WAY (YIELD) signs (see Figures 9.2 and 9.3) are also regulatory signs,

.   warning signs, which alert the driver to potential hazards ahead (Figure 10.5 above), and

. information signs, which give drivers information about route directions (such as destinations, tourist facilities, services; see Figure 13.17).

Each of these types of sign should follow standard conventions concerning colour and shape to aid recognition and credibility (see Chapter 3). Careful planning, installation and maintenance of road signs can contribute to the safe and efficient operation of the road network. They need to be designed to convey clear and unambiguous messages to road users so that they can be understood quickly and easily. Road signs are often used in conjunction with pavement markings (Ross Silcock Partnership, 1991, p 120).

It is important also to note the importance of correct location, the need to use standard signs, and the need to maintain and replace signs. Signs are an accepted part of the traffic system, but much of the information they provide is of transient value only and therefore if the driver is to recognize the sign, accept its message, and act upon it, it is essential that the sign satisfy requirements of conspicuity, legibility, comprehensibility and credibility outlined in Chapter 3. The overuse of signs should be avoided, since their effectiveness will be reduced if they are used too freely.

*Regulatory signs*

Regulatory signs contribute to safety by conveying essential control information to drivers, such as the legal requirement to stop, yield right of way to another road user, travel in the correct direction, etc. As such, it is the message rather than the sign that is important, but to do that, adherence to the principles outlined above concerning siting, the use of standard shapes and colours, maintenance, etc is necessary.

*Warning signs*

Warning signs give advance notice of potential hazard such as intersections, curves, crests, pedestrian crossings, etc, and are of particular use when the design element is sub-standard.

Since warning signs are an integral part of the road system, it is difficult to isolate the safety effects of them. However, Tignor (1993) quotes US studies which indicate that for traffic signs as a whole, the expected benefit is a 29 per cent reduction in fatal accident rates, a 14 per cent reduction in injury accident rates, and an overall benefit cost ratio of 7.3:1. Reported effectiveness of other devices includes:

.  Tignor (1993) has indicated that the installation of *curve warning signs* leads to a 20 per cent average accident reduction. Pak-Poy and Kneebone (1988, p 40) quoted a Canadian study which in turn drew on other references which claimed a reduction of 20-57 per cent in accidents when such signs were provided; in one such study, a 71 per cent reduction in fatal accidents was recorded.

.  Tignor (1993) indicates an average 20 per cent accident reduction following installation of *advance curve warning signs showing an advisory speed* (Figure 10.5). Kneebone (1964) reported that the installation of a number of such signs in Australia reduced casualty accidents by 62 per cent and all accidents by 56 per cent. This was associated with a reduction in speeds at those sites. Pak Poy and Kneebone (1988, p 40) quote other US studies which have shown a reduction in accidents following programs of this sort ranging from 20 per cent to 37 per cent.

.  *Advisory speed signs* have shown a 36 per cent average accident reduction in the USA (Tignor, 1993).

.  Pak Poy and Kneebone (1988) cite another study which suggested accident reductions of around 20-30 per cent for other warning signs, such as *side road signs*.

.  Jackson (1981) reported that improved *signing at intersections* gave an accident reduction of 34 per cent in a British county.

In particularly hazardous situations, greater emphasis can be given to the special need for drivers to take care by the use of special signs. An example of this is the use in Britain of bright, highly reflective yellow backing boards to frame a conventional warning sign (Figure 9.14). An independent study carried out for the manufacturer of one such product by the TMS Consultancy (1993) indicated that these signs 'have made a significant contribution to accident reduction in a number of individual sites, and a significant contribution to an overall reduction in accidents throughout this study. In some cases the ... sign was the only change, and the whole effect is therefore likely to be attributed to that feature.'

*Information signs*

Information signs contribute to road safety by minimizing unnecessary travel, allowing drivers to position their vehicles prior to making turns, reassuring drivers so that they are not hesitant and thereby potentially disrupting traffic flow, and drawing attention to the presence of major intersections.

No specific information on the safety effectiveness of information signs could be found.

*Sign maintenance*

Signs will remain functional and achieve their safety objectives only if they are adequately maintained. They fade under sunlight, are subject to accidental and vandal damage, and often do not command a high profile in an agency's maintenance program. National Association of Australian State Road Authorities (1988f) suggest that all signs should be subject to regular maintenance and inspection (including night time inspection) to ensure:

. that they have not become obscured by foliage or other roadside installations,

. that each sign is in good physical condition,

. that each sign is performing its function and conveying its message under both daylight and night time conditions,

. that the sign's function is still relevant and necessary, and that there is not a need to update or replace it,

. that all signs and markings are cleaned sufficiently often, and

. that supporting structures are in sound condition.

*Road signs are an integral part of a modern road system. They convey significant safety benefits as well as user amenity. It is essential that they be installed and maintained in accord with relevant warrants and guides, in particular those concerning shape, colour, size, location and*

*application. Attention to on-going maintenance is essential, since signs can only be effective if they are maintained in sound condition.*

## Street lighting

In urban areas, street lighting of appropriate standard contributes to road safety. It can be particularly important where there are pedestrians or cyclists. Lighting has benefits other than accident prevention, and is more often justified, especially in residential streets, as a general amenity contributing to security and crime prevention.

Lighting standards are well-established, providing guidelines or standards for particular classes of road and street (Lay, 1986, Chapter 24). Street lighting should aim to provide a uniformly lit road surface against which objects can be seen in silhouette, with higher lighting intensity to provide direct illumination at conflict points such as major intersections and pedestrian crossings.

Various studies have claimed accident rate reductions of around 30 per cent over the urban road system (Stark, 1975; Scott, 1980; Teale, 1984; Foyster and Thompson, 1986). Tignor (1993) reports US studies which indicated a reduction of 41 per cent in fatal accidents and 16 per cent in injury accidents, with an overall benefit:cost ratio of 12:1 from lighting improvements. At intersections, up to 75 per cent of night-time accidents can be affected by lighting.

Urban freeways in particular appear to be safer if well-lit (Box, 1972), although Nairn (1987, p 35) suggested that the benefits of lighting may need to be compared with other possible improvements such as better delineation (raised reflective pavement markers, edge lining, etc).

In rural areas, lighting of isolated grade intersections can be a worthwhile safety benefit (Lipinski, et al, 1970). In the UK, it is common to light rural roads (especially freeways/motorways), and Sabey and Johnson (1973) have found a statistically significant reduction of about 50 per cent at such sites.

It should also be noted that the safety benefits of improved lighting can be offset to an extent if the lighting poles are poorly located, since a high proportion of urban single vehicle accidents involve utility poles (see Chapter 12). The lighting layout should therefore aim to minimize the number of poles, and should ensure that poles are not located in vulnerable positions.

In summary, to quote Nairn (1987, p 35), 'there is little doubt that street lighting is an important component of urban road design. It fulfils the roles of providing an improved road safety potential and added personal security for urban dwellers. The applications and standard of design must however be carefully considered.' The Federal Highway Administration (1982, p 12-14) suggested that 'the more complex the decision required of the driver at any particular location, the more likely lighting will be of benefit. The presence of raised channelization, roadside development, and/or high degrees of curvature are good indications of the need for fixed roadway lighting.'

*Street lighting contributes to road safety on urban arterial roads, urban freeways, and in some circumstances in rural areas. However, care needs to be taken with its design, especially with the location and type of poles, as these can be a major hazard in themselves.*

# 11 Road maintenance and construction

*Road construction and maintenance activities can directly influence the safety of roads. In this chapter, we review these factors, considering the effects of pavement maintenance, and in particular resurfacing for its effects upon skid resistance and pavement roughness, and road safety at work zones. Other maintenance activities include the maintenance of signals (Chapter 9), signs and markings (Chapter 10) and roadside maintenance (Chapter 12).*

## Pavement condition

Pavement condition includes both the skid resistance of the pavement surface, and the roughness of the pavement itself. The former is much more significant in accident terms, but the latter is more significant in terms of economic efficiency through its effects on vehicle operating costs. Road maintenance activities which involve resurfacing may therefore be directed at either friction or roughness, or both.

*Skid resistance*

Skidding is a contributory factor to many accidents, especially on wet roads and on the approaches to intersections. Accidents which occur in wet weather typically (Kumar and Cunningham, 1992):

. occur at 2 to 3 times the rate of accidents in dry weather, all else being equal,
. represent about 20-30 per cent of total accidents,
. involve skidding, and

.   in up to 70 per cent of cases, improved skid resistance may be helpful.

In Britain, about 15 per cent of all vehicles involved in injury accidents have skidded prior to the collision, and these accidents produce 41 per cent of vehicle user deaths and 30 per cent of serious injuries (Ho, 1991). The accidents most involved in skidding accidents include rear-end, run-off-road, sideswipe, head-on and pedestrian accidents (Geoffroy, 1993a; Ward, 1992).

Skidding accidents are a result of reduced friction between the tyres and the road pavement. Lay (1988) has suggested that a coefficient of friction of above 0.55 is usually enough to significantly reduce braking and turning accidents, although a value as high as 0.75 might be needed when risks are high, and as low as 0.30 may be tolerated when risks are low, such as on long straight stretches of road with no interruptions to traffic. Wet surfaces reduce the available friction, particularly at the start of rain after a long period of dry weather when the frictional resistance can decrease by as much as half (Sabey and Storie, 1968; Organisation for Economic Cooperation and Development, 1984).

However, the frictional resistance can be substantially improved by providing a suitable road surface texture, with resultant potential for accident improvement. Such treatments involve either application of an overlay of high-friction asphalt, or grooving/grinding an existing surface (Figure 11.1) (Geoffroy, 1993a). The need for such a treatment can be assessed by use of machines capable of measuring pavement skid resistance, such as the SCRIM device (Sideways Force Coefficient Routine Investigation Machine) (Hosking and Woodford, 1976).

The mechanism by which friction develops between the road pavement and the tyre involves the tyre deforming into fine irregularities in the pavement surface (Organisation for Economic Cooperation and Development, 1976, 1984; Roe, Webster and West, 1991). These irregularities occur at two levels: a 'macrotexture' which is the rough surface texture visible to the naked eye, and the 'microtexture' which is the detailed surface characteristics of the aggregate (stones) forming the pavement. At low speeds, a harsh microtexture is required, while the macrotexture is more important at higher speeds. The effect of traffic is to reduce the harshness of the microtexture, i.e. the surface becomes 'polished'. Coefficients of friction between a locked tyre and the pavement vary from around 0.6 when both microtexture and macrotexture is rough, to 0.05 when both are smooth.

**Figure 11.1 Grooved pavement**, to increase frictional resistance on a horizontal curve.

The presence of moisture has little effect on skid resistance when vehicles are travelling at low speeds, but as speeds increase the water must be squeezed away from the surface before the tyre can grip. This is the role of macrotexture - to provide channels to drain the water away. Hydroplaning, in which the tyre does not develop full grip over an area because of the presence of a film of water about 6 mm thick, is more likely at higher speeds, with bald tyres, and a fine macrotexture (Lay, 1986, p 542).

The safety benefits of providing skid-resistant pavements to counter wet weather accidents have been reported in a number of studies (Cleveland, 1987; Federal Highway Administration, 1982, p 2.2 ff; Kumar and Cunningham, 1992). Typical results are:

. In London, a large scale anti-skid resurfacing program led to a statistically significant 30 per cent accident reduction, with wet weather accidents falling by 47 per cent (Young, 1983). Sites treated were those with higher than expected proportions of wet or skidding accidents, including pedestrian crossings and approaches to intersections.

.  The County Surveyors' Society (1989) reported a study in the UK that indicated a statistically significant 25 per cent reduction in total accidents following application of high friction surfacing.

.  A US study (Adam and Shah, 1974) identified reductions in total accidents in the range 26-54 per cent, and in wet weather accidents of 64-83 per cent, following application of high friction surfacing to heavily trafficked multi-lane roads in Louisiana.

.  Wet weather accidents on a steep 2-lane section of highway in California were reduced by 72 per cent following the grooving of the pavement surface (Wong, 1990).

.  Kumar and Cunningham (1992) report a Canadian study which indicated that after treatments aimed at wet weather accidents at intersections, total accidents fell by 46 per cent, with wet pavement accidents falling by 71 per cent, and dry pavement accidents by 21 per cent. Rehabilitation to improve skid resistance at freeway/motorway locations produced an average overall 29 per cent accident reduction, with 54 per cent reduction in wet pavement accidents, and 16 per cent in dry pavement accidents.

.  Roe, Webster and West (1991) report a British study which found that both skidding and non-skidding accidents, in both wet and dry conditions, were less if the pavement macrotexture was coarse than if it was fine, indicating the potential safety benefits of maintaining a coarse macrotexture.

Finally, it is relevant to note that splash and spray, which is associated with accident occurrence (Colwill and Daines, 1987), is related to wet roads, and in particular to heavy vehicles on wet roads. Splash and spray can be reduced through the use of open-graded, or porous, asphalt (Daines, 1992; van Heystraeten and Moraux, 1990). This is also much less noisy than regular asphalt or concrete surfaces. However, splash and spray is mainly controlled through on-vehicle devices (Ivey and Mounce, 1984; Sandberg, 1980).

*Pavement roughness*

Considerable attention has been given to the effects of road roughness on vehicle operating costs and therefore to the economic efficiency of road provision and optimum maintenance intervention levels (Lay, 1986, Chapter 26). However, much less attention has been given to safety aspects of road roughness. Perhaps this is because, in developed countries at least, roads are maintained at a sufficiently high level that roughness does not become a safety issue.

Nevertheless, there is some evidence that roughness and related surface irregularity is a matter of concern in a small proportion of accidents. Geoffroy (1993a) quotes a number of studies to illustrate this:

.   a study in North Carolina (Ivey and Griffin, 1976) found that about 2 per cent of accidents involved 'discontinuities' in the traffic lane, including non-pavement conditions like rocks and manhole covers,

.   a Finnish study found that pavement condition contributed to 2 per cent of fatal accidents,

.   on the other hand, an Israeli study (Craus, Livneh and Ishai, 1991) found no correlation between pavement surface condition and accidents,

.   in New York State in 1991, fewer than 1/3 of one per cent of accidents were reported as having road pavement defects (other than slippery pavements) mentioned as a causal factor.

Surface roughness may also be a much larger factor in truck accidents and motor cycle accidents than in car accidents. An Australian study of truck accidents (reported in Ogden and Pearson, 1991) found that 10.7 per cent of such accidents were associated with drivers losing control due to potholes. Jackson (1986) cites cases in the US where failure of a mechanical component of the truck (e.g. spring) was due to pavement roughness, and quotes another study which found that certain wavelengths of surface discontinuity may resonate with the truck suspension, causing either mechanical failure or loss of control by the driver. Smith (1986) notes that rough surfaces can cause load shift in large trucks, or rollover, or both. It is also interesting to note that a survey of the attitudes of Australian truck drivers conducted by Axia (1986) found that truck drivers considered road pavement conditions to be 'the cause of a large number of accidents', and that poor roads were the cause of unwarranted damage to their vehicles.

It could be argued that ideally, roads carrying large volumes of trucks should be less rough than other roads for this reason. However, the reverse is the norm, as roads carrying high truck volumes are likely to be rougher due to the pavement deterioration associated with truck use.

In summary then, while intuitively it seems reasonable to suppose that irregularities or defects in the road surface could adversely affect the ability of the driver to control the vehicle, there is little research on the subject, and what there is seems to suggest that, in developed countries at least, this a factor affecting only a small percentage of accidents, although it may be more significant for trucks.

*Pavement resurfacing*

Pavement resurfacing may be undertaken as part of an accident-related mass action program, or as part of routine pavement maintenance. In the first case, sites for treatment are identified through the mass accident data base (see Chapter 4). Depending upon the format of the data base and the items coded into it, such sites may be identified either as those which have accidents involving skidding as factor, or those having wet pavement as a factor. The UK County Surveyors' Society (1989) has noted that the former calls for a subjective assessment by the police officer, and that it may be more cost-effective to identify sites simply on the basis of wet pavement or wet weather. Similarly, they suggest that since it is sometimes difficult to pinpoint where exactly on a bend a skidding accident has occurred, the whole bend, or whole road segments, may need to be treated.

Pavement resurfacing undertaken as part of routine highway maintenance work would be part of an ongoing resurfacing or rehabilitation works program. However, Transportation Research Board (1987a, p 96) has noted that the potential effect of resurfacing on safety is a result of two factors working in opposite directions. First, since resurfacing reduces surface roughness and improves ride quality, it may lead to increased average speeds. Second, resurfacing often increases pavement skid resistance, which reduces stopping distance and improves vehicle controllability when the pavement surface is wet. The report went on to suggest the following tentative findings concerning the safety effects of resurfacing:

. Routine resurfacing of rural roads generally increases dry weather accident rates by an initial amount of about 10 per cent, probably because of increased speeds.

. Dry weather skid resistance and stopping are unaffected by resurfacing unless the original pavement was extremely rough.

. Routine resurfacing of rural roads generally reduces wet weather accident rates by an initial amount of about 15 per cent. Apparently, this follows from improvements in wet weather stopping distances and vehicle controllability that more than compensate for any effects of somewhat higher speeds following resurfacing.

. For most rural roads, the net effect of resurfacing on accident rates is small and gradually diminishes over time.

. Resurfacing improves the safety performance of roads that experience an abnormally high frequency of accidents in wet weather.

. Resurfacing projects provide the opportunity to correct deficient pavement cross slopes at little or no extra cost. Correcting cross slopes allows better drainage of the pavement surface and improves vehicle control in wet weather. On individual resurfacing projects, careful attention to the removal of surface defects and necessary improvements to skid resistance, surface drainage, and superelevation may help offset the potentially adverse effects of increased speeds.

These comprehensive findings provide a good summary. The one that is perhaps most deserving of emphasis from a road safety engineering viewpoint is that, as with other remedial programs, the effectiveness is much greater and not likely to be counter-productive if the site treated is one which has a history of accidents which are potentially amenable to treatment by the resurfacing program such as those involving skidding or loss of control. This is of course the basis of site selection for any mass action road safety program, and once again underlines the necessity for a good data base and sound analysis of the data to ensure that road safety resources are well-spent.

*Wet weather accidents represent typically 20-30 per cent of accidents. Most of these involve skidding, and up to 70 per cent can potentially be ameliorated by improving skid resistance. Various methods are available to improve the skid resistance of road surfaces, including the application of a high-friction overlay, or cutting grooves into the pavement. From a road safety engineering viewpoint, the need is to target resurfacing works at sites with a history of accidents which are potentially amenable to treatment by pavement resurfacing. Sites which are resurfaced for other reasons (to do with vehicle operating costs) may show little if any safety benefit if they lead to an increase in travel speeds.*

## Work zones

Data from the US suggests that work zones are hazardous from a road safety viewpoint. The Federal Highway Administration (1982, p 101 ff) has reported various studies which show a greater incidence of accidents on road segments where roadworks are in progress. For example, a Californian study showed a 21 per cent increase; an Ohio study showed a 7 per cent increase; resurfacing projects in Georgia showed a 61 per cent increase, and a freeway widening project in Virginia showed a 119 per cent increase. However, American results were variable. A multi-state study of 79 projects showed an average increase of 7.5 per cent, but 24 sites indicated an increase of more than 50 per cent while 31 sites showed a decrease. Those showing the worst increases were short duration, short length construction zones, perhaps reflecting either driver expectancy (or lack thereof) or poor roadworks signing, or both.

In the UK, Summersgill (1985) has reported that the rate of personal injury accidents at work zones on motorways/freeways is about 50 per cent greater than elsewhere on the motorway. Importantly, this rate is still less that experienced off the motorway network, which has implications for re-routing traffic away from the work site.

Heavy vehicles face particular difficulties at work zones (Graham, 1988; Federal Highway Administration, 1986; Lumenfeld, 1988). These include median crossovers, reduced number of lanes, reduced lane width, trucks being required to travel closer (because of their width) to potential hazards such as excavations or drop-offs, short merge zones, and flashing signals which are at truck driver's eye height causing visibility problems. All of these mean that explicit consideration should be given to warning, delineation and control devices for trucks at work sites. Federal Highway Administration (1986) has reported that trucks are over-represented in work zone accidents in the US, being associated with 24 per cent of work zone fatalities compared with 13 per cent of all fatalities. However, Council and Hall (1989, p 102) have compared the involvement of trucks in accidents at work zones with that of all vehicles, and found very little difference. Trucks were slightly over-represented in work zones on freeways and slightly under-represented on other roads.

Organisation for Economic Cooperation and Development (1989) have reported that excessive speed, traffic management at the work site, adverse weather, heavy traffic, and the hours of darkness are all associated with accidents at work zones.

Bryden (1993) has summarized the principles involved in safely and effectively controlling traffic at work sites:

. traffic safety should be an integral and high priority element of every construction job, from planning, through design, to construction,

. construction and maintenance operations should inhibit traffic as little as possible,

. clear and positive guidance must be provided to drivers approaching and traversing work zones,

. routine inspection of traffic control elements is essential to ensure acceptable levels of traffic safety and operations,

. roadside safety must be given sufficient attention because of the potential increase in hazards associated with the work activities,

. appropriate training of all relevant personnel is essential,

. adequate legislative authority is necessary for the implementation and enforcement of traffic regulations applicable to work zones (for example, Figure 11.2 shows a work zone speed limit sign), and

. maintaining good public relations, and keeping the motoring public informed, is essential.

**Figure 11.2  Work zone speed limit sign**

More particularly, Organisation for Economic Cooperation and Development (1989, p 79) has developed the following guidelines for traffic management at work zone sites:

. capacity restrictions must be carefully evaluated and monitored,
. lane closures should normally start from the fast lane,
. buffer zones should be provided wherever possible,
. incident control is important, especially with contra-flow techniques, and
. speed limits should be realistic; they should be supported by appropriate accompanying measures and not rely solely on signing.

*Road work zones can represent a particular hazard to road users. It is important that work sites have adequate advance warning, clear and unambiguous traffic control through the work zone, and that the work zone is left in a safe condition when work is not in progress.*

266

# 12  The roadside

*Many accidents involve the vehicle leaving the road and striking a roadside object. In this chapter, we review the ways in which this problem may be tackled, including the development of a roadside clear zone, the establishment of a roadside hazard management program (including its application to utility poles, traffic signs, bridges and culverts, and trees), the installation of crash barriers, and treatment of the road shoulder.*

## The forgiving roadside

Collisions with fixed roadside objects typically account for 25 - 30 per cent of fatal accidents. In the US, over the decade of the 1980s, the distribution of objects in fatal accidents hit was as shown in Figure 12.1.

Collisions with roadside objects are significant in both urban and rural environments. In a study of rural single vehicle accidents in Australia, Armour and Cinquegrana (1990) found that a roadside object was considered to have increased the severity of 27 per cent of the accidents investigated.

As with other road safety programs, measures to address this problem may be directed at reducing either the frequency of accidents, or reducing their severity. The former would include such measures as certain types of shoulder treatment (which we will consider in this chapter), control of speed (Chapter 13), and programs aimed at combating driver fatigue or alcohol abuse.

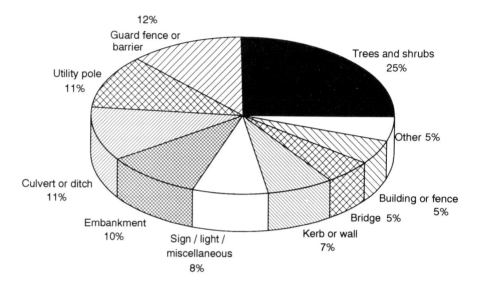

**Figure 12.1 Distribution of roadside objects in fatal accidents, USA**

Source: Cirillo (1993).

However, while accident prevention is clearly the ideal, vehicles can and do leave the roadway for a variety of reasons associated with the driver (e.g. fatigue, inattention, distraction by a passenger), the vehicle (e.g. tyre or steering failure, truck load instability), traffic conditions (e.g. another accident, animal or pedestrian on the road), the road environment (e.g. weather), or a combination of these. The aim then should be to provide a *forgiving roadside*, that is to develop cost-effective ways of reducing the severity of those accidents where a vehicle leaves the roadway.

Broadly speaking, there are two strategies here. The first is to attempt to provide, where possible, a *roadside clear zone* so that if a vehicle leaves the roadway, it is less likely to strike a fixed roadside object. The second is to accept that such a clear zone is impractical in many cases (especially in urban areas) and that therefore it is necessary to develop a *roadside hazard management program* aimed at reducing the severity of accidents with both fixed roadside objects, and also with pedestrians and cyclists who may be struck by an errant vehicle.

These two approaches are considered in the following sections of this chapter.

## Roadside clear zones

*Recovery area*

As noted above, there will be instances where vehicles leave the roadway. The recovery area is a term used to describe that zone beside the road within which the driver is likely to be able to regain control of the vehicle if it has not struck a fixed roadside object or rolled over. This area is defined by the distance the vehicle travels along the roadside and the distance which it penetrates into the roadside, which in turn depend upon the speed at which the vehicle is travelling, and the angle at which it leaves the roadway.

Early studies in the US (Stonex, 1960) established that with flat sides slopes, 80-85 per cent of vehicles travelling at highway speeds could recover within 9 m (30 ft) from the edge of the roadway. This distance was considerably greater on a curve, or if the batter slope was steeper.

*Clear zone*

It is not practical or cost-effective to universally provide a distance corresponding to the recovery area, so road authorities over time have developed the concept of the *clear zone*, which is an area within the recovery area which is ideally kept fee of roadside hazards, and which reflects the probability of an accident occurring on that road and the cost-effectiveness of providing such a zone.

Various attempts have been made to define such a clear zone. (See Federal Highway Administration, 1982, p 3-3 ff for a review of US studies, Troutbeck (1983) for a review of Australian studies, and Hedman (1990) for a review of Swedish studies). Basically, the conclusion from these studies is that a clear zone of around 9 m (30 ft) width from the travelled pavement is appropriate. Clear zone are therefore areas adjacent to traffic lanes which are free from roadside hazards such as poles, trees and shrubs with trunks greater than about 100 mm (4 inches), culvert end walls, steep batters (greater than about 6:1, or ideally 4:1), drains, etc which pose a danger to errant vehicles. Any obstacles within the zone should either to be removed or shielded with guard fencing.

The clear zone is therefore dependent upon the traffic speed, roadside geometry, and traffic volume, and is a compromise between safety, economic and in many cases environmental considerations (Graham and Harwood, 1983; Sicking and Ross, 1986; Transportation Research Board, 1987a, Appendix F). Figure 12.2 shows a typical clear zone relationship, applicable to tangent (straight) sections of road if it is practicable to provide such a width; if it is not practicable to do so, it may be necessary to consider alternative remedial treatments, such as guard fencing.

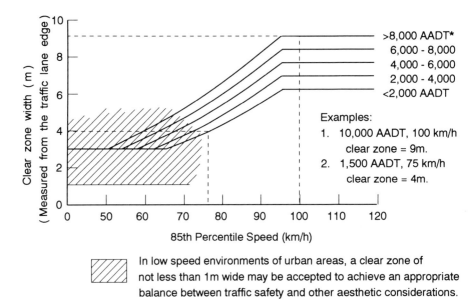

Notes: The clear zone is measured from the edge of the trafficked lane. For curves with a radius of less than 600 m (2,000 ft), the clear zone width on the outside of the curve should be doubled.

**Figure 12.2 Desirable clear zone widths**

Source: Symons and Cunningham (1987).

The effectiveness of providing roadside clear zones is well-established. To illustrate this, Table 12.1 shows the expected reduction in related accident types (i.e. those accidents types influenced by the treatment) with increased clear zone width on both straight sections and horizontal curves, based on US experience.

**Table 12.1**
**Accident reduction factors for increasing roadside clear zone width**

| Amount of increased roadside recovery distance in m (ft) | Reduction in related accident types (percent) | |
|---|---|---|
| | straight | curves |
| 1.5 m (5 ft) | 13 | 9 |
| 2.4 m (8 ft) | 21 | 14 |
| 3.0 m (10 ft) | 25 | 17 |
| 3.6 m (12 ft) | 29 | 19 |
| 5.0 m (15 ft) | 35 | 23 |
| 6.0 m (20 ft) | 44 | 29 |

Source: Zegeer and Council (1992); Zegeer, Twomey, Heckman and Hayward (1992).

*Cross section*

Flatter roadside slopes have been found to have a significant effect on accidents, especially single-vehicle accidents (Zegeer and Council, 1992, 1993). Accident rates fall steadily as side slopes are flattened from 3:1 to 7:1 or flatter. However, little accident reduction is expected from flattening a 2:1 slope to 3:1. Side slopes of 5:1 or flatter are needed (Zegeer and Council, 1992).

Clear zones and side slopes are closely related, since the clear zone, by definition, must include a flat traversable slope of 4:1 or flatter (Cirillo, 1993). Slopes steeper than 4:1 are too steep to allow recovery of control, and vehicles encroaching on such slopes can be expected to travel all the way to the bottom if they do not roll over.

These cross sectional considerations mainly apply to new works, and provide some guidance to road designers. They may however on occasions be useful in remedial treatments, especially on horizontal curves. An American study produced the results shown in Table 12.2.

**Table 12.2**
**Accident reduction factors for flattening side slopes on curves**

| Percent reduction in total curve accidents | | | | |
|---|---|---|---|---|
| Side slope, before condition on curve | Side slope, after condition | | | |
| | 4:1 | 5:1 | 6:1 | 7:1 or flatter |
| 2:1 | 6 | 9 | 12 | 15 |
| 3:1 | 5 | 8 | 11 | 15 |
| 4:1 | - | 3 | 7 | 11 |
| 5:1 | - | - | 3 | 8 |
| 6:1 | - | - | - | 5 |

Source: Zegeer, Twomey, Heckman and Hayward (1992)

*Establishing and maintaining a clear zone, free of fixed obstacles, beside a road has definite safety benefits. It appears to be cost effective on rural roads even at quite low traffic volumes. For volumes in excess of 4000 veh/d and speeds of around 100 km/h, a clear zone of 9 m is indicated. Side slopes need to be flatter than 5:1 to significantly reduce the probability of vehicle rollovers.*

**Roadside hazard management**

Where it is impractical or too expensive to provide a roadside clear zone, there are likely to be roadside hazards which present some measure of risk to errant vehicles, or pedestrians at risk from such vehicles. These hazards include those listed in Figure 12.1.

The objective of a roadside hazard management program is to keep this risk to a manageable level. Following the strategy outlined in Chapter 2 for road safety engineering, it will involve single sites, route actions, or mass action programs. Area-wide actions are less likely to feature because collisions with fixed roadside objects are not typically the sort of problem addressed through these programs; an exception may be an area-wide program involving the provision of pedestrian fencing.

In some cases, especially with mass action programs, there is scope for a pro-active approach predicated on the notion that the probability of an accident at any given site is low, so what is required is to identify the features associated with accidents of a given type, and then treat in priority order all sites which exhibit those features (Ogden and Howie, 1990).

Jarvis and Mullen (1977) have proposed a hierarchy of treatments of fixed roadside hazards as follows:

.  Eliminate all obstacles from the roadside, either by good design and technology for new facilities, or the removal or resiting of all existing obstacles.

.  If it is not possible to eliminate all roadside objects, then either:

   .  identify those most likely to be struck, establish priorities, and organise removal or resiting, or

   .  make harmless those obstacles most likely to be struck, but impossible to remove.

.  Use a safety barrier to shield those obstacles which cannot be removed or modified.

Typical treatments may include:

.  treatment of rigid utility poles by relocation, undergrounding of cables, or replacement with frangible poles,

.  enhancing the safety of bridges and culverts through the provision of upgraded approach guard fencing and/or bridge railing, and improved delineation,

.  flattening of batters, or installation of guard fencing on steep or high embankments,

. installation of impact attenuators,

. shielding (with guard fence) or removing trees which are within the clear zone,

. removal of culvert headwalls and/or extension of culverts to provide increased recovery area,

. replacement of old guard fencing which does not meet current standards, or

. enhanced delineation (roadside devices and pavement markings - see Chapter 10).

A key component of any roadside management program is maintenance, since all items must be maintained when in use, and works programs are typically carried out by maintenance crews. Training of such personnel is critical, since proper installation and ongoing maintenance of many of these treatments is essential to their continued effectiveness.

It is difficult to enumerate the effectiveness or cost-effectiveness of such programs, because of the low probability of an accident at any one site, and the difficulty in specifically relating accidents (or their absence) to the program. However, many studies have testified to the fact that such programs are a highly cost-effective form of road safety investment (e.g. Transportation Research Board, 1987a; Teale, 1984; Pak-Poy and Kneebone, 1988, Graham and Harwood, 1983; County Surveyors' Society, 1989; Johnson, 1980; Hedman, 1990).

There is an extensive literature on the safety aspects of specific roadside features[1]. In the following sections, we briefly review treatments aimed at some of the more significant roadside hazards identified in Figure 12.1, namely utility poles, road signs, trees, and bridges and culverts. The function, design, installation and maintenance of safety barriers (guard fencing and crash cushions) is discussed later in this Chapter.

*Utility poles*

Although utility poles are present in a significant proportion of accidents involving fixed roadside objects, not every pole represents a hazard. Identification of hazardous sites through the mass accident data base is therefore one way to develop remedial measures. An alternative, applicable more to mass action, pro-active programs, and to new works, is to identify those characteristics of pole location which make them more likely to be struck (Good, Fox and Joubert, 1987; Zegeer and Council, 1992). In general, the hazard increases with traffic flow, pole density (poles per length of road), and offset from the edge of the road, and is greater for poles on the outside of horizontal curves, and at sites where the road-tyre friction is reduced. Good, Fox and Joubert (1987) indicated that range of relative risk of a pole being involved in an accident was about 1000:1, indicating that a program which targeted the most hazardous poles would in fact deal with a very small proportion of the total number poles along the roadside. Treatment of hazardous poles may involve:

. relocation of the pole further away from the roadway or to an alternative, safer, location (e.g. locating light poles on the inside, rather than the outside of a horizontal curve);

. removal of some poles by increasing the pole spacing, inter-poling to replace a pole in a particularly hazardous location, joint use of poles by different utilities (e.g. electric power supply, street lighting, telephone), or undergrounding of cables,

. shielding of poles with a safety barrier (guard fence or impact attenuator); the benefits of this need to be offset against the hazard associated with the barrier and its end treatment;

. use of slip-base poles which break away at the base when impacted (Figure 12.3a and Figure 12.4); these include special electrical connections to ensure electrical safety; they do not retard the impacting vehicle, and may give rise to secondary accidents, especially in areas of high pedestrian activity or on narrow medians;

. use of impact absorbing poles, which fail by yielding progressively, entrapping the impacting vehicle (Figure 12.3b); these are particularly suited to areas where there is high pedestrian use;

. where the pole is on a curve, provision of a high friction pavement (see Chapter 11) may be worth considering;

. as a last and least satisfactory resort, attaching reflective delineators to the pole.

Impact absorbing and slip base poles are collectively referred to as 'frangible' or breakaway poles, and are currently used mostly as street lighting poles (luminaires). The development of frangible poles for other utilities is more difficult, but experimental work is under way (Cirillo, 1993; Ivey and Morgan, 1986).

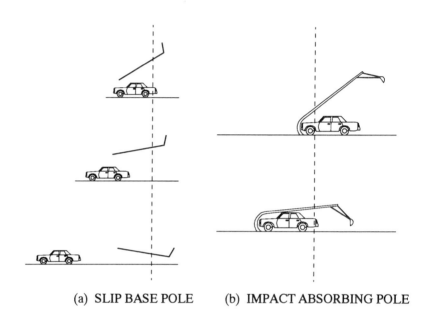

(a) SLIP BASE POLE    (b) IMPACT ABSORBING POLE

**Figure 12.3 Collapse modes of slip-base and impact absorbing poles**

Cirillo and Council (1986) have reported injury reductions of 30 per cent from the use of breakaway luminaire supports. They also note that such supports are ineffective if impact speeds are less than about 50-60 km/h (30-35 mph). There are also difficulties in using frangible devices in areas where there are likely to be pedestrians, because of the potential for pedestrians to be struck by a collapsing pole or luminaire.

Another aspect of utility poles is that, at the planning stage of a road project, existing poles can act as a control on the location of a new road (e.g. in road duplication). However, this can often result in the poles being quite close to the edge of the new roadway. The safety benefits of relocating the poles should be considered at this stage; this may be a factor to be considered during a safety audit (see Chapter 15).

**Figure 12.4 Slip-base pole**

*Trees*

Perhaps the most difficult aspect of roadside hazard management concerns trees. Trees and shrubbery along a road add to its aesthetic appeal, and can be helpful in shielding headlights and providing a visual barrier between the road and abutting property. In some instances, where adjacent land has been cleared for agriculture, the trees in the road reserve may be important ecologically, being the only vestiges of historic fauna in the locality. Trees can also form an important subliminal delineation function - although in some cases it can be misleading (see Chapter 3).

On the other hand, substantial trees close to the roadway constitute a hazard, as will any other substantial item within the recovery area (Figure 12.5). In rural areas, removing trees which are in particularly hazardous location can be highly effective; e.g. trees which are on heavily trafficked, high speed roads, close to the roadway, on the outside of horizontal curves, and at sites where the road-tyre friction is reduced. Zegeer and Council (1992) quote a US study which suggested that clearing trees to provide even an additional 0.9 m (3 ft) of recovery space could reduce

277

related accidents by 22 per cent; 71 per cent of such accidents could be eliminated if the trees were cleared to a depth of an additional 4.5 m (15 ft).

In situations where there are many trees, growing close to the edge of a high speed, heavily trafficked road, and where clearance is not feasible on ecological, environmental or aesthetic rounds, a possible treatment is to shield the whole stand of trees with guard fencing. However, as always, the benefits of this approach need to be considered in the light of the hazard associated with the guard fence and its end treatment, and may not be feasible where there are frequent access points.

*Road signs*

Unless located behind a safety barrier, all road signs should have a frangible post. Larger signs such as advance direction signs should be of a frangible design so that if it is struck, the supporting post shears and the vehicle passes beneath it (Figure 12.6). Attention to detail in the installation of such devices is important; the bolts must be correctly tensioned to ensure that they will shear, the base section must not be too low (perhaps allowing debris to accumulate and impede break away) nor too high (where it can snag an impacting vehicle), and the base plate must be aligned correctly to the direction of travel.

Frangible designs are not suitable for use in lower speed environments such as roundabouts, where the vehicle does not have sufficient speed to satisfactorily clear the falling pole. In this case, a smaller, lighter sign may be more appropriate, mounted on a lightweight post.

Such lightweight posts, which are applicable to many smaller road signs such as warning signs, chevrons and regulatory signs, are commonly light gauge steel pipe or channel section, which readily deforms on impact. However, it should be noted that such posts can be a hazard to bicyclists and motor cyclists, so careful attention to their location is needed.

Similarly guide posts (Chapter 10), which by their nature tend to be closer to the edge of the roadway, should be of lightweight material so that they do not themselves become a hazard. Common materials are timber, steel or plastic.

**Figure 12.5 Trees close to the pavement are hazardous**

*Bridges and culverts*

Hazards associated with bridges can be significant. Narrow bridges increase the probability of a vehicle colliding with the bridge and reduce the opportunity for safe recovery. Bridge approaches are often on a downgrade, and the approaches may be curved. Bridges are over-represented in accidents relative to their length of the road system, and bridge accidents are more severe than accidents as a whole.

**Figure 12.6 Frangible road sign post**, which shears if struck by an errant vehicle.

Culverts can be a problem also, since the culvert end wall or pipe end is often located quite close to the pavement; in many cases, the road pavement has been widened into the shoulder, leaving the culvert very close to the pavement, and producing a constriction in the width of the formation at the point of the culvert. In some cases, there are culverts running parallel to the roadway, carrying a drain under a side road or access driveway (Figure 12.7). In both cases attention to the detail of the design with safety in mind can resolve the problem. For example, the culvert end wall can be rendered less hazardous by being designed to match the slope of the embankment, it can replaced with a grated inlet structure, or the culvert can be extended or relocated so that the end wall is further from the roadway.

**Figure 12.7  Roadside hazard: culvert on side road or driveway**

However, the probability of an accident at any one site is quite low, so unless there are specific sites with a problem revealed in the mass accident data base, bridge safety management programs need to be based upon the mass application of low cost countermeasures at a large number of sites (Ogden and Howie, 1990; Transportation Research Board, 1987a, p 86, 158).

Ogden and Howie (1990) have produced guidelines for the treatment of bridge sites. Their recommended order of priority (based upon a Texas model, (Ivey, et al, 1979)) was dependent upon bridge width, traffic flow, and bridge length. Treatments included delineation and guard fencing, as follows:

. Unless street lighting is present, install guideposts and reflective post-mounted delineators to provide effective long range delineation (see Chapter 10).

. Where warranted, install bridge width markers on or adjacent to the bridge end posts, piers, or abutments on both the left and right side of the carriageway.

. Where bridge width markers are installed, provide edge lining, together with raised reflective pavement markers to provide short range delineation and thus facilitate good lane control.

. Except for road sections with an overall low geometric standard, if the bridge is on or adjacent to a curve with a radius of 600 m (2000 ft) or less install chevron signs on the outside of the curve. This will assist the driver to negotiate both curve and bridge.

. Where the bridge does not have guard fencing installed, ascertain whether guard fencing is warranted, and if so, install in accord with the current standards.

. Where the bridge has guard fencing already in place, determine whether the fencing conforms with the requirements of current design and installation practice. Where it does not, upgrade the installation to conform with the current standards.

*Other roadside hazards*

While there are many other potential hazards which may be found at the roadside, the principles outlined for the above specific features may, in general, be followed. Care needs to be taken with pedestrian and bicycle facilities (see Chapter 14), where devices aimed at protecting these vulnerable road users can potentially conflict with some of these principles. For example, where there are very large pedestrians flows on roadside footpaths, solid bollards may be erected at the kerb line to provide a measure of protection from errant motor vehicles (Figure 12.8). These obviously contradict the 'forgiving roadside' objective discussed above, but in this case, there is clearly a tradeoff to be made between the safety of vulnerable road users and the safety of motorists.

**Figure 12.8 Pedestrian protection using bollards** to separate pedestrians and moving vehicles.

However, even in cases such as these, the roadside feature should be made as safe as possible. In particular, horizontal rails, which can spear an errant vehicle, should be avoided (Figure 12.9); any pedestrian or other fencing should comprise essentially vertical elements which is less hazardous to motorists and is also more difficult for pedestrians to climb and thereby walk on the roadway (Figure 12.10). In some cases, the road safety engineer in a local authority will need to be alert to the activities of colleagues in other Departments, because it can happen that through ignorance or oversight, potentially hazardous features such as these can be installed for reasons that have little to do with traffic, such as landscaping (Figure 12.11).

283

**Figure 12.9 Roadside hazard: horizontal rails which can spear an errant vehicle**; this should be avoided, and replaced with fencing using predominantly vertical elements (see Figure 12.10).

*The establishment of a formal roadside hazard management program, in the overall context of a hazardous road location program, is important since fixed roadside hazards are involved in a significant proportion of accidents. This will identify suitable site, route and mass action priorities for the treatment of roadside hazards, and will develop programs aimed at removing, relocating or shielding the hazard, making it less hazardous, or replacing it with a frangible device.*

**Figure 12.10    Roadside pedestrian fence using mainly vertical elements** will be much less likely to spear an errant vehicle, and is more difficult for pedestrians to climb.

## Safety barriers

Safety barriers include (American Association of State Highway and Transportation Officials (1989):

. guard fences, which are safety barriers on the edge of a carriageway/roadway; if used in a median they may be referred to as median barriers; guard fences are of three types:
  . flexible (e.g. cable barriers),
  . rigid (e.g. concrete barriers), and
  . semi-rigid (e.g steel W-beam or box beam barriers).

. crash cushions, which are devices installed at fixed installations, such as bridge piers; they are also referred to as impact attenuators, and

. bridge barriers.

**Figure 12.11**    **Roadside hazard: landscape features** comprising
                    formidable objects should be avoided.


All safety barriers are required to serve dual and conflicting roles.
They must, on the one hand, be capable of redirecting and/or containing
an errant vehicle, while on the other hand, they must not impose excessive
deceleration forces on the vehicle occupants. Accordingly, all types of
safety barrier have been subjected to rigorous crash testing to verify their
performance and action during crash conditions, and standards and guides
for their use and installation are continually evolving[2]. Much of this
research is reflected in the warrants and guidelines for the installation of
guard fencing (e.g. American Association of State Highway and
Transportation Officials, 1989; Department of Transport (UK), 1985;
National Association of Australian State Road Authorities, 1987).

These warrants typically refer to a range of applications, including
(Lay, 1986, p 567):

. on embankments, where slope and height exceed certain values; Figure 12.12 shows a US warrant,

. near roadside hazards; as noted above, any hazard within about 9 m (30 ft) of the roadside may justify shielding,

. on narrow medians, to prevent head-on accidents, where the flow exceeds a threshold value, typically about 5,000 veh/d,

. where the road formation narrows, e.g. at some bridges and culverts,

. on the outside of sub-standard curves, typically where the difference between 85 percentile speeds and advisory speed is greater than say 15 km/h (10 mph), or

. to protect structures and pedestrians.

The benefits of safety barriers are entirely dependent upon their ability to reduce accident *severity*, since of necessity they are closer to the road and longer than the hazard they guard, and therefore may have a higher accident rate than the hazard in question; in fact Cirillo (1993) says that these devices 'should be a last resort alternative ... only used when it is impossible to eliminate a hazard through design'. In some cases, safety barriers may help to prevent accidents since they assist in delineation of the roadway.

The following discussion briefly outlines the essential features of each of the aforementioned types of safety barrier, and refers to their application and effectiveness.

*Steel guard railing*

Steel guard railing, commonly of a rolled W-section, but also of a rectangular hollow section, acts by resolving the kinetic energy possessed by an impacting vehicle into components in three dimensions (vertical, parallel to the rail and perpendicular to the rail). If the vehicle is to be redirected effectively, the perpendicular and vertical components must be reduced or dissipated. This energy dissipation is accomplished through bending and crushing of various parts of the vehicle and guard rail installation, including the soil.

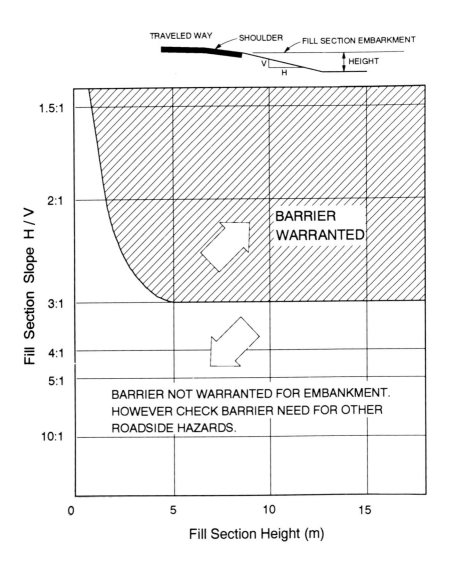

**Figure 12.12    Comparative risk warrants for embankments**

Source: From *Roadside Design Guide*, Copyright 1989 by the American Association of State Highway and Transportation Officials, Washington, DC. Used by permission.

To be effective, guard railing must be installed to allow this energy dissipation to occur, and in such a way that the end product is not more hazardous than an unprotected roadside object. This requires attention to detail in the assembly and installation of all of the components of the barrier. While the details may vary from agency to agency, the important point to stress here is the need for correct installation, in accord with the local agency's current practice. Guard railing which is not correctly installed may be hazardous (possibly forming a greater hazard than the object it is shielding), and may render the installing authority open to a charge of negligence in the case of an accident (Epstein and Hunter, 1984).

Although steel W-beam guard railing is the most common form of semi-rigid safety barrier, other forms exist, such as steel box section, thrie-beam sections (which are particularly effective in reducing snagging for small vehicles while restraining larger vehicles), the self-restoring barrier, and steel backed timber railings (American Association of State Highway and Transportation Officials, 1989).

There have been numerous studies of the effectiveness of guard railing in reducing accident severity. This work will not be reviewed in detail here; suffice it to say that if properly installed at appropriate locations in accordance with warrants, safety barriers can be effective in reducing the severity of accidents (Ross, et al, 1993). Conversely, as noted above, if not properly installed, it can be ineffective or even counter-productive; a training program for those responsible for deciding about guard rail programs and those responsible for actual installation is an important element of a safety barrier program (Crowley and Denman, 1992).

*Existing barriers.* Because steel guard railing has long been recognised as a useful safety device, many installations have been in place for many years. However, as standards and knowledge improves these barriers cease to conform to the requirements of current practice. This does not necessarily mean that it is unacceptable, but, as the National Association of Australian State Road Authorities (1987) guidelines for the provision of safety barriers notes, 'a decision regarding the acceptance, removal, modification or replacement of the barrier can be based on an assessment of the performance of the particular installation concerned and the significance of the departure from current practice.'

Factors which need to be considered in this assessment include:

. potential hazard of the barrier compared with that of the feature being shielded or with that of a modern barrier,

. suitability of the barrier, its post-spacing, terminals, transitions, etc,

. barrier length, alignment, clearances, and location relative to the adjacent lanes,

. barrier height,

. condition of the roadside between the traffic lane and the barrier, and

. alignment of the adjacent traffic lane.

Examples of deficient or inappropriate guard rail installation are many and include:

. Guard railing which is too low, with the risk that vehicles may roll over the device rather than be retarded (Figure 12.13).

. Guard railing which is too high, due perhaps to the approach embankment height and width; in this case, a vehicle may pass beneath or be trapped under the guard rail (Figure 12.14).

. Exposed 'fish tail' approach end to the guard rail, and guard rail not anchored; the exposed end constitutes a hazard in itself, while the lack of anchorages may result in the guard rail being demolished in a collision, rather than staying in place and redirecting and decelerating the vehicle (Figure 12.15). For comparison, Figure 12.16 shows the standard UK installation, and Figure 12.17 shows a current standard installation with a bullnose end and a Breakaway Cable Terminal as used in parts of the US and Australia.

. Guard railing with inadequate taper. A correctly tapered guard rail will have its end well away from the pavement, and will be unlikely to be struck end-on (Figure 12.17).

**Figure 12.13**     **Guard railing too low,** with the risk that vehicles may roll over the device; note also that it is not attached to the bridge end post, so that the guard rail may actually direct an errant vehicle into a collision with the rigid end post (c.f. Figure 12.19).

.   Guard railing with inadequate post spacing, particularly on the approach to a bridge or other rigid object (Figure 12.18). By contrast, Figure 12.19 shows a satisfactory installation, with post spacing decreasing near the bridge end post to stiffen the transition between guard rail and bridge.

In summary, an important component of any roadside hazard management program should be an inspection of all current guard rail installations, and a program of upgrading these installations so that they conform with the requirements of current practice. Once again, included in this should be an educational program aimed at field personnel and design staff with the objective of disseminating information about the importance of correct design and installation (Crowley and Denman, 1992).

**Figure 12.14**     **Guard railing too high**, with the risk that vehicles may be trapped beneath it.

*Concrete barriers*

The concrete safety shape, commonly known as the New Jersey barrier (Figure 12.20) is the most widely used concrete barrier. It is primarily used for median barriers on divided roads (see below) or as a component of a bridge barrier.

As with other barrier types, warrants are in place in most jurisdictions providing directions for the use of this treatment. Concrete barriers are very rigid systems, and therefore in all but very shallow angle collisions, they represent a significant hazard to errant vehicles. Hence they should only be installed in accord with the warrants developed for their use.

**Figure 12.15** **Exposed, unanchored 'fish tail' approach end** may spear an errant vehicle.

**Figure 12.16** **Buried guard rail terminal as used in the UK.**

**Figure 12.17**   **Bullnose end and breakaway cable terminal** is less likely to spear an errant vehicle, while the cable anchor assists the guard railing to remain upright so that it can absorb the energy of the vehicle striking it; note also that the guard fence is tapered away from the direction of traffic so that it is less likely to spear an errant vehicle.

**Figure 12.18** **Inadequate guard rail post spacing**; note also that the guard rail is not stiffened near the bridge end post (c.f Figure 12.19), and is not attached to the end post.

**Figure 12.19** **Variable post spacing, to stiffen the transition between guard fence and bridge**; note also rigid connection between approach guard fencing and bridge end post.

**Figure 12.20** **Concrete safety shape barrier** physically prevents errant vehicles from encroaching into the path of oncoming traffic, and tends to divert an errant vehicle back into its traffic lane.

Mak and Sicking (1990), while noting that 'the degree to which the concrete safety-shaped barrier has been successful in reducing deaths and serious injuries is unknown' claimed that 'hundreds, perhaps thousands, of lives may be saved each year because of the deployment of these barriers.' They listed the advantages of such devices as:

. the design of the barrier is intended to minimise or prevent damage to vehicles during low-angle impacts,

. the barrier does not deflect to any appreciable degree, even under severe impact conditions, and

. maintenance costs are negligible.

However, they also noted that small vehicles and large vehicles with a high centre of gravity are more prone to roll over in a collision with such a barrier, and that such accidents are more severe than those where a vehicle does not roll over. They went on to suggest a modified section with a constant side slope that may reduce the incidence of roll overs.

## Cable barriers

Although much less common than rigid or semi-rigid safety barriers, flexible barriers using a cable system have also been used (Figure 12.21). They are cost-effective in low to moderate traffic flows, and in situations where the roadside or median design can accommodate the large deflection inherent in these types of barrier (Cirillo, 1993). In the UK, new designs have been developed which are more favourable for light vehicles (Himus, 1990).

## Median barriers

The provision of medians has been discussed in Chapter 8, and it was noted that they served a variety of functions. A median barrier may be warranted in situations of high flow and/or narrow median width. Figure 12.22 shows a US warrant for the installation of median barriers.

Median barriers are effective in reducing or eliminating head-on accidents on divided roads, but they have may tend to increase other types of accident. A study of their installation on a motorway/freeway in the UK (Johnson, 1980) found that:

. fatalities reduced by 15 per cent,
. injury accidents were little changed, and
. non-injury accidents increased by 14 per cent.

**Figure 12.21    Flexible barrier using a cable system**

In another UK study, Sowerby (1987) found that the injury accident rate for accidents involving a vehicle entering or crossing the median was 30 per cent lower in the sections with a median barrier, and for all accident types the fatal accident rate was 26 per cent lower on the sections with a median barrier. He calculated that on new roads, median barriers were cost-effective on roads carrying more than about 10,000 veh/d.

*Bridge barriers*

A bridge barrier typically comprises a rigid longitudinal rail fixed at intervals to vertical posts. It is designed to prevent a light vehicle running off the edge of a bridge; railings designed to retain or deflect a heavy vehicle are much heavier and more expensive and their use is only generally warranted in exceptional situations where the consequences of an accident are extreme (Bronstad and Michie, 1981).

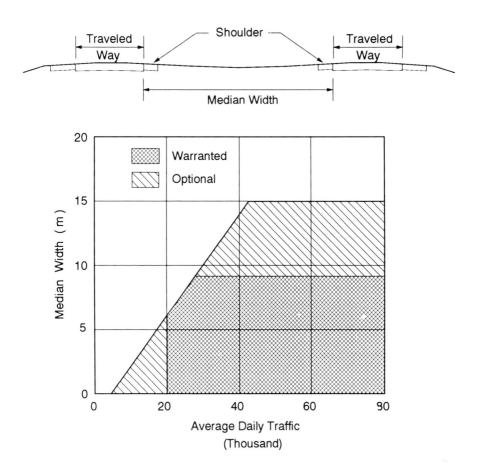

**Figure 12.22    Median barrier warrant for freeways and expressways**

Source: From *Roadside Design Guide*, Copyright 1989 by the American Association of State Highway and Transportation Officials, Washington, DC. Used by permission.

Bridge barriers built to current standards will therefore not generally present a problem. However, there are many older bridges on the road network which do not meet current standards, and which may present a hazard. Examples include older bridges with timber rails which can lead to 'spearing' accidents. In these cases, replacement or modification of the railing may be an appropriate treatment, for example by integrating the bridge railing and the approach guard railing to provide a continuous rail. This may replace the pre-existing bridge rail.

A related issue at bridges is the importance of a transition between the rigid bridge end post and/or railing and a semi-rigid steel guard rail on the bridge approach. Commenting on this, Bligh, Sicking and Ross (1987, p 1) note that 'approach guard rails are typically much more flexible than the bridge rails or parapets to which they are attached ... these flexible barriers can deflect sufficiently to allow an errant vehicle to impact or 'snag' on the end of the rigid barrier, even when the two barriers are securely attached.' Figure 12.18 shows such a situation, while Figure 12.13 shows a related problem, where the approach guard rail is not attached to the bridge at all.

In general, transitions between steel guard railing and a bridge end post requires a physical connection and stiffening of the guard rail near the bridge (Figure 12.19 above) (Bronstad, et al, 1987; McDevitt, 1988). Development of a program of upgrading transition arrangement at existing bridges may therefore be an important component of a roadside hazard management program.

*Crash cushions*

There are a wide variety of types of crash cushions, or impact attenuator, some of which are proprietary systems (Figure 12.23), and some of which use readily available materials such as sand or water filled barrels (American Association of State Highway and Transportation Officials, 1989).

However, all are based upon the principle of absorbing some of the kinetic energy of an errant vehicle before it impacts the object. These are described by Griffin (1984), Pigman, Agent and Creasey (1985), Institute for Road Safety Research (1986), and Proctor and Belcher (1990).

Research indicates that such devices are effective at the ends of longitudinal safety barriers in medians and freeway/motorway gore areas, bridge piers in narrow medians, the end of concrete barrier walls, toll plazas, etc. Cirillo and Council (1986) describe crash cushions as 'one of the most effective (highway safety) devices to date', and claim that they can reduce fatalities and serious injuries by 75 per cent.

**Figure 12.23** **Crash cushion** at the approach end of a median barrier.

*Safety barriers and heavy vehicles*

There has been a lot of research, particularly in the US, to develop safety barriers capable of restraining an errant truck or bus. The problem is twofold: because the vehicle is heavier, it requires a stronger installation to restrain it, and because its centre of gravity is higher, it is more susceptible to rollover.

Ross and Sicking (1986) describe several roadside barriers which include those capable of withstanding an impact from a 36 t vehicle travelling at 80 km/h (50 mph) at 15 degrees impact angle. However, they concluded that these barriers were 'only justified at special locations where the encroachment of a large truck could be catastrophic'; examples given included bridges adjacent to a school or apartment building, or near a petrochemical plant. Laker (1988, p 45) described a British study of an open box steel barrier and a precast concrete barrier which were partially effective in restraining and/or redirecting vehicles up to 39.2 t. Ross and Sicking (op cit, p 239) conclude that as a general rule, barriers capable of withstanding a vehicle weighing more than 9 t are only warranted where traffic flow exceeds 100,000 veh/d, or where the consequences of an accident would be catastrophic.

Michie (1986) summarized the situation by noting that 'longitudinal barriers such as bridge rails, guard rails, and median barriers are being designed to accommodate the largest vehicles but are relatively expensive and therefore sites must be carefully selected'.

Finally, it is important to note that Michie (1986) also concluded that 'crash cushions are not technically feasible for heavy trucks. However, designs to accommodate light trucks (up to (4.5 t) should be considered.'

*Provided that they are properly installed and placed at locations which satisfy road agency warrants, safety barriers (guard fences, bridge barriers, and crash cushions) can be effective in reducing the severity of accidents. However, few existing installations are suited to heavy vehicles. Roadside hazard management programs may need to develop explicit programs to upgrade, on a priority basis, older installations which do not meet current requirements. Maintenance is a key issue, as is the training of personnel who are responsible for installation and maintenance.*

## Shoulder treatments

Shoulders, where they are provided, serve a variety of functions:

. provide structural support to the roadway pavement,
. provide drainage to keep water out of the roadway pavement base,
. provide lateral clearance from roadside objects and structures,
. provide a recovery area for errant vehicles,
. allow stopped or disabled vehicles to stand clear of the traffic lane,
. allow slow vehicles space to pull over, so that faster vehicles may overtake, and
. on single lane roads, allow vehicles travelling in opposite directions to pass.

Some of these are safety-related. The two major aspects of shoulders relate to shoulder sealing, and pavement edge drops.

*Sealed shoulders*

There is ample evidence that sealed (paved) shoulders are much safer than unsealed shoulders on rural roads. Sealed shoulders reduce the incidence of run-off-the-road and head-on accidents by providing a greater recovery and manoeuvring space. They also (Burns, et al, 1984) reduce the potential for vehicles which stray from the sealed pavement to lose control in loose shoulder material; Armour (1984) found this to be a contributing cause of over 50 per cent of fatal run-off-the-road accidents in an Australian study.

In a recent major study of rural single vehicle accidents in Australia, Armour and Cinquegrana (1990) found that the presence or condition of unsealed shoulders was considered to have contributed to 33 per cent of the accidents investigated.

A number of other studies have examined the safety benefits of sealed shoulders:

.   In a comprehensive review of Australian conditions, Armour (1984) found that roads with sealed shoulders had a fatal accident rate 60-70 per cent less than roads with unsealed shoulders. There was some evidence that the benefits were greater on road sections with curves or grades; the ratio between accident rates for roads with unsealed and sealed shoulders was about 3:1 for straight, flat road sections and 4:1 for curves or grades. It should also be noted that wide shoulders are usually associated with pavement edge lines, the safety benefits of which have been discussed in Chapter 10.

.   Ogden (1993) in a study of Australian rural roads which had been treated with sealed shoulders as part of a maintenance program (typically with a sealed shoulder of 0.6 - 1.2 m (2-4 ft)) found that such treatments had a 43 per cent lower accident rate on a vehicle km basis (Figure 12.24). Using cost data appropriate to this situation (i.e. the marginal cost of additional material to be provided during a routine maintenance operation) and Australian accident cost data, he found that the benefit cost ratio could be expressed as:

B/C = 2.6 x (AADT in thousands)

That is, the treatment becomes cost-effective (with a benefit:cost ratio of 1.0) at an AADT of only about 350 vehicles per day, and increases linearly beyond that.

. A study in Texas (Rogness, Fambro and Turner, 1982; Turner, Fambro and Rogness, 1981) found that the addition of shoulders to a 2 lane rural road reduced the total number of accidents. At low volumes (AADT 3000 veh/d) there were significantly fewer single vehicle (run-off-the-road and hit-fixed-object) accidents, indicating the effectiveness of the sealed shoulder in providing recovery space. At moderate volumes (3000-5000 veh/d) the addition of sealed shoulders reduced both the total number of accidents and their severity, suggesting that the shoulders were being used for both accident avoidance and recovery. At higher volumes (5000-7000 veh/d), again accident frequency was reduced, but there was increased severity of those that did occur; this was attributed to 'increased operating speeds after the shoulder was added to roadways in this volume category'. The study concluded that full-width shoulders (i.e. a width approximating that of the through lane) on 2-lane roads were effective in reducing accidents, but were probably not cost-effective for roads carrying less than 3000 veh/d.

. A detailed review of the safety effects of road cross-section design for 2-lane roads in the US (Zegeer, Hummer, Herf, Reinfurt and Hunter, 1987, 1988) included consideration of the effects of 'stabilised' shoulders. This study was based on a large sample of roads (1801 rural road sections covering 7700 km (4700 miles) and detailed equations incorporating a number of traffic and roadway variables were developed. The results indicated that sealed shoulders were only marginally better than unsealed shoulders for similar road and traffic conditions. (For example, a road carrying 3000 veh/d in rolling terrain with a moderate roadside hazard ranking was about 8 per cent safer with 1.8 m (6 ft) sealed shoulders compared with 1.8 m (6 ft) unsealed shoulders.)

. A Texas study (Woods, Rollins and Crane, 1989) examined the safety effects of various shoulder configurations and concluded that while shoulder width had no statistically significant effect, 'a significant difference in accident rates for driveable and non-driveable shoulders were present ... these results were consistent for total, fatal, injury and for all AADT levels with the exception of instances where sample sizes were too small to accurately test the relevant hypothesis' (op cit, p 4). The study concluded that sealed shoulders (1.8 - 3.0 m (6-10 ft) wide) were cost-effective in safety terms for volumes in excess of 1500 veh/d on rural 2-lane roads.

.    In a review of US experience, Skinner (1986) suggested that run-off-the-road and opposite-direction accidents could be reduced by 5-15 per cent with sealed shoulders, depending primarily on lane width. The greatest benefit occurred on roads with narrow lanes (2.4 m - 2.7 m) (8-9 ft).

.    A major review of the safety effects of road geometric design was conducted by the Transportation Research Board (1987a). It concluded that sealed shoulders on 2-lane rural highways were cost-effective for traffic volumes in excess of 2000 veh/d.

In summary, the literature shows that there are clear safety benefits from sealed shoulders on 2-lane rural roads. The benefit results mainly from reductions in single vehicle run-off-the-road accidents (which may be due to reducing or eliminating loss of control when a vehicle strays onto an unsealed shoulder, and also increased recovery space) and multi-vehicle opposite-direction accidents (which may be due to the above, together with increased avoidance space). The literature indicates that sealed shoulders are cost-effective at quite low traffic volumes, with the actual value depending upon the cost of the treatment and the evaluation of benefits.

*Pavement edge drops*

Pavement edge drops (vertical discontinuities at the edge of the paved surface) result either from resurfacing activity unaccompanied by desirable shoulder improvements, or wear and erosion of weak shoulder materials. A particularly susceptible location of edge drops is the inside of horizontal curves, due in part to the off-tracking of the trailing wheels of vehicles, especially trucks. These have been identified as being associated with about 1-1.5 per cent of accidents in the US in various studies (Glennon, 1987a).

**Figure 12.24**     **Narrow sealed shoulder** provides considerable safety
benefits at little cost.


Recent research (Ivey and Mounce, 1984; Glennon, 1987a;
Transportation Research Board, 1987a, p 98; Ivey and Sicking, 1986) has
identified drop height and shape as being important, and that novice
drivers are particularly at risk. Transportation Research Board (1987a, p
99) summarised by saying that 'current understanding of the edge drop
hazard is incomplete. In the interim, edge drops of any height or type must
be considered potentially hazardous, and should not be built into the cross
section as a result of either pavement surfacing or resurfacing.'

*Where shoulders are provided on rural roads, it seems to be cost-*
*effective in safety terms to seal them, unless traffic flows are very low*
*(around 500 veh/d). Ideally, the shoulder should be fully sealed*
*(around 2 m (7 ft)), but if that is not possible, a narrow sealed*
*shoulder of around 0.6 m (2 ft) produces worthwhile benefits.*
*Pavement edge drops (discontinuities between the pavement and the*
*shoulder) have been shown to be associated with a small number of*

*accidents, and particular attention should be paid to this in resurfacing work and maintenance activities.*

## Notes

1. Reviews of the safety effectiveness of roadside hazard management treatments are presented in Pak-Poy and Kneebone (1988), Transportation Research Board (1987a), National Association of Australian State Road Authorities (1987, 1988a), Hedman (1990), Cirillo (1993) and Zegeer and Council (1992, 1993).

2. There has been a good deal of experimental and theoretical work on the design of safety barriers over the years (e.g. Michie and Bronstad, 1972; Troutbeck, 1983; Bronstad, Michie and Mayer, 1987; Institute for Road Safety Research, 1986).

# 13 Traffic management

*Traffic management refers to the adaptation of the use of the existing road network. Safety benefits from traffic management can result from changes in the patterns of traffic flow, changes in traffic speed, and management of parking and loading arrangements. Traffic management may also be carried out for reasons other than safety, in particular to pursue environmental, traffic efficiency (capacity) or access objectives, and in some instances these objectives may conflict with safety objectives. These aspects are reviewed in this chapter, and in the following chapter we consider a related aspect, namely the safety of pedestrians and bicyclists.*

## Road networks and functional hierarchy

*Traffic management*

Traffic management refers to the general process of adjusting or adapting the use of the existing road system to improve traffic operations without the need for major new construction. Often, a traffic management project will have multiple objectives. These may include objectives related to:

. traffic efficiency (e.g. road capacity),
. improved environmental amenity (e.g. reduced noise),
. enhanced access (e.g. better access for particular groups of road users, such as pedestrians, bicyclists or freight vehicles) and/or
. road safety.

These objectives can often be potentially in conflict with each other, and priorities may have to be determined. However, most traffic management projects would seek to improve road safety as either the major or a subsidiary objective.

*Road functions and functional hierarchy*

The prime determinant of the management of any given road within the overall network is that road's function, and its relationship to other roads with which it connects. This means that any discussion of traffic management in general, or the use of traffic management to pursue safety objectives, must take place in the context of a clear view of the functions of a road network, usually expressed as a functional hierarchy.

The road network serves a multitude of purposes, but from a road function point of view, there are essentially two needs which the road network allows:

. *The traffic movement function*, i.e. the role of roads in providing a means by which people and goods can get from one place to another; these roads constitute the *arterial road network*.

. *The access function*, i.e. the role of roads in providing access to abutting properties and land uses; these roads (or streets as they are perhaps more commonly called) constitute the *local road network*.

Perhaps in an ideal situation, each and every road would perform only one of these functions, but in practice, there are many roads which do both. The reason for this, as Brindle (1989) has clearly pointed out, is that whereas the movement function is a variable (i.e. traffic flow can be any value from almost nothing to many thousands of vehicles per day), the access function is binary: either a road performs an access function or it does not. From the point of view of access, the road outside the front of a property serves the same function whether that road is a minor cul de sac or a major highway. Thus, the only roads which do not have an access function are those which are 'access controlled'; i.e. where:

. the only access to the road reserve is via ramps at interchanges (such as freeways/motorways),

. access from abutting properties is oriented away from the road (as is sometimes done with distributor roads serving residential neighbourhoods), or

. there are frontage roads paralleling an arterial road; this may be thought of as effectively two roads within the same reserve, the frontage road serving the access function and the through roadway serving the movement function (Figure 8.2).

All other roads serve an access function. Many (perhaps the majority of the length of road in many cities) have this as their only function; they do not carry 'through traffic'. But there are also many roads which as well as serving their access function, also, whether intended or not, serve a traffic movement function.

This latter class of roads, sometimes referred to as 'mixed function' roads, create a major challenge for traffic management. In particular, they tend to have a very poor accident record, as a result of their mixed and inherently conflicting functions (Brindle, 1986a, 1989; Institution of Highways and Transportation, 1987, p 31). On the one hand, those living and working along them seek to use them for access purposes, exiting and entering properties, parking in the street, having visitors park nearby, and in residential areas, having significant pedestrian and sometimes bicycle activity. These activities (and even more domesticated activities like using the road as a playground) can all be satisfactorily carried out if the traffic flow is light and vehicle speeds are low.

On the other hand, those using the road to satisfy the movement objective (even if they live very close by), want to travel at higher speeds, and if there are a lot of them, then traffic volume increases also. This problem is exacerbated by some residential estate road networks, which deliberately arrange the local streets around a long, continuous collector-distributor road running across the estate, often built to quite high geometric design standards, and with access to abutting property. This type of road has been referred to as the 'difficult distributor' (Brindle, 1986a) because of the difficulty of reconciling the conflicting needs of mobility and access.

*Road hierarchy as a network planning tool*

The basis of any traffic management plan is usually the development of a road hierarchy, and agreement to it by the various stakeholders, such as residents, local businesses, emergency service providers, etc. The importance of doing this, and some guidelines as to how to do it are outlined in many of the planning documents which have sought to reconcile road network and land use planning issues[1]. These principles

311

typically attempt to reconcile a number of objectives related to safety, amenity, function, etc. This is not the place for a detailed discussion of these objectives, but from the perspective of modifying an existing network with the aim of enhancing safety, the main objectives are (Organisation for Economic Cooperation and Development, 1986, p 91):

. to prevent residential areas being used by through traffic, except under exceptional circumstances,

. to influence driver behaviour so that drivers are induced to follow planned routes at moderate speeds, with proper attention being given to pedestrians and bicyclists, and

. to use physical devices in support of legal and statutory regulations in order to overcome the lack of enforcement of such measures as speed limits, one-way streets and turning prohibitions.

The road hierarchy plan can form the basis for the development of a traffic management plan. Roads which are clearly 'local', i.e. have solely an access function, will have objectives related to local amenity and safety; if the road configuration does not allow these objectives to be met, then the road may need some form of treatment. Similarly, roads which are 'mixed function' are likely to need to need some form of traffic management for them to carry out their mix of functions, since in many cases it will be unlikely that the access and movement functions can both be achieved satisfactorily without such treatment.

Roads with primarily a movement or traffic function will in most cases be managed to maximize flow and traffic efficiency, since this represents good use of a valuable community resource. Indeed often a significant component of any traffic management scheme aimed at enhancing amenity and safety on local or access roads will include improving conditions, where possible, on nearby arterial roads, so that there is less incentive for drivers to use local streets as a 'rat run'.

However, maximizing traffic efficiency is not always the appropriate objective for an arterial road. There has emerged in recent years in Europe and Australia the notion of an 'environmentally adapted through road', i.e. one where an arterial road is not managed to develop its full movement potential, but is adapted to achieve explicit environmental goals. (We return to discuss this concept later in this chapter).

Gunnarsson (1993), has taken this philosophy a step further, and suggested that the spectrum of road functions is in fact broader than that hinted at above, and that beyond the road which has a purely access function there is an 'urban space' which is motor vehicle-free, i.e. mobility is solely provided by walking and bicycling. He further suggests, just as there is a transition between access roads and movement roads, so there is a transition between these vehicle-free spaces and local roads; these he refers to as 'pedestrian streets', of which the Dutch *Woonerf* (see Figure 13.1) is perhaps the best-known example (Royal Dutch Touring Club, 1979).

**Figure 13.1 Woonerf: integrated vehicle/pedestrian space** where vehicle speeds are very low and pedestrians have priority.

313

Gunnarsson thus defines three classes of road (Figure 13.2), F (exclusive foot space), C (local streets), T (exclusive transport space), with transitions at F/C and T/C. This is quite a useful concept since it helps provide a conceptual framework for different sorts of what has come to be referred to as *traffic calming*; Gunnarsson describes the local street zone and the two transition zones as 'traffic calming space'. We will return to a discussion of traffic calming later in this chapter.

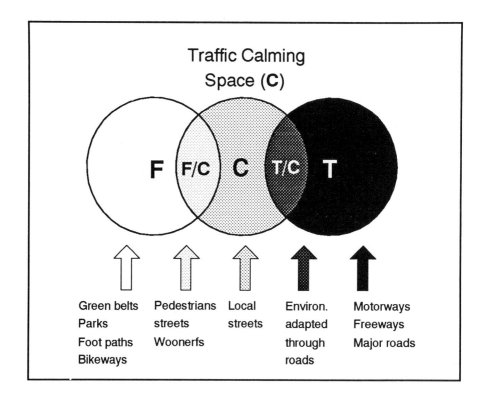

**Figure 13.2 Traffic calming space**

Source: Gunnarsson (1993). Copyright Institute of Transportation Engineers, 525 School Street SW, Washington, DC, USA. Fax (+1) 202 863 5486. Used by permission.

*Safety or security?*

Before doing that however, it is necessary to introduce another important question into the discussion, and that relates particularly to the safety objective, recalling that safety is likely to be an objective of most if not all traffic management schemes. The question is, what is meant by this objective? In most applications, the objective of seeking to have safer roads leads directly to a need for data on accident occurrence, and monitoring programs to ensure that accidents are indeed reduced. This is the philosophy underlying most of road safety engineering, as outlined in Chapter 2.

However, in dealing with local streets, and particularly those in urban areas, this crisp definitions needs perhaps to become a little fuzzier. In these instances we are dealing with people's living space; mobility and access are important parts of that living space, but there is not a clear distinction between the transport-related needs that the living space fills, and other needs. People take a holistic view of their local environment, and are more likely to find it acceptable if it 'feels' safe and secure than if it does not. In other words, the safety issue becomes part of a wider amenity issue. This distinction between *safety* and *security* (Hauer, 1993; Wallwork, 1993) is always important, but is critical in local areas. As Hauer so succinctly puts it: 'much of what we do is because people wish to feel safe'.

Thus, traffic management schemes which aim to reduce speeds on local streets and maybe reduce traffic volumes are likely to be supported by the community because people will feel more secure. But the objective will almost always be expressed as a *safety* objective, and most likely people will say that they feel 'safer'. This is important because although, as we will see later, many well-designed traffic management schemes have achieved safety benefits which have been measured in the usual way, this is only one indication of success, and may not be the indicator which is most important for achieving community acceptance of the scheme.

For this reason it is interesting to note that research on traffic management for local streets has included not only investigation of objective or measurable safety (accident numbers), but also investigations about subjective safety, i.e. whether people *believe* that safety has been enhanced (e.g. Proctor, 1990, 1991a,b; Lynam, Mackie and Davies, 1988).

315

*More than safety?*

Similarly, since schemes involving local areas aim to enhance the totality of the local environment, they may need to go beyond measures which simply aim to reduce vehicle speeds and traffic volumes. In other words, as emphasized in the introduction to this chapter, traffic management schemes have multiple objectives.

The problem is that the safety/security objectives could very often be achieved quite easily, but in a way that contributes nothing to other objectives, and indeed detracts from them, for example by very crude road humps or street closures which make the locality look ugly and degraded. The need to ensure community acceptance will however in most cases demand more than this; in some cases there will be a demand for enhancement of the physical environment, or at least no degradation of it, with appropriate landscaping and attention to detail in implementation. Good civic design is what is needed, not just good traffic engineering.

This objective can create difficulties in implementation, where the funding sources for traffic management and for amenity or environmental enhancement are separate. In the UK for example there are institutional difficulties in spending 'transport' money on 'environmental' projects, and many traffic management projects of the sort we are describing here have to have money from both funds, since if only the former was available, the result would be a very basic engineering effort with little by way of civic design. Thus, for example, the Devon County Council (1994) in the UK noted that 'there is a need to develop schemes in the future which will achieve road safety objectives, whilst at the same time contributing to environmental enhancement, urban regeneration, and local distinctiveness', and indicated that this would need funding from the County's 'urban regeneration budget', contributions from private developers, and by coordinating work with maintenance operations.

*Lessons for new networks*

Most traffic management schemes, and particularly those involving what was described above as 'traffic calming' on local streets, involve retro-fitting devices to existing streets, to rectify problems caused by poor previous decisions, or modifying street networks that were not designed for contemporary living and mobility patterns. The question then naturally arises, what can be done to ensure that these problems are not built into new networks? As Wallwork (1993) has said, 'traffic calming is a negative reaction to a problem caused by bad planning, zoning and/or street design. We need to be pro-active in our approach and learn from the past and others.'

Mainly, this involves attention to network layout, to ensure that problems are not built in, and attention to detail in civic design to ensure that an appropriate balance of built and open spaces, and the connections between them, are provided.

The safety aspects of road network design have been well-researched over the last 2 or 3 decades. It is generally accepted that traditional street layouts involving long straight streets with multiple intersections are associated with accidents (Bennett and Marland, 1978; Clark, 1985; Brindle, 1986a, 1989; Organisation for Economic Cooperation and Development 1979; 1986). These studies confirmed the safety benefits of local networks based on short culs-de-sac, loops, and streets which do not have long straight or curvilinear sections allowing higher speeds. They also showed the safety advantages of t-intersections and controlled intersections (in particular, roundabouts).

These findings have been reflected in the principles for road network development in urban areas[1]. The Organisation for Economic Cooperation and Development (1986, p 91) has summarized the key road network planning principles for *new* residential areas as follows:

.   strict differentiation of streets according to their traffic function leads to safer residential areas,

.   distribution of traffic into a residential area with multiple access from a ring road is safer than central distribution,

.   full segregation of vehicle and pedestrian and bicycle movements is accompanied by very low accident rates (although there may be other reasons for wishing to integrate rather than segregate traffic - see Chapter 14),

.   cul-de-sac streets are safer than loop streets, which in turn are safer than ordinary through streets with long straight sections and numerous intersections (especially cross intersections), and

.   on roads providing a distributive (arterial) function, accident rates are minimized where frontage access is prohibited.

317

*Traffic management involves the adaptation of the use of the existing road network. The development of a traffic management plan usually requires the development of a road hierarchy, with each road and street being managed in accordance with its primary function. Mixed function roads, which provide both access and movement functions, are a particular problem and will usually need some form of traffic management to achieve an acceptable balance between safety and efficiency objectives. Other access roads may or may not need explicit treatment, depending upon their role and performance, while roads serving primarily a movement function will need to be managed, usually but not always to maximize transport efficiency. The need to distinguish safety (which road safety engineers can measure and provide) and security (which is probably what the community expects) can be important.*

## Traffic calming

We noted above the usefulness of defining three classes of road (Figure 13.2), F (exclusive foot space), C (local streets), T (exclusive transport space), with transitions at F/C and T/C (Gunnarsson, 1993). The local street zone, and the two transitions are candidates for what has come to be referred to as 'traffic calming'. In this section, we discuss the principles of traffic calming and its application at these points, but first, we need to clarify the meaning and use of the term 'traffic calming', since it has come to mean different things to different people.

*Traffic management or traffic calming?*

The term 'traffic management' is one which has long been used in the sense defined in the previous section. Various techniques, which we will discuss later, have been developed (and are still being developed) to achieve the disparate aims of traffic management schemes worldwide. The German term *verkersberuhigung* means much the same thing, and has been predominantly used to describe the use of physical traffic control measures, especially for speed reduction. This term variously translates into English as 'traffic calming' or 'traffic pacification'.

However the term 'traffic calming' has come to be used in the English-speaking literature to also refer also to something quite different (Brindle, 1992; Hawley, et al, 1993). In non-traffic engineering literature, the term embraces a philosophy and set of goals that go far beyond mere physical control and management of traffic, but extends into city-wide suppression of traffic, questions of alternative urban structure, and substantial lifestyle changes aimed at achieving what is claimed to be an environmentally sustainable future. The result is an uneasy tension between the traffic or road safety engineering profession and the environmental movement; that while what some engineers call 'traffic calming' is contributing to a safer and more pleasant environment, this is seen by others who attach a much broader meaning to 'traffic calming' as merely supporting the 'car culture' (Proctor, 1991b).

For example, in the UK the term 'traffic calming' has been enshrined in legislation ('The Traffic Calming Act, 1992'). However, while its objectives relate to 'promoting safety and preserving or improving the environment', the means to achieve this is through speed reduction and access control, and this is to be done through physical devices supported by regulation (Department of Transport, 1993a,b). The Royal Society for the Prevention of Accidents (1994) defines traffic calming as simply 'self-enforcing engineering measures implemented mainly in residential areas to reduce vehicle speeds to around 20 mph' (about 30 km/h).

In the United States, the term 'traffic calming' is becoming increasingly commonly used in traffic engineering in a very similar way. For example, Wallwork (1993) describes it as involving 'physical changes to streets to reduce vehicle speeds and to decrease the cars' dominance'.

Even in Devon, where the concept has been taken as far as anywhere in the UK, traffic calming is described as follows (Devon County Council, 1994):

'Traffic calming seeks not only to improve road safety, but to address the wider issue of the 'quality of life' in our towns and villages. Noise, pollution, severance and visual intrusion combine to seriously degrade our living environment. Traffic calming is therefore a means to restore a proper balance between the motor vehicle and the community... Within this broad strategy there seems little doubt that, at least for the foreseeable future, there will still be a need for a network of high standard motorways and rural roads.'

Compare this with the much broader interpretation of Newman and Kenworthy (1991) that 'traffic calming in the broad sense ... is aimed at reducing total dependence on the car and promoting a transport system more oriented to pedestrian, bicycle and public transport use', or Hass-

Klau (1990) who defined it as 'the combination of transport policies intended to alleviate the adverse environmental, safety and severance effects motor vehicles continue to impose on both the individual and society at large.'

So clearly, the term 'traffic calming' as used by traffic engineers and road safety officials is more limited than its use in the city planning and environmental literature. A useful resolution of this conflict of interpretation has been proposed by Brindle (1992), who suggests that the broader sense in which the term traffic calming is used encompasses two axes:

. the scope of the measure: local, intermediate or citywide, and

. the type of measure: technique oriented (e.g. use of physical devices and regulations), or based on an ethos about contemporary society (i.e. social/cultural change)

The result is a matrix of the form indicated in Figure 13.3. Brindle makes the critical observation that most existing examples of 'traffic calming' fall into the top left hand cell (local/devices), with some (such as environmentally adapted through roads) in the cell below it. That is, most success in traffic calming has involved application of traffic management techniques.

However, importantly, the rest of the traffic calming philosophy is essentially untouched by these measures. As Brindle says, 'successful traffic calming may require more than physical treatments in specific streets and areas. Citywide suppression of traffic (the result of decisions to move by automobile) goes beyond traffic calming as it is currently understood and practiced. This approach to urban traffic problems is in fact promoting TSM (transportation system management) and TDM (travel demand management).'

This explains the tension between road safety/traffic engineers and some in the environmental movement. While there may well be deep philosophical differences of opinion (and no doubt a wide range on both sides), the essential problem is semantic; both are using the same term - traffic calming - but its use by the traffic management profession implies a narrower focus than its use to describe more fundamental social/cultural change.

| Scope of measure | Type of Measure | |
| --- | --- | --- |
| | Physical/Environmental (Technique) | Social/Cultural (Ethos) |
| **L:** Local (street or neighbourhood) | **LE:** Local area traffic management Speed control devices Most reported speed and accident physical countermeasures | **LC:** Neighbourhood speed watch Community action Attitudinal change |
| **I:** Intermediate (zone, precinct, corridor, regional) | **IE:** Environmentally-adapted through roads Shared zones, lower-speed zones Pedestrianized shopping precincts Corridors | **IC:** Voluntary behaviour change Mode choice, speed |
| **M:** Macro (citywide) | **ME:** Transportation systems management (TSM) Total system measures (fares policy, citywide road pricing) | **MC:** Travel demand management Urban form and structure |

**Figure 13.3  A framework for classifying traffic calming measures**

Source: Brindle (1992).

However as we have just seen, within the traffic engineering and traffic management profession, the term 'traffic calming' is becoming quite firmly entrenched as referring to the management of traffic with the explicit aim of reducing its adverse effects, and in particular with reducing traffic speed. So, while recognizing the use of the term to refer to something much broader than simply traffic management, we will nevertheless adopt the pragmatic approach, and use the term here as it is becoming increasingly used within traffic engineering and road safety circles, to refer to the management of traffic to pursue amenity and safety goals, as distinct from traffic efficiency (e.g. capacity) goals.

As noted previously, traffic calming (as defined above) can be applied at three levels following the schema developed by Gunnarsson (1993) and described in Figure 13.2 above: by the development of shared zones which integrate motor vehicles into a pedestrian environment, by the development of area schemes, and by the development of environmentally adapted through roads. The application of each of these is discussed in this section, (including a review of their safety effectiveness), while the techniques used in their implementation are reviewed later in this chapter.

*Integrated or shared zones*

The first level of application of traffic management to the resolution of safety and environmental problems in local networks (Figure 13.2) involves the use of 'shared zones'. These are based on the concept of integration rather than separation of road users, where motor vehicles are required to travel at near walking speeds. This idea is usually associated with the Dutch *Woonerf* (Living Space), and developed in cities where the streets were very narrow and residential densities were high. The *Woonerf* concept involves completely re-designing the street layout, with no formal footways or sidewalks, and with vehicle speeds being constrained by a range of physical devices and road surface treatments. Much effort goes into the civic design, with extensive landscaping, play areas, parking bays, etc. Early *Woonerf* schemes were often street-specific, rather than area-wide, and were very expensive. The *Woonerf* concept was seen a suitable solution for the older residential precincts in high-density European cities, and cities throughout Europe, especially in Denmark, Germany, and France, as well as The Netherlands, began to adopt this concept from the mid-1970s (Organisation for Economic Cooperation and Development, 1979; Kjemtrup and Herrstedt, 1992; Vis, Dijkstra and Slop, 1992; Gunnarsson, 1993).

*Safety effectiveness.* The *Woonerf* is only in part a safety device; it is much more about amenity and environmental enhancement. Therefore Gunnarsson's (1993) summary is apt: 'some studies have proved safety effects, while others have shown no safety effects but reduction of conflicts between road users'.

*Area treatments*

The concept of integrating vehicular and vulnerable traffic led to problems in implementation, and was certainly not applicable everywhere. (Kjemtrup and Herrstedt (1992) give an excellent review of the stages of development of speed management devices in Europe, and the introduction of the *Woonerf* idea in particular.) This led during the 1970s to the evolution of a segregated road traffic system (i.e. with a designated lane or lanes for vehicles and footpaths or sidewalks), involving extensive use of physical devices. These were typically applied to a local network, so that traffic problems in one street were not simply transfered to an adjacent street. Compared with the shared zone concept, these are much more economical, highly effective in reducing accidents, especially to vulnerable road users, and are more readily adapted to applications on an area-wide basis.

Area treatments may usefully be divided into two distinct types: those which are more applicable to low density residential developments, and aim to control speeds which are in excess of a statutory speed limit of around 50-60 km/h (30-35 mph), and those used in higher density cities where the aim is to reduce speeds to around 30 km/h (20 mph).

Schemes in low density areas typically utilize a range of physical devices including vertical and horizontal displacement, limited network changes such as closures and turn bans, and intersection treatments, especially local area roundabouts (see below). They have been widely used in Australia since the mid-1970s (Brindle, 1992, National Association of Australian State Road Authorities, 1988c). They have found application to a more limited extent in the United States (Wallwork, 1993; Homburger, et al, 1989) and elsewhere.

In higher density cities, precincts tend to be smaller, and the aim is to achieve much lower speeds, to around 30 km/h (20 mph). This target figure has emerged as a result of European experience; as Vis, Dijkstra and Slop (1992) state: 'it was generally acknowledged that with regard to safety in residential areas, the speed of traffic would have to fall significantly below the legal 50 km/h limit. For residential areas, a speed of 30 km/h was considered acceptable, as the braking distance of passenger cars is about 15 m (50 ft) in that case and the collision speed in the event of an accident is less than 30 km/h (20 mph). Under these circumstances, the probability of serious injury is minimal.'

Such schemes use a similar battery of techniques to those described above and reviewed in detail later in this chapter, but at greater intensity to achieve the lower speed outcome. Schemes of this sort are now in place in:

.   The Netherlands: *The 30 km/h zone* (Vis, Dijkstra and Slop, 1992),
.   France: *Better Living and Moving in Towns* (Faure and de Neuville, 1992),
.   Denmark (Engel and Thomsen, 1992),
.   Germany: *Tempo 30 zone* (Kjemtrup and Herrstedt, 1992),
.   Sweden (Gunnarsson, 1993),
.   UK: *20 mph Speed Limit Zones* (Department of Transport, 1991, 1992), and
.   Japan: *Road-Pia Concept* (Fujitsuka, 1991; Yamanaka and Odani, 1991).

*Safety effectiveness*. As noted previously, traffic management schemes applied to low density areas are usually predicated on increasing the amenity of the area to residents, part of which involves a perception of safety by residents in the area treated. Such schemes are usually successful in this since they can reduce vehicle speeds and sometimes traffic volumes but whether they increase objective safety (as measured by accidents) is open to question. The main reason for this is that accidents are in fact very rare at any given site within a local area and to demonstrate statistically significant accident reductions is difficult. Based upon a comprehensive survey of international reported outcomes of such schemes, and an in-depth analysis of accident patterns within case study areas in Sydney, Australia, Fairlie and Taylor (1990) concluded that:

> 'Many of the traffic management devices used extensively in Local Area Traffic Management (LATM) fail to resolve the dominant types of accidents occurring on local streets... These were cross traffic, right-through, rear end and hit parked vehicle accidents... Current LATM schemes may not be as effective in reducing accidents as many practitioners believe.'

With this cautionary note, we can however report the results of several studies which have examined the effects of traffic management schemes at the local level, excluding for the moment those which aimed to have very low speed outcomes (30 km/h or 20 mph). These include:

. Brindle (1986b), based upon an international review, concluded that 'there is a persuasive body of opinion ... that lower speeds are essential if safety is to be improved in neighbourhoods.' Reduced speeds (even in the speed range encountered in urban local streets) will reduce conflicts and accident severity, but to achieve these speed reductions, some form of physical change to the street is necessary.

. Andreassen and Hoque (1986) reviewed the accident patterns in local areas in Australia, and found that 'most of the present (traffic calming) devices do not address known accident problems'. In particular, they found that most reported accidents involved two vehicles at an intersection, but these were mostly one accident per site, which 'does not indicate any obvious site-specific treatment'. The next most frequent accidents were 'hit parked vehicle' and 'run off road', and observed that the effects of traffic calming devices on these accidents 'are unknown'.

. Hagan and Amamoo (1988) in a study of two local areas in Adelaide, South Australia, examined the accident experience before-and-after the installation of a range of devices (principally street closures, roundabouts and upgrading of arterial roads on the boundary). They found a statistically significant reduction in the total reported accident rate and the personal injury accident rate, but no statistically significant change in property damage accident rates.

. In the UK, the results of a major experiment involving five towns showed positive effects. It is important to note that the traffic management strategies used involved only network changes (closures, turn bans), intersection treatments (mini-roundabouts), threshold treatments, parking and pedestrian refuges, i.e. no vertical or lateral displacement devices were used. This study (Mackie, Ward and Walker, 1990) found total accident reduction varying from 9 to 18 per cent, with an average of 12 per cent across the five towns. Major benefits accrued to pedal cyclists (33 per cent) and motor cyclists (16 per cent) with only a small 5 per cent benefit to pedestrians. Accident reduction occurred mostly on the surrounding arterials (14 per cent reduction) and the residential streets (18 per cent) with little change in the 'local distributor' roads.

With the European and Japanese schemes used in higher density areas, which have an overt aim of reducing speeds to 30 km/h (20 mph) or thereabouts, the evidence as to the safety benefits is clearer. For example:

.   Engel and Thomsen (1992) and Kjemtrup and Herrstedt (1992) have reported a study involving 44 experimental streets in Denmark, totalling 223 km (134 miles); following the introduction of 30 km/h (and in some cases 15 km/h) treatment, casualties per 'road user km' fell by 72 per cent, with no change in total accident frequency. There was a 78 per cent reduction in serious injuries.

.   In The Netherlands, a demonstration project involving changes to the street network in two residential districts resulted in a 25 per cent reduction in casualty accidents and 5 per cent reduction in all accidents (Vis, Dijkstra and Slop, 1992; Janssen, 1991).

.   Kjemtrup and Herrstedt (1992) reported a study of 263 *Tempo 30* zones in Hamburg, Germany, which led to a 27 per cent reduction in injured persons.

.   Proctor (1990) reports the effects of two more German studies: a 44 per cent reduction in casualties in Heidelberg, and a Berlin study which showed a 43 per cent reduction in pedestrian accidents, a 66 per cent reduction in child accidents, and a 16 per cent reduction in bicycle accidents.

.   Institute for Road Safety Research (SWOV) (1985) in The Netherlands indicate that accidents within residential areas can be reduced by up to 50 per cent.

.   Fujitsuka (1991) reports a reduction from 32 casualty accidents in 4 years prior to the implementation of a project in Nagoya, Japan, to two in the 2 years after its completion.

*Environmentally adapted through roads*

The third level of application of traffic management to the resolution of safety and environmental problems (Figure 13.2) involves what is sometimes called an environmentally adapted through road. This is one which retains its status as an arterial road, but the traffic efficiency role is curtailed to some extent so that other environmental or amenity goals may also be realized.

There are two typical application, one involving bypassed towns, and the other involving adaptation of roads still fulfilling their arterial function.

*Bypassed towns.* In the first case, the typical situation is that of a town astride an old traditional 'High Street'. The town perhaps grew up around or along the road, with a time period in some countries measured in centuries. Recently, with the overt and explicit aim of enhancing the environment of the town, a bypass route has been built, so that 'through' traffic no longer travels through the town. However, if nothing is done to the old 'High Street' route, problems can arise; it is still serving an arterial function, in the context of the town and perhaps local region, so it may still attract a reasonable amount of traffic, and it is likely that there will be roadside land uses (retail, commercial, business) that attract traffic and generate parking demands. Speeds may be quite high.

This scenario is typical of many towns and villages, particularly in Europe, and in several countries explicit traffic management measures for application on that route have been applied to 'reclaim' the former trunk road and make it more appropriate to its new role. Typical examples are described for the UK by Davies and Barrell (1993) and Department of Transport (1993e) and in France by Faure and de Neuville (1992).

*Environmentally-adapted arterial.* In the second case, the situation is typically that a major road runs through a rural town, or a suburban centre, and creates environmental and safety problems within that town and centre. The strategy is then to manage the traffic on that road, without building a bypass to take through traffic away, but to moderate the traffic efficiency function of the road to some extent with the aim of reducing the adverse impacts of the through traffic. A number of applications have been reported, from Denmark (Herrstedt, 1992), France (Kjemtrup and Herrstedt, 1992), Germany (Schnull and Lange, 1992), Australia (Westerman, et al, 1993; Roads and Traffic Authority, 1989; Armstrong, et al, 1992) and the UK (Department of Transport, 1994c).

The safety effectiveness of these treatments appears to be encouraging. For example:

.   in one town in Denmark, accidents have been halved and casualties reduced to one-third (Herrstedt, 1992),

327

. in France, the average number of accidents in treated towns fell by 60 per cent (Kjemtrup and Herrstedt, 1992),

. in the UK, average speeds and 85 percentile speeds have been reduced where these schemes have been applied in villages with a through road (Wheeler, Taylor and Baker, 1994),

. in Germany, an experiment involving 27 communities situated on through traffic routes has been reported as having 'mixed success' in reducing vehicle speeds, with a 3 mph (about 5 km/h) reduction in the mean speed from 40 mph (about 68 km/h) being considered a 'good result' (VISP Working Group, 1994).

*Treatments.* In either case, treatments typically involve some or all of the following:

. a form of 'gateway' treatment using signs and town entry features (to emphasize the changed status of the road, encourage slower driving, and provide a sense of identity),

. speed restriction devices like road narrowings and road humps,

. enhanced pedestrian and bicyclist facilities,

. improved parking (especially for bypassed towns), since the town can rejuvenate as a business centre when through traffic is removed; Kjemtrup and Herrstedt (1992) even mention that in Denmark, local traders have paid for the treatments,

. changed traffic furniture like lighting and seating,

. enhanced signing,

. a roundabout at the start and end of the town, to ensure that the traffic slows,

. narrower lanes,

. changes in road surface, including colour and texture, and/or

. additional traffic control measures such as traffic signals and pedestrian crossings.

*Problems and difficulties*

While a traffic calming scheme which is well-designed and sensitively implemented, with good community consultation in the planning phase, can produce safety and amenity benefits, there is often some negative response from affected parties, which needs to be carefully considered. For example, Brindle (1992) has reported a citizen's group in Australia called CRASH (Concerned Residents Against Speed Humps) which submitted its opposition to traffic calming (specifically speed humps) in the following terms:

. they discriminate against law-abiding road users,
. they are dangerous to bicyclists and motor cyclists, especially when wet,
. they cause unnecessary wear and tear on motor vehicles,
. they disadvantage some local businesses,
. their lighting is a source of annoyance to some residents,
. they hinder emergency vehicles,
. they waste taxpayer's money,
. they make some motorists more aggressive and impatient,
. they detract from the environment - lights, signs, noise,
. they devalue property,
. they are inappropriate for heavy vehicles,
. they increase road maintenance costs, and
. they cost people time.

Some of these points are not without validity, and considerations such as these mean that the development of traffic calming schemes require careful design and sensitive implementation. For example, the Kent County Council (1994a) list the following potential disbenefits which that organisation considers in designing and implementing its traffic calming measures:

. effects on buses (journey times, passenger comfort, injuries to passengers, bus maintenance costs),

. effects on bicyclists (noting that lower vehicle speeds make bicycling safer),

. effects on emergency services (effect of humps on access time, the need to be able to negotiate chicanes, street closures and their effects on access time and the turning circles in culs-de-sac, and clearance from street furniture such as bollards and posts),

. effects of street lighting on amenity,

. loss of parking,

. noise (especially braking and acceleration, and vehicles thumping as they pass over speed humps),

. effects on energy consumption and emissions caused by vehicles accelerating and decelerating, compared with a steady speed,

. public opinion after implementation, due to some people perceiving themselves to be less safe (or less secure - see above) after implementation of the scheme, and

. transference of traffic which, while often an explicit objective of a scheme, can sometimes change traffic patterns in unexpected and undesirable ways.

This is not the place for a discussion of these issues and how to resolve them. It is necessary to note only that if traffic calming measures are to be introduced with safety objectives, the design and implementation of the scheme must be carefully and sensitively carried out. Later in this chapter, we review some of devices and techniques which may be used to 'traffic calm' an area.

*Traffic calming is a term used to describe the introduction of physical devices aimed at enhancing amenity and safety, especially through speed reduction. It's prime application is within local residential precincts, but there are some situations where the balance of objectives for an arterial road may call for a degree of 'calming'. The safety benefits and the security benefits of traffic calming can be demonstrated. These benefits stem primarily from speed reductions, and these are achieved by development of an overall scheme rather than by specific devices at discrete locations. For this reason, it is vital that traffic calming schemes be developed and implemented on an integrated area-wide basis.*

## Speed management

In the introduction to this chapter, we alluded to the central importance of vehicle speed as a critical factor in road safety, especially in urban areas. Speed may be managed in two ways, through traffic calming using physical devices aimed to restrict the speed of vehicles as discussed above, or through the imposition of speed limits. We discuss the latter in this section.

### Speeds and safety

There is clear evidence of the effect of speed on accident rates and accident severity. The energy to be dissipated in an accident is proportional to the square of the impact speed; for example, an impact speed of 130 km/h involves more than twice the energy of one at 90 km/h. Moreover, in many accidents the impact speed is well below the travel speed, as drivers have managed to brake but not stop their vehicles before the collision. As travel speeds drop therefore, the impact speed drops also, and the collision may in fact be avoided.

Lay (1986, p 363) has suggested four factors which contribute to the greater hazard at higher speed, namely that the vehicle becomes less stable at higher speeds, the driver has less time to react, other road users have less time to react, and the severity of accidents increases, as mentioned above.

Organisation for Economic Cooperation and Development (1981a, p 2) has quantified the effect of speed on accidents and accident severity, based upon Swedish data, as follows:

the percentage drop in accident rates outside built up areas is $n$ times the percentage drop in mean speed, where $n = 4$ for fatal accidents, 3 for personal injury accidents, and 2 for all accidents.

In urban areas, there are two distinct speed-related accident problems. The first involves injury to drivers and passengers of vehicles where speed

331

is in excess of posted speed limits, or an inappropriate speed limit, leads to 'loss of control' accidents. The second involves injury to vulnerable road users - pedestrians and bicyclists; in many cases the driver is within the speed limit. A recent Australian study (McLean, et al, 1994) based on a detailed study of 146 fatal pedestrian accidents found that 45 per cent of these would probably have survived if the vehicles that struck them had been travelling just 10 km/h slower before the emergency arose.

*Speed limits*

It follows from the above that, to the extent that speed limits affect travel speed, speed limits should affect accidents.

While there is little controversy about this conclusion as it applies to urban areas and roads of limited design standard, the evidence for rural freeways is less clear. The United States undertook what amounted to a massive nationwide experiment when speed limits on rural Interstate freeways were reduced to 55 mph (88 km/h) in 1974, and increased to 65 mph (104 km/h) in 1987.

Analysis of the effects of these changes is not straightforward, because of the need to correct for other safety initiatives, changes in enforcement patterns, changes in travel behaviour, etc. As a result, some researchers (e.g. Anon, 1988a; Garber and Graham, 1990) claim to have detected a relationship between accidents and speed. (Garber and Graham for example concluded that for rural Interstates there were roughly 15 per cent more fatalities following the increase in speed limit.) However, others were either unable to detect any statistically significant effect (e.g. Chang and Paniati, 1990) or have found that the increase in speed limits led to a decrease in accidents. (E.g. Lave and Elias (1994) found that 'the 65 mph limit reduced statewide fatality rates by 3.4 to 5.1 per cent, holding constant the effects of long term trend, driving exposure, seat belt laws, and economic factors'. They explained this somewhat counter-intuitive outcome as being the result of the higher speed limit encouraging drivers to use the freeways rather than the more dangerous non-freeways, and redirection of enforcement away from the Interstates to other roads.)

*Speed limits and travel speeds*

It is axiomatic that speed limits affect safety only if they affect actual travel speeds. The influence of speed limit on speed is somewhat tenuous, and relies firstly on the speed limit as being regarded as 'reasonable' by the driver, and secondly on enforcement.

*Reasonableness of speed limits.* In relation to the former, the Organisation for Economic Cooperation and Development (1981a, p 2) concluded that 'in order to bring about a reduction in mean speed and speed dispersion, a speed limit should be set at the 85 percentile of existing speeds, or at a lower level (but not too far below)'. Ross Silcock Partnership (1991, p 126) note that not only will drivers not observe speed limits which are 'not consistent with the nature and type of road' but that too many changes in speed limit 'make enforcement difficult and cause confusion to drivers.' On the other hand, a speed limit set too high may have negative effects because road users often interpret the speed limit as the recommended speed rather than a ceiling.

Road environment factors affecting drivers' perception of what is 'reasonable' include alignment, road category, whether the road is in an urban or rural environment, lane width, roadside development, traffic density, sight distance, parked vehicles, pedestrians and day and night vision (Fildes and Lee, 1993, p 78).

*Enforcement.* The Organisation for Economic Cooperation and Development (1981a, p 6) noted that 'traditionally, the underlying assumption has been that enforcement would result in a reduction in mean speed and in the spread of speeds, and this in turn would lead to a reduction in accident numbers and severity. This assumption can no longer be made without serious and specific limitations. In particular, enforcement at a specific site and time brings the average speed close to the posted speed; the effect on variability is less pronounced... (but) despite reservations about the effect on *speeds*, high levels of surveillance reduce the numbers of *fatal and injury accidents*' (their emphasis).

This is not the place for a detailed discussion of the effectiveness of enforcement, but it is relevant to note that these conclusions are consistent with the observations of Axup (1993) and Zaal (1994).

Automated speed enforcement, using high-volume speed cameras capable of taking one photograph per second, are likely to become more common in the future. Where they have been used, for example in Britain (Swali, 1993; Winnett, 1994) and Australia (Axup, 1993), they have been effective in reducing speeds, not only at the sites where they have been set up, but also in leading to a change in attitudes towards speeding. Bearing in mind the point made in Chapter 2 that the prime enforcement-related factor affecting driver behaviour is the probability of detection, the widespread use of speed cameras has already produced a change in driver attitude in Australia where portable speed cameras have been in use for several years. However, such is the capacity of these devices to detect large numbers of vehicles that they run the danger of being perceived as revenue raising devices and not a road safety measure. As Axup (1993) warns, 'to avoid undue criticism of the use of such devices and to win community support, it is essential to carefully establish the criteria for selection of the sites in which they are to be deployed. Acceptance in Australia has largely been a result of very good police implementation and a focus on only those sites with a legitimate speed problem.'

*Differential speed limits for heavy vehicles.* Notwithstanding the above arguments about the relationship between speed and safety, there is evidence that accident rates are related to the *dispersion* or variance of speeds of vehicles in the traffic stream. Federal Highway Administration (1982, p 4-2), Solomon (1964), Taylor (1965) and Munden (1967) have all reported that the chance of being involved in an accident follows a U-shaped distribution, with the minimum occurring when the vehicle is travelling at about the average speed of traffic, or slightly above (Figure 13.4). As vehicle speeds move significantly above or below the average speed of the traffic stream, the probability of being involved in an accident increases dramatically. Sweatman, et al (1990, p 36) in a study of fatal accidents involving trucks in Australia found that vehicles travelling slowly were a factor in 20 per cent of accidents, and vehicles travelling at excessive speed were a factor in 39-47 per cent of accidents.

However, Fildes and Lee (1993, p 5) have cautioned against drawing simplistic conclusions from these studies, noting that excessively fast drivers are likely to be young, on business, travelling long distances, behind schedule, and driving newer vehicles. Slow travellers are more likely to be older, travelling for domestic or recreational purposes, and driving older vehicles. They suggest that it may be these sorts of factors, rather than speed variance per se, which is behind the observed relationship between speed variance and accident occurrence.

Nevertheless, this is the basis of the argument that there should not be a speed limit differential (and thus travel speed differential) between heavy vehicles and other road vehicles. Evidence to support the argument has been produced in the US, where, following the introduction of nationwide 55 mph (88 km/h) car speed limits in 1974, the observed speed differential between cars and trucks was reduced. Radwan and Sinha (1978) examined the effect of this on truck accidents and concluded that there had been reductions in heavy truck accident rates in all severity types (property damage, injury and fatality) on freeways. On four-lane and two-lane rural highways however, the reduction occurred only for injury accidents. The reductions were attributed to an absolute reduction in speeds and decreased speed dispersion.

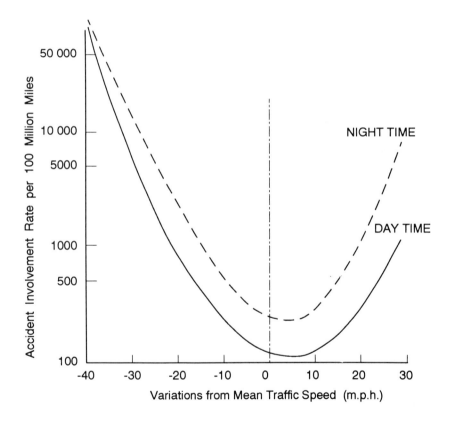

**Figure 13.4 Accidents are minimised when there is little variation from average speed.**

Notwithstanding this evidence, there are still jurisdictions which have a statutory speed limit differential. This is predicated upon the argument that trucks have poorer braking and handling than cars, and therefore should not travel as fast. However, as noted above, this will likely be counter-productive in safety terms if truck drivers obey the limit, at least on two lane roads (Ogden and Pearson, 1991). It also leads to a substantial deterioration of level of service on those roads, as one of the key factors affecting drivers' perception of service quality is the extent to which they are forced to travel in bunches (Hoban, 1988).

*Setting speed limits*

As noted above, speed limits which are perceived as reasonable for the road conditions will be respected and voluntarily observed by the majority of motorists, with only limited enforcement effort. Speed limits which are set too low will not be respected (and may in fact lead to increased vehicle speeds, since drivers ignore them) and require substantial enforcement effort to have any effect. There are four types of speed limit:

. general limits, which are imposed by statute and are applicable to all roads in an area unless signed otherwise, e.g. a general urban limit and a general rural limit,

. speed zones, which are speed limits applied to a specific road (perhaps varying by time of day) in the light of an assessment of that road's design characteristics and its traffic and abutting land use characteristics,

. vehicle limits, which may apply to specific classes of vehicle (e.g. trucks and buses), and

. driver limits, which may apply to specific classes of driver, such as learners.

Formal management of vehicle speeds by the use of any of these legally enforceable speed limits involves:

. establishing a balance between safety, mobility, and amenity for users of abutting developments,

.   meeting driver expectations (consistent with the above), thereby making speed limits more or less self-enforcing,

.   achieving consistency across the jurisdiction (and in many cases, nationally),

.   the ability to deter offenders by appropriate levels of enforcement,

.   developing a culture of compliance, and

.   minimizing the costs of signing and enforcement.

An example of a formal, systematic approach to the setting of speed limits in a speed zoning context is the expert system called VLIMITS developed by the Australian Road Research Board (Jarvis and Hoban, 1988). This takes account of the factors shown in Table 13.1.

VLIMITS has been used as the basis of a recent major statewide speed limit review in Victoria, Australia. Guidelines for the use of the various speed limits are summarized below (VicRoads, 1994). It can be seen that these mostly relate to the road configuration, and as a result, drivers in most cases will be able to assess the speed limit for any road segment by its appearance, perhaps without even noticing the speed limit signing:

*Shared zone (10 km/h (6 mph))*: where it is desired to have vehicles and pedestrians sharing the same road space, with pedestrians having priority (e.g. service vehicles in shopping malls).

*Local traffic area zone (40 km/h (24 mph))*: applicable to roads where traffic management works have been undertaken to physically limit speeds to about 40 km/h.

*Local street speed limit (50 km/h (30 mph))*: Applicable to local streets where the general urban limit of 60 km/h is considered too high; typically local access or collector roads with abutting development.

*General urban limit (60 km/h (36 mph))*: Applies to all urban roads that do not meet criteria for higher or lower speed limits; typically includes undivided arterial roads where there is substantial abutting development, but occasionally used also on divided roads having intense abutting development, e.g. strip shopping centres with 'friction' generated by driveways and parking turnover, pedestrian and bicycle activity, etc. The general urban limit also applies to some collector roads, if they are of higher standard (greater than 8 m (25 ft) between kerbs), and carrying above 5,000 veh/d.

*Urban (70 km/h (42 mph))*: Applies to divided roads where there is substantial abutting development having direct access to the through roadway, and undivided roads with low traffic volumes, little or no abutting development, and wide verges on both sides.

*Urban (80 km/h 48 mph))*: Applies to divided roads where there is substantial abutting development but little or no direct access (because of frontage roads or the orientation of development inwards away from the road), and undivided roads with only a limited amount of abutting development. This limit also applies to 'hamlet' zones, where a road passes through a small rural settlement, but where there is only a limited amount of abutting development, and also as a 'buffer zone' inserted on the approach to a rural town, between the rural zone of 100 km/h and the urban zone of 60 km/h or less.

*General rural limit (100 km/h (60 mph))*: The general speed limit in rural areas, used where there is little or no abutting development and widely spaced intersections. Normally, no allowance is made for alignment, but sub-standard elements (especially horizontal curves) may have advisory speed signs; sections with an extended length of uniformly low standard and cross section may be speed limited to a lower value.

*Rural freeway (110 km/h (66 mph))*: Applies to high-standard rural freeways, which meet current design standards, have a 9 m roadside clear zone, an accident rate of less than one casualty accident per 2 kilometres (1.2 miles) per year, and widely spaced interchanges (greater than 3 km).

While these criteria, and the values nominated, may not be applicable to all environments and applications, they are presented as a guide to what may be appropriate to given situations, and the circumstances under which speed limits may be differentiated. The important element is their consistency, reasonableness, and explicit, non-arbitrary, criteria for determination of the speed limit appropriate to any given situation.

**Table 13.1**
**Factors considered in setting of speed limits**

| Criterion | Factors |
|---|---|
| Road environment | road classification<br>undivided or divided road<br>number of lanes and lane widths<br>presence of footpaths/ sidewalks<br>clearance to roadside obstacles<br>vertical and horizontal alignment |
| Abutting development | number and density of abutting developments<br>type and extent of traffic generated<br>land use (schools, houses, apartments, shops, etc) |
| Road users and their movements | cars<br>trucks<br>buses<br>bicyclists and pedestrians<br>parked vehicles<br>peak hour traffic<br>recreational traffic |
| Existing speeds | average speeds<br>85 percentile speeds |
| Accident history | to give an indication of speed-related safety problems |
| Adjacent speed zones | to be consistent<br>minimum lengths for buffer zones are specified |
| Other factors | intersections<br>schools<br>pedestrian crossings<br>road alignment |

Source: Jarvis and Hoban (1988).

*All else being equal, a reduction in the mean speed of traffic reduces accidents. This will involve the establishment of speed limits which are appropriate to the traffic environment, and seen to be reasonable by motorists.*

### Devices and techniques for managing speed and volume

Earlier in this chapter, we introduced the notion of 'traffic calming', and pointed out that the safety benefits of physical devices for managing traffic flow mainly from reducing excessive vehicle speeds. Speed limits were then discussed in the previous section, and it was noted that, while a degree of enforcement is essential, it is impossible to enforce every road continuously, so speed limits must be, to an extent, self-enforcing.

In this section, we briefly review the main devices and techniques for managing traffic speed and traffic volume. Particular attention is paid to local networks, since these are the areas where speed management through the use of physical devices is most relevant. However, in considering the introduction of any speed management, or traffic calming scheme, it is essential that devices and individual streets are not considered in isolation, but that traffic calming schemes are developed and implemented on an integrated area-wide basis. This approach is also vital if the objective is to reduce traffic volumes as well as speeds, otherwise the effect of a treatment may be to merely relocate traffic to an adjacent local street, not onto a traffic route.

Detailed discussion of the design and implementation of traffic management and traffic calming devices is beyond the scope of this book[2]. However, it is useful in this discussion of road safety engineering and the role of traffic calming and speed management in safety to at least summarize the types of devices and techniques which are available for reducing speed or (more importantly) keeping speeds low once they have been reduced, and for constraining traffic volumes. These broadly fall into six categories:

. regulatory devices,
. network modifications,
. devices used at intersections,
. devices relying on vertical displacement,
. devices relying on horizontal displacement, and
. gateways.

*Regulatory devices*

Traffic regulations are the requirements placed upon road users which they are legally required to obey, and which carry a sanction (e.g. a fine) if disobeyed. They constitute the 'rules of the road' (e.g. by assigning priority), indicate acceptable codes of behaviour (e.g. speed limits), and can be used as a tool for managing road user activity (e.g. traffic control). In the context of managing traffic on local street networks, the following regulatory devices may be used.

*Speed limits.* These have been discussed in the previous section. Speed limits of themselves are most unlikely to reduce speeds to levels which are generally considered appropriate in 'calmed' streets (e.g. less than 50 km/h (30 mph)) unless associated with other physical devices or network discontinuities.

*STOP and GIVE WAY/YIELD signs.* These have been discussed in Chapter 9. They are important within any road or street network to indicate priority at intersections, and may be used with or without other devices (such as roundabouts or channelization).

*No-turn signs.* These may be used to control entry into a local street, sometimes only at designated hours of the day to deter rat-running (Figure 13.5). Since enforcement is often likely to be minimal, these are sometimes referred to as 'bluff signs', i.e. they operate more by bluff than by active enforcement or physical deterrence. Homburger, et al (1989, p 84) note that the effect of such prohibitions may be to 'force motorists to make turns at less safe locations or by means of hazardous manoeuvres', and therefore 'the analyst should determine that safe and reasonable alternatives to the proposed prohibited manoeuvre do exist.'

*One-way operation.* This practice is discussed later in this chapter in relation to arterial roads, but in local networks, it may be part of a strategy to prevent traffic from entering a local network at a particular gateway, e.g. one that could be used as a rat-run, or because the street is too narrow to permit two-way operation. Needless to say, alternative access must be provided. Where irregular patterns of one-way streets are used, careful treatment is essential at intersections where one-way streets signed in facing directions meet, and where a two-way street faces a one-way street across an intersection (Homburger, et al, 1989, p 85).

**Figure 13.5 'Bluff' sign indicating turn prohibition**

*Network modifications*

Problems with traffic in local streets, and in particular accident problems, began to be recognized as an unfortunate and unacceptable by-product of motor vehicles during the period of rapid motorization in the 1950s and 1960s. The Buchanan Report in Britain, *Traffic in Towns* (Buchanan,

1963) represents a clear watershed in our thinking about the relationship between urban areas and their transport needs. The initial response was to seek to solve these problems by modifying the road and street network. This was based on the premise that, having identified the two basic types of road defined above (arterial roads and local streets), it was necessary to reinforce that designation by modifying the street pattern. Hence, much early traffic management work which aimed at resolving local network problems used this approach, and indeed, it still forms the basis for much such work in the UK (Proctor, 1990). There are numerous techniques, but most involve variations upon those detailed below. It should be noted that since all of these techniques involve a change in local street connectivity, they can be unpopular with residents in the street which is affected, since the travel patterns are disrupted. Problems can also be created for emergency vehicles, both in terms of access to the closed street, and also the provision of a turning circle at the end of the street.

*Street closure at intersection.* This procedure involves the closure of one or more legs of an intersection, e.g. to convert a cross-intersection into a t-intersection, or to eliminate the intersection entirely (Figure 13.6). The intention of these closures is to alter local connectivity, so that traffic is prevented from using the path which included that street. Safety may also be enhanced by the conversion of the cross intersection, or the elimination of the intersection entirely. Of course, access to the street must be maintained from another direction.

*Link closure.* This procedure is similar to the above, except that the closure is made mid-block (i.e. not at an intersection). The single through street then becomes two culs-de sac.

*Partial street closure.* This method typically involves preventing access to or egress from a street. For example, egress may be allowed, but access (which may be hazardous if the vehicle is turning from a busy arterial road) may be prevented (Figure 13.7). Usually two-way operation in the rest of the street is permitted.

*Diagonal closure of intersection.* This involves the placement of a barrier diagonally across a cross-intersection, to create two right-angle bends instead of an intersection.

**Figure 13.6 Street closure at intersection** eliminates intersection conflicts and prevents extraneous traffic from entering the street.

*Closure of median opening.* In order to deter rat-running through a local network, and/or to eliminate hazards associated with traffic turning into or out of a local street across a median in an intersecting arterial road, the median may be closed. This is a less severe measure than any of the above since it leaves the local network intact, but a consequence is that traffic must make a turn (e.g. a U-turn) elsewhere, and it will be important to check that this manoeuvre can be performed safely. Homburger, et al (1989, p 95) claim that the safety of the major street is 'inversely proportional to the number of openings permitted in the median'.

*Pedestrian refuge and/or narrow median.* Although primarily a measure directed at pedestrian safety, the status of a road may be altered by narrowing the lanes to provide a continuous median, typically around 1.0-1.2 m (3-4 ft), with periodic pedestrian refuges. The combination of narrow lanes and the series of refuges combine to alter the visual cues provided to a driver, and thus tend to affect behaviour and speed.

**Figure 13.7 Partial street closure** to allow access or egress only.

*Intersection devices*

Intersection safety was discussed in detail in Chapter 9. In the context of traffic calming and speed reduction, devices at intersections have an important role to play. These devices, especially roundabouts, have been widely used in Australia (Brindle, 1992), and are the most readily accepted form of traffic calming treatment in that country (Fairlie and Taylor, 1990). They have the considerable advantage that it is at intersections where most accidents occur in local areas, and thus by reducing speed and resolving priority at intersections, they are more likely to contribute directly to safety than do most other methods (Fairlie and Taylor, 1990).

*Roundabouts*. Roundabouts in local streets resolve priority issues, and provided that the vehicle is required to divert from a straight line, also reduce vehicle speed. Klyne (1988) has established an empirical relationship between speed and path radius:

345

$$V = 6\, \frac{\sqrt{R}}{S}$$

where:  V = 95 percentile speed (km/h) of through vehicles
R = radius of centre line of vehicle path (metres)
S = sight distance factor (S = 1.0 for good sight distance, up to 1.53 for poor sight distance).

This formula suggests that to keep 95 percentile speeds through an intersection to 30 km/h, for example, the roundabout geometry should be such that the path radius developed cannot be greater than 25 m (about 80 feet).

To ensure that adequate deflection is developed (i.e. the path radius is limited), Australian practice is generally to provide splitter islands on the approach to a local area roundabout and to provide a raised central island of reasonable radius; this will involve in some cases realignment of kerb lines (Figures 9.5 and 9.6). In the UK, mini-roundabouts have been successfully used. However, since these rarely have splitter islands and are usually either painted or have minimal vertical dimensions so that vehicles can and do drive over them (Figure 9.8), they have little effect upon speed, although they do have a satisfactory safety performance (County Surveyors' Society, 1987; Walker and Pittam, 1989).

*Channelization.* Once again, channelization was discussed in Chapter 9. In the context of traffic calming, a typical application would be to re-allocate priority at an intersection, e.g. at a t-intersection to give priority to vehicles travelling around a curve (Figure 13.8), or to deter speeding by motorists on the top of the t-intersection by requiring them to slow down to negotiate the device (Figure 13.9).

*Vertical displacement*

Properly designed, humps (i.e. devices which cause vertical displacement of a vehicle) are highly effective in causing vehicles to reduce speed in their vicinity. They have become widely used as a speed management device for this reason, and in some countries are much preferred to devices which alter network connectivity (because they do not affect local access). They have disadvantages however, in that they are noisy, not particularly aesthetic, and can cause problems for buses and emergency vehicles if they are not well-designed (Jarvis, 1992).

**Figure 13.8 Redirected priority at t-intersection**, to alter local street connectivity.

*Road humps*. Road humps are of several types. The earliest type was a *bump*, akin to a pipe half-buried in the roadway. These impart a very severe vertical acceleration to low-speed vehicles, which can potentially damage the vehicle, and may even cause loss of control. Paradoxically, for larger vehicles, the vertical acceleration is less if the vehicles cross them at speed. This device therefore has very limited application, and is generally only found in environments where speeds are required to be very low, such as where pedestrians cross car park lanes.

Research in the UK in the early 1970s showed that a much more satisfactory arrangement was to have a long, low device; these could impart the necessary vertical acceleration, were effective on both light and heavy vehicles, and did not lead to loss of control. The first types, often referred to as the *TRRL* or *Watts profile* hump (Watts, 1973) were circular in shape, typically about 100 mm (4 inches) high and 3-4 m (about 10-13 ft) in length (Figure 13.10). Today, there are a range of Watts profile speed humps in use, ranging in height from 50 mm (2 inches) to 120 mm (about 5 inches) in height; humps less that 50 mm in height have little if any effect upon speed.

In response to the problems with circular humps, an alternative device was developed which was similar in effect but more user-friendly, especially to buses (Jarvis, 1992) and arguably more aesthetic. This is the *flat-topped or plateau* road hump (Figure 13.11). It is of similar height to the Watts profile device, but has straight approach and departure ramps (typically 1:10 to 1:15) and a flat top; the length varies from being quite short (about 2 m - 7 ft) to being much longer (perhaps 7 m (24 ft)), so that the vehicle actually has both axles on the plateau momentarily.

**Figure 13.9 Treatment at t-intersection**; horizontal deflection leads to reduction in vehicle speeds.

**Figure 13.10**    **Circular profile road hump** is effective in reducing vehicle speeds.

**Figure 13.11**    **Flat-top or plateau road hump** is effective in reducing vehicle speeds and has less adverse effect on buses and emergency vehicles than a circular profile road hump.

As a way of avoiding the problems with buses, a device sometimes known as a *speed cushion* has been used; this involves a road hump centrally located in a lane between bollards or similar, with a width greater than that of the axle width of a car but less than that of a bus. The device therefore has no effect on the bus but retains its effectiveness for a car.

Another variation is to use a *speed table*, whereby the whole road space at the intersection of two roads is raised; this has the advantage that speeds are lowered at the intersection, with no loss of car parking spaces.

Humps are intrusive devices, and their design and location should be carefully undertaken. National guides should be followed where appropriate (e.g. Institution of Highways and Transportation, 1987, Chapter 22; Institute of Transportation Engineers, 1993b; National Association of Australian State Road Authorities, 1988c).

*Rumble devices.* Rumble devices may be placed transversely across the pavement itself on an approach to an intersection or pedestrian crossing to alert the driver to the approaching hazard (Sumner and Shippey, 1977; Harwood, 1993). Their use and effectiveness has been described in Chapter 10.

*Horizontal displacement*

Instead of (or in conjunction with) the use of vertical displacement devices, horizontal displacement may be used. These devices, which cause the driver to change direction quite sharply, also change the visual cues presented by the street, for example by breaking up a long, straight vista into a series of much shorter intervals between devices. There are numerous devices of this form, including the following:

*Chicanes.* These devices involve the use of a feature extending into the roadway from the kerb around which the driver must manoeuvre; these features are variously referred to as 'build outs' (UK), 'kerb extensions' (Australia), 'chokers' (USA) or 'forts' (Japan). Chicanes may be single lane, two lane, or one lane in each direction, depending upon traffic flow and street width (Figure 13.12). These devices need to be carefully designed and landscaped to ensure that they do not increase the hazard for pedestrians and bicyclists. Unfortunately, by their nature they can provide a challenge for certain motorists who, perhaps, associate such devices with the motor racing circuit, and seek to travel through them at speed!

350

**Figure 13.12**   **Chicane**, (a) single lane and (b) two-lane; in both cases the horizontal deflection is effective in reducing vehicle speeds.

351

*Pinch points*. A pinch point (sometimes alternatively referred to as a 'slow point') is a short section of narrow road, usually one lane only, which introduces a sudden change in road configuration (Figure 13.13). Like a chicane, it alters the visual cues and perhaps provides space for landscaping. Lane width may be considerably reduced (say 2.7 m (9 ft)) to lead to a significant speed reduction. They may be combined with a hump, e.g. as a gateway device (see below), or a pedestrian crossing. In the latter case, they have the added advantage that pedestrians and drivers have better vision of each other, and the pedestrian takes a shorter time to cross the road, with advantages for both pedestrian safety (less exposure) and traffic performance (shorter delay).

*Restructured parking*. Rearrangement of parking can be an effective speed control measure, by altering the kerb alignment. This changes the visual cues offered by the street and thus influences driver behaviour. If used in conjunction with pedestrian crossings they also enhance safety (Figure 14.2), albeit at the cost of a reduction in the number of parking spaces.

**Figure 13.13**     **Pinch point, or slow point**, can be effective in reducing vehicle speed by altering visual cues, with drivers tending to slow at the road narrowing.

*Gateways*

Gateways or entry treatments may be used at the entrance to towns to announce the start of the built-up environment (Figure 13.14), or on side roads so that drivers will appreciate that they are leaving an arterial road and entering a local network (Figure 13.15). They would typically use one or (more commonly perhaps) a combination of devices, such as pinch points, changes in surface texture and/or colour, road humps or plateaux, signing, landscaping features such as planting or street furniture, and/or rumble devices.

**Figure 13.14    Gateway: town entrance**

*Implementation*

The previous discussion has briefly reviewed the range of treatments and devices. However, as has been emphasized throughout this chapter, these are not to be introduced piece-meal, but must be planned and developed as part of an overall traffic management plan for an area as a whole, including adjacent arterial roads. As Brindle (1992) has commented, 'the key seems to be to encourage integrated design, combining considerations of length, visibility, texture and materials, cross-section, edge treatments, human activity, roadside development,and planting. Design rules and standards cannot guarantee a pleasant and safe low-speed environment.' Similar sentiments are expressed by Organisation for Economic Cooperation and Development (1986, p 91), which noted that traffic calming measures 'are likely to prove most effective when applied on an area-wide basis, and with the additional objective of improving the quality of the environment.'

However, in implementing schemes containing such devices, there are some useful guidelines which have emerged, based upon various researchers worldwide (e.g. Ogden and Bennett, 1989; Brindle, 1992; Wallwork, 1993; Kent County Council, 1994a; Devon County Council, 1992; Vis, Dijkstra and Slop, 1992; Organisation for Economic Cooperation and Development 1979, 1986; Homburger, et al, 1989):

**Figure 13.15    Gateway: residential precinct**

. network configuration should be such that the amount of traffic on any residential street is limited; suggested upper limits as acceptable volumes in residential streets are typically in the range 2000 - 3000 veh/d,

. wide, long streets with house frontages have a poor safety record and should be avoided if possible,

. use can be made of network discontinuities and circuitous travel paths to discourage the entry of non-local traffic into a local area,

. the influence of various factors on traffic speeds (and hence accidents) in local areas are as follows:

   . speeds are low in streets shorter than 200 m (about 670 ft),
   . of secondary importance is micro-alignment,
   . the influence of streetscaping is positive but of unknown extent, and
   . of doubtful influence are flowing alignments and subtle sight distance restrictions,

. streets shorter than about 200 m (670 ft) generally will not require speed management devices if the 85 percentile of speeds is to be below 50 km/h (30 mph); the corresponding length for a speed of 30 km/h (20 mph) is 100 m (330 ft),

. intersections along streets within a residential network should be separated by at least 20 m (about 70 ft),

. action is usually required when 85 percentile speeds exceed 60 km/h (35 mph),

. the effect of speed control devices is quite localized, so as the desired speed for the street reduces, they need to be more closely spaced; as a general guide, the following relationships between spacing and 85 percentile speed seem reasonable:

   . spacing about 75 m (250 ft): speed 30 km/h (18 mph)
   . spacing about 100 m (330 ft): speed 40 km/h (24 mph)
   . spacing about 150 m (500 ft): speed 45 km/h (27 mph)
   . spacing about 200 m (670 ft): speed 60 km/h (36 mph)

. chicanes should probably not be used in any street in which it is expected that traffic volumes will exceed 600 veh/h,

. chicanes and other devices involving the use of kerb realignment are most effective if they are closely spaced; a chicane will constrain vehicle speed to less than 30 km/h (20 mph) if it is 10-15 m (30-45 ft) long,

. however, at this spacing buses and other long vehicles will have difficulty in manoeuvring through the device and a larger spacing will be needed; in this case the speed reduction potential of the device depends upon there being sufficient traffic in the opposing direction to inhibit the speed of travel,

. chicanes and road humps should only be used on straight sections of road, not on curves, so that drivers have clear visibility, and so that the potential for vehicle instability is reduced,

. rumble devices can be a problem for bicyclists and pedestrians, so it is suggested that they should not exceed about 15 mm (0.6 inches) in height and that a gap of about 750 mm (30 inches) be left between the device and the kerb to allow passage for bicycles,

. road humps lower than about 50 mm (2 inches) in height give little or no slowing effect,

. gradients on the approach to a plateau or flat-top road hump need to be greater than 1:20 to have any effect on speed; generally 1:10 is appropriate unless the road is on a bus route when 1:15 is appropriate,

. pinch points, slow points and other road narrowings need to be 2.7 m (9 ft) or less in width to achieve a speed reduction.

*There are numerous devices which have been used to keep traffic speeds at an acceptable level and/or deter extraneous traffic. However, it is important that in applying such devices, the focus is on the development of an overall scheme rather than upon installing individual devices at discrete locations. That is, traffic calming schemes should be developed and implemented on an integrated area-wide basis.*

## Parking

Vehicles spend the majority of their time at rest. An important aspect of traffic management therefore revolves around how and where to store (i.e. park) vehicles. While there is an extensive literature on parking design and layout (e.g. McCluskey, 1987; Institution of Highways and Transportation, 1987; National Association of Australian State Road Authorities, 1988d; Institute of Transportation Engineers, 1990), for present purposes we will only consider the safety aspects of parking.

In the UK, parked vehicles or those which are in the process of parking or unparking represent about 10 per cent of traffic accidents (Ross Silcock Partnership, 1991, p 128). Parked or parking vehicles are particularly associated with pedestrian casualties; Lawson (1990) in a study of pedestrian accidents in Birmingham, England found that over 30 per cent of pedestrians involved in traffic accidents had impeded vision of moving vehicles, and over 40 per cent of drivers involved in such accidents said something made it difficult to see the pedestrian. In both cases, a parked vehicle was the most common source of the obstruction.

Several American studies have examined the accident experience of on-street parking, comparing angle with parallel parking (Federal Highway Administration, 1982; McCoy, et al, 1990). These have mostly reported parallel parking to be safer. However, McCoy, et al (1991) in a study in Nebraska concluded that, while there were significantly more parking-related accidents following conversion from parallel to angle parking, when the increase in exposure due to the increase in the number of spaces was taken into account, there was no significant difference in parking-related accident rates between parallel and angle parking. They concluded that 'where the supply of parking spaces is sufficient, the conversion of on-street parking from parallel to angle should not be considered (but) converting on-street parking from parallel to angle may be a cost-effective way of increasing the supply of parking.' National Association of Australian State Road Authorities (1988d, p 19) recommends that angle parking should be avoided in on-street situations, particularly on arterial roads.

Centre of the road parking may be appropriate in streets where there is little through traffic and vehicle speeds are low. By separating opposing streams of traffic, it facilitates pedestrian crossings, but it also generates pedestrian activities as drivers and passengers move to and from their parked vehicles. In combination with parallel parking, it can provide for a large number of parking spaces per unit length of road, provided there is sufficient street width.

It remains the case however that off-street parking is safer than on-street parking.

Parked vehicles also affect intersection safety (although a London study found that accidents involving parked vehicles were over-represented relative to all accidents in mid-block locations (London Accident Analysis Unit, 1994)). For this reason, parking prohibitions in or near intersections contribute to safety (Organisation for Economic Cooperation and Development, 1976, p 53). However, where parking space is at a premium, as in many European cities, it is common to find vehicles parked within the intersection (Figure 13.16).

**Figure 13.16**    **Where kerb space is at a premium, drivers will park anywhere**, even on a corner or across a pedestrian crossing (Paris).

Ross Silcock Partnership (op cit, p 129) suggest that planning for parking involves consideration of three factors: the need to maximize access to traffic generating facilities, the need to minimize interruptions to moving traffic, and the need to minimize traffic accidents. They suggest that this involves the following procedures:

. parking on arterial roads carrying large volumes of traffic should be avoided; parking should be displaced to side streets through partial or all-day bans on the main road,

. major traffic generators along main roads should, where feasible, be required to provide off-street parking,

. careful attention needs to be given to pedestrian circulation within off-street car parks to reduce conflict in terms of both aggregate exposure to risk and the exposure of vulnerable road users (pedestrians and bicyclists),

. in busy streets, road narrowing can be used to create a clear distinction between the roadway for moving traffic and that for stationary vehicles (Figure 14.2),

. in residential areas, off-street parking should be provided wherever possible; if this is impossible, on-street parking can be grouped nearby to create special resident parking zones, and

. in industrial areas, large articulated trucks need lanes to be about 3.5 m (about 12 ft) wide; unless kerbside parking is prohibited and enforced, an additional 3 m (10 ft) will need to be provided as parking space.

*There are clear safety benefits from prohibiting parking on arterial roads, and where feasible, parking should be provided off-street. Where this is not feasible, parallel parking is safer than angle parking, although of course this is at the expense of parking capacity. Pedestrians are particularly affected by parking, both on-street (where parked vehicles may impede visibility) and off-street, where care must be taken in arranging pedestrian circulation within car parks to minimize conflict with moving vehicles.*

## One-way streets

One-way streets have a number of effects on traffic, some of which tend to contribute to safety, and some of which do not. Generally, one-way operation leads to higher speeds, and to longer trips. They can also be more confusing for pedestrians. On the other hand, conflicts at intersections are reduced, there may be fewer stops, and traffic flow tends to be more orderly, creating gaps for both pedestrians and vehicles to enter or cross the traffic stream. Homburger, et al (1989, p 85) summarize that 'one-way streets tend to be inherently safer than two-way streets because the 'friction' from an opposing traffic stream has been removed.'

The safety of one-way street systems has been typically assessed by comparing accidents before and after conversion to one-way operation, and often relate to streets in central business districts (CBD). These studies have tended to indicate that one-way streets are safer, by perhaps 20-30 per cent. The number of mid-block accidents is generally reduced more than the number of intersection accidents, with the smallest effect being at non-signalized intersections (Wainwright, 1993; Zegeer and Zegeer, 1988).

However, the generality of these findings have been questioned in a recent study by Hocherman, Hakkert and Bar-Ziv (1990). They compared accident rates on all one-way and all two-way undivided streets in a section of Jerusalem, Israel, and found that in non-CBD locations, accident rates (per vehicle kilometre) were higher on one-way streets, with pedestrian accidents being particularly affected. These differences were mainly a result of accidents at unsignalized intersections; the mid-block rates were comparable for one-way and two-way streets. In CBD locations, there was some indication that one-way streets may be safer for pedestrians, but otherwise the sample was too small to be reliable.

*Although there is a paucity of recent information, experience suggests that one-way streets are somewhat safer than two-way streets in central business district environments. The evidence is less clear in other environments, with pedestrian accidents and accidents at low-volume unsignalized intersections possibly being particular problems.*

## Truck routes

Control of trucks through some form of truck routing is sometimes suggested as a means of implementing an urban traffic management scheme. However, its application in this area is essentially to pursue amenity objectives, not safety objectives (Figure 13.17).

The only reference to truck routing from a safety viewpoint is in relation to hazardous materials routing. This is not a trivial problem however; a 1977 American study quoted in Federal Highway Administration (1982, p 13-14) found that 13 per cent of trucks carried hazardous goods, and trucks carrying hazardous materials were involved in 6 per cent of truck accidents and 7.1 per cent of fatal truck accidents.

**Figure 13.17**    **Truck restrictions** are more commonly introduced for amenity rather than safety reasons.

A number of studies related to risk assessment for the purposes of designating routes for hazardous vehicles have been undertaken (Organisation for Economic Cooperation and Development, 1988). These have led to certain ideal guidelines, which have been summarized by Ogden (1992, p 145), as follows:

. all freeways and controlled access facilities are likely to be suitable,

. routes should be as direct as possible, all else being equal,

. where there is no direct freeway to freeway connection, a suitable route to facilitate such travel should be sought,

. routes should be less densely populated than alternatives,

. routes should avoid centres of concentrated population, such as shopping centres, schools, hospitals, cinemas, etc,

. routes should be largely free of physical characteristics likely to contribute to accidents, such as steep grades, narrow lanes, low overhead clearances, sharp bends or ramps, poor shoulders, etc,

. rail level crossings should be avoided,

. crossings over open water supply aqueducts should be avoided, and

. the choice of route should take into account relative levels of exposure to risk, as measured by travel distance, persons exposed to risk, time of day, etc.

Other forms of truck route, such as routes designated for high-productivity vehicles (e.g. twin or triple trailered trucks), or for more general truck activity, need to satisfy a range of geometric, environmental and functional criteria. Safety is usually reflected implicitly in some of these criteria, such as geometric standards, traffic control, access limitations, and vehicle characteristics like turning radius, braking, power-weight ratio, trailer swing and splash-and-spray requirements (Ogden, 1992, p 140).

*Truck routing may be a valid measure in some cases, particularly in pursuit of amenity objectives in residential areas, and for hazardous goods transport. However, each case must be assessed on its merits, particularly bearing in mind that there must be exceptions to a general truck routing ordinance to permit access by trucks with legitimate access needs.*

**Notes**

1.  Discussion of urban road networks, and their relationship to land use planning are contained in *national guides* such as Institution of Highways and Transportation (1987, 1990c, UK); Institute for Road Safety Research (1985, The Netherlands); Department of Industry, Technology and Commerce (1990, Australia); Homburger, et al (1989, USA); the SCAFT guidelines (Swedish National Board of Physical Planning, 1968); and in *general reviews* such as Appleyard (1981), Organisation for Economic Cooperation and Development (1979), and Brindle (1989).

2.  Discussion of the design and implementation of traffic management and traffic calming devices may be found in any of the *national guides* such as those produced by the Institution of Highways and Transportation (1990c), County Surveyors' Society (1994), National Association of Australian State Road Authorities (1988c), or Homburger, et al (1989); in *local guides* such as those produced by the UK Kent County Council (1994a), the Devon County Council (1992), or the Western Sydney Regional Organisation of Councils (Hawley, et al, 1993); or in *general reviews* such as those presented by Wallwork (1993), Yamanaka and Odani (1991), or Organisation for Economic Cooperation and Development (1979).

# 14 Vulnerable road users

*Pedestrians, bicyclists, and other vulnerable road users require specific consideration in traffic design and management, particularly from a road safety viewpoint. In this chapter, we examine the range of devices and treatments that are available to facilitate safe mobility by vulnerable road users, and review their safety effectiveness.*

## Pedestrian safety

*Pedestrians at risk*

There are clear gender and age patterns evident in pedestrian injury risk. US research (Zegeer, 1993) indicates that the number of pedestrian injuries per head of population is highest for males in the 5-9 age group, while the elderly are more likely to suffer serious injury.

Several studies of child pedestrian accidents (Grayson, 1975; Lawson, 1989; Carsten, et al, 1989; Homburger, et al, 1989, p 19) have shown that most such accidents occur near the victim's home, most involved the victim running across the road, most occur in the afternoon, most occur away from a pedestrian crossing facility, and in many cases the victim did not see the vehicle at all, or saw it too late.

A number of studies have demonstrated that there are important behaviourial and psychological differences between children and adults in traffic. For example, Shinar (1978) has commented that:

'Children ... lack the skills and habits that are typically acquired at a later age, which enable people to behave safely on the road. Unintrusive observations of children walking to and from school have led to the realization that the child pedestrian, particularly under the age of 10, lives in a different conceptual world than the adult pedestrian ... they have only a fragmentary understanding of the rules and structure of the traffic system, their attention level fluctuates and they are easily distracted, and their knowledge of traffic signs is incomplete.'

The other vulnerable group of pedestrians, the elderly, although having a lower pedestrian accident rate than most age groups, are more vulnerable to serious injury. For example, in America the percentage of pedestrian accidents resulting in death exceeds 20 per cent for pedestrians over age 75 years, compared with about 8 per cent for pedestrians under age 14 years (Zegeer, 1993). In Britain about 50 per cent of pedestrian deaths involve people aged over 60 years (Carthy, et al, 1995). As with child pedestrians, the road and traffic environment faced by the elderly can be unfriendly. Carthy, et al (1995) for example note that when crossing a road "the combined failure of initial judgement (made more likely by sensory loss with age) and failure to accommodate or modify behaviour to avoid a developing incident (made more likely by physical and intellectual impairment), mean that in traffic (particularly where speed is excessive, the flow system is complex, or where it is assumed that the pedestrian can grasp novel signals or rules) there are several interacting sources of threat to the older pedestrian."

Moreover, this study found that elderly women are more at risk than men; even taking account of the distance walked and the roads crossed, women over 75 years are "up to two and a half times more at risk than males in the same age group".

Alcohol impairment has also been shown to be a significant factor in adult pedestrian accidents. Zegeer (1993, p 187) notes that in the US, around 40 per cent of fatally injured pedestrians had a blood alcohol concentration (BAC) of 0.10 g/mL or greater, while Carsten, et al (1989) found that alcohol was a contributory factor in a conservatively-estimated 11 per cent of accidents involved adult pedestrians in the UK, compared with 4 per cent of all adult road accidents.

Finally, it is pertinent to recall the information presented in Figure 1.1 that per passenger hour, the walk mode is comparatively less safe than travel by public transport modes or in motor cars.

*Factors contributing to pedestrian accidents*

Apart from the aforementioned age and gender variations, there are some environmental factors which have been found to be associated with pedestrian accidents. For example, Davies and Winnett (1993) report a detailed UK study of pedestrian accidents which found that:

. 44 per cent of pedestrians involved in an accident did not see the vehicle which struck them, with a further 34 per cent saying that they saw it too late; this obstruction was mostly due to parked or stationary vehicles (i.e. vehicles not involved in the collision),

. 8 per cent of pedestrian accidents occurred near a bus stop, with 22 per cent of these involving a bus; the most common behaviours which preceded the accident involved the pedestrian trying to catch the bus or the pedestrian walking in front of a bus,

. 20 per cent of pedestrian accidents occurred at pedestrian crossings (zebra or pelican crossings), with most involving either pedestrian error or driver non-compliance,

. in 8 per cent of pedestrian accidents, the speed of the vehicle was considered to contribute to the occurrence of the accident; these mostly involved individual vehicles travelling 'too fast'.

Zegeer (1993, p 187) quotes US research which indicates that pedestrian accidents are most prevalent during morning and afternoon peak periods with Fridays and Saturdays being over-represented and Sundays under-represented. Further, 67 per cent of pedestrian accidents occurred away from an intersection (i.e. they occurred at mid-block locations). This is because child pedestrian accidents mostly occur at such locations; adult pedestrians aged 45-65 years are equally likely to occur at mid-block or intersections, while for elderly pedestrians, accidents at intersections are more prevalent.

A recent Australian study (McLean, et al, 1994) found that 85 per cent of urban pedestrian fatalities occurred on non-local roads, with relatively few on residential streets. This suggests that pedestrian safety treatments should be concentrated on the more heavily trafficked roads.

*Pedestrian safety treatments*

Although there are education, enforcement and vehicle design measures aimed at promoting pedestrian safety (Zegeer and Zegeer, 1988, p 5), in keeping with the purpose of this book we will consider here only road safety engineering treatments.

Design strategies for pedestrians are fundamentally of three types *segregation*, through the spatial separation of pedestrian and vehicular networks, *separation*, through the allocation of either time (e.g. pedestrian signals) or space (e.g. sidewalks) within a shared pedestrian-vehicle facility, or *integration*, through shared use of a facility, such as a Woonerf (see Chapter 13).

**Table 14.1**
**Pedestrian facilities**

| Facility | Types |
|---|---|
| Footpaths | footpaths in the road reserve (sidewalks)<br>separate footpath network<br>shared footpath/bicycle network |
| General crossing treatments | pedestrian refuge islands<br>traffic islands and medians<br>kerb extensions (build outs, chokers)<br>pedestrian fencing<br>unsignalized crosswalks |
| Time separated facilities | pedestrian crossings (zebra, pedestrian-operated signals),<br>Pelican, etc.<br>supervised children's crossings<br>pedestrian facilities at signalized intersections |
| Space separated facilities | subways (pedestrian tunnels or underpasses)<br>pedestrian bridges<br>pedestrian malls |
| Integrated facilities | shared vehicle-pedestrian spaces |

Within these categories, there are a range of specific treatments, as shown in Table 14.1 (Zegeer, 1993; Austroads, 1995; Institution of Highways and Transportation, 1987).

Different jurisdictions use these facilities to varying degrees, and where they are used, there are often local warrants or guidelines governing their use. This is not the place for a review of such guidelines, the important point being that if any facility is used, it should be installed and operated in accord with local practice.

## Safety effectiveness of pedestrian treatments

*Footpaths or sidewalks.* Except where pedestrian flow is very light (e.g. many rural roads), vehicular flow is very light (e.g. a cul de sac serving only a handful of residences), or where there is deliberate policy of integration of pedestrian and vehicle flow, some form of pedestrian footpath or sidewalk is generally considered to be desirable.

American research reported by Zegeer (1993, p 190) indicates that sidewalks (footpaths running parallel to the roadway) have significant safety benefits in residential and business districts, with, not surprisingly, the greatest benefit occurring where pedestrian volumes are highest.

Footpaths in segregated facilities (i.e. where the pedestrian network departs from the vehicular network) may be presumed to have road safety benefits and perhaps other benefits such as those related to aesthetics or convenient access. However, there may in some instances be undesirable negative effects, such as night-time security. Consideration may need to be given to the provision of security lighting.

*Refuge islands.* These are islands provided in such a way as to permit pedestrians to cross traffic one stream at a time, with a relatively safe waiting area in the centre of the roadway. They include formal pedestrian refuges (Figure 14.1), splitter islands at the approach to an intersection or roundabout (Figure 9.5), medians, etc. Such devices are often appropriate where pedestrian crossing movements are concentrated, but overall numbers do not warrant a pedestrian crossing. They should be designed to assure adequate refuge widths for wheelchairs, prams, etc, with ramped approaches (also referred to as 'dropped kerbs' or 'kerb cuts') on either side so as not to create a vertical barrier. They can generally only be installed where road width is adequate.

Such devices are very common in cities with medium to high residential density (such as many European cities), but the approach is equally applicable to lower density cities where the conditions are suited; as mentioned, splitter islands and medians effectively serve this purpose. However, Zegeer and Zegeer (1988, p 28) caution against their use on narrow streets where only a narrow island can be provided, where there is a high volume of turning trucks, where the alignment is such that the island is obscured from motorists' view, and where they create difficulties for snow clearance.

A London study reported by Ward (1992) found that the installation of refuges near pedestrian generators reduced pedestrian accidents by as much as 60 per cent. However, where refuges were installed at uncontrolled intersections for safety reasons, the reduction was only 13 per cent, while if refuges were installed for reasons other than safety, an increase in pedestrian accidents was found.

**Figure 14.1 Pedestrian refuge** allows the pedestrian to cross the road in two stages, with some protection while waiting for a gap in the traffic at the second stage.

*Kerb extensions.* This treatment (also known as a footpath extension, a build out, or a choker) consists of a local widening of the footpath into the roadway. It typically comes at the expense of car parking spaces (see Chapter 13). Their provision means that pedestrians do not have as far to walk to cross traffic streams, hence reducing their exposure. As a consequence, there is less vehicular delay. They also enable pedestrians and motorists to have better mutual visibility. On arterial roads, they may be provided in association with a zebra crossing or a pedestrian operated signal, often with some form of streetscaping (Figure 14.2). On local streets, they may be integrated with a plateau road hump (Figure 13.13).

*Pedestrian barriers.* In locations of high pedestrian activity it is often necessary to utilize some form of barrier or fencing to control the movement of pedestrians. Applications include median barriers to prevent pedestrians from crossing a divided road, fences at the roadside to discourage pedestrians from walking onto the road, and bollards. As noted in Chapter 12, it is very important that these fences be designed without stiff horizontal rails which could spear errant vehicles (see Figures 12.9 and 12.10).

**Figure 14.2 Kerb extension for pedestrian crossing** reduces the time required for the pedestrian to cross the traffic stream, and assists in mutual visibility of pedestrian and motorist.

Ward (1992) has reported a London study where pedestrian fencing was installed; in some cases this involved a new facility and in others it involved an extension of an existing facility. Overall, there was a significant 27 per cent reduction in pedestrian accidents. However, the effect was greater at the sites where the existing fencing was extended, leading the author to conclude that long lengths of fencing are needed in order for the treatment to be effective.

Zegeer and Zegeer (1988, p 23) report a 1975 American study which found that the incidence of pedestrians crossing at midblock locations was significantly reduced with median fences, while darting out from behind parked cars was reduced through the use of chains suspended from parking meter posts.

Bollards at the roadside (Figure 12.8), unlike fences, do not prevent pedestrians from crossing the road, but provide a measure of protection to pedestrians from errant vehicles. They also prevent vehicles from using the footpath for parking or loading.

Zegeer and Zegeer (1988, p 23) suggest that pedestrian barriers are most beneficial in particular situations, including

.   in conjunction with pedestrian overpasses,
.   where vehicle speeds are high,
.   where there are high volumes of child pedestrians,
.   where there is little separation between the roadway and sidewalk on high speed roads,
.   near schools, sporting arenas, and other major pedestrian generators, or
.   on bridges where there is both pedestrian and vehicle traffic.

*Traffic signals.* Pedestrian facilities at traffic signals may (Greenberg, 1995):

.   have no explicit recognition, with pedestrians having to observe the vehicular signals,

.   have concurrent phasing, with a 'walk' and 'do not walk' display (either in words or symbols) that permits use in parallel with the vehicular movement (Figure 14.3); this may be activated automatically in every cycle or may require the pedestrian to use a push button, and at the appropriate time of the cycle the display appears, with sufficient time allowed for the pedestrian to clear the crossing, or

**Figure 14.3 Pedestrian 'walk' displayed while the parallel traffic stream is running**

. have exclusive pedestrian phasing, such that there are no potential conflicts with any vehicular movement.

There may sometimes be a conflict between capacity and the provision of pedestrian facilities at signals. This is particularly so where the third option is used. For example, in the UK, where concurrent phasing is not used, the consequence is that there are relatively few intersections with pedestrian facilities, since exclusive phasing reduces the capacity of the intersection, and therefore most intersections have no pedestrian indication.

Zegeer, Opiela and Cynecki (1982) caution that signals with pedestrian facilities may be no safer than those without such facilities, but which provide a green phase at least equal to the pedestrian clearance time. Based upon an analysis of pedestrian accidents in the US, they showed that there was no statistical difference between intersections that had walk/don't walk control and those which had no pedestrian indication. Zegeer (1993, p 193) suggests that pedestrian displays are necessary when vehicle displays are not visible to pedestrians, when the timing is complex (including situations where there are exclusive turn phases), at school crossings, and where an exclusive pedestrian-only phase to allow pedestrian movements in any direction is provided.

However, in situations where there is dynamic adaptive traffic signal control, signal phases can be variable and quite short if there is only a small demand. In this situation, pedestrian facilities are necessary to ensure that adequate pedestrian clearance time is provided. Hunt (1993) has shown that pedestrian facilities at signalized intersections in a linked network have very little effect on vehicular delay, but some effect on pedestrian delay because pedestrians must wait until the relevant time in the cycle before they receive a green 'walk' signal.

Although there have been a number of studies of pedestrian behaviour at signalized intersections (e.g. Knasbasis, Zegeer and Cynecki, 1982; Short, Woelfl and Chang 1982; Garder, 1989), links between behaviour and safety are not yet clearly established. The available evidence seems to indicate that pedestrian involvement in accidents at signalized intersections is mainly associated with pedestrians crossing against a red light, or turning vehicles striking a pedestrian.

A recent study (Garder, 1989) concluded that reducing the number of red-walkers (i.e. increased pedestrian compliance) was the most important measure, but this would require a change in attitude amongst pedestrians. Shorter cycle times and higher levels of enforcement were specifically mentioned, although there are questions as to the cost effectiveness of these types of measure.

*Pedestrian crossings.* These devices provide explicit right of way for pedestrians at mid-block locations, by requiring motorists to stop (if necessary) to allow the pedestrian to cross. There are several types, including:

*Zebra crossings*, which comprise a striped crossing and flashing signals (usually yellow) to alert the motorist to the presence of the crossing. Pedestrians have right of way over vehicles, but only when the pedestrian has been able to step onto the crossing. The absence of positive control means that this device is unsuitable for heavy or fast-moving traffic (e.g. greater than 60 km/h (about 35 mph)), or where pedestrians are constantly using the crossing. Zegeer (1993) notes that zebra crossings are 'used sparingly in most parts of the United States because of the uncertainty regarding their potential safety effects'.

*Pedestrian operated signals* display a red-green-yellow display to approaching vehicles, identical to that faced at an intersection. The sequence is initiated by the pedestrian pressing a button (although with some modern variants, pedestrians are detected automatically). They are more positive than zebra crossings since pedestrians do not have to expose themselves to risk by stepping onto the crossing. Importantly, they are suitable for use where signals are linked, the pedestrian phase being delayed until the appropriate time in the cycle. They are suited to situations where there is heavy or fast moving traffic or heavy pedestrian demand.

*Pelican crossings* are effectively a combination of a zebra crossing and a pedestrian operated signal. They provide a safe initial crossing period for pedestrians by displaying a red signal to motorists. It then reverts for a short period to flashing yellow, during which time any pedestrian still on the crossing has right of way. For the remainder of the time it displays green to motorists. They are widely used in Britain on more heavily trafficked roads, on roads with a speed limit of 70 km/h (40 mph) or greater, where there are heavy pedestrian flows such that a zebra crossing would cause undue delay to motorists, or where sight distance is limited.

*Marked crosswalks* are used in some countries to indicate a place where pedestrians may cross, but without any provision for active control of motorists (Figure 14.4). A sign may used to indicate that pedestrians have priority, while in other cases there is no indicated priority for pedestrians. Zegeer (1993) has noted that these do not necessarily improve pedestrian safety since they 'may present a false sense of security to pedestrians'.

Daly, McGrath and van Emst (1991) have developed empirical relationships expressing annual accident frequency (Y) as a function of site characteristics, based upon UK data. Their results for total accidents were:

Zebra crossing: $\quad Y = (3 \times 10^{-4}) \, V$

where V is daily traffic flow (in the range 1406 - 8364 veh/d)

Pelican crossing: $\quad Y = (3 \times 10^{-3}) \, V^{0.6} \, P^{0.2} \, T$

where V is daily traffic flow (in the range 1599 - 14755 veh/d); P is the daily pedestrian flow (in the range 43 - 8278 persons/d); T is the city population with T = 1 for a population over 1 million, and T = 0.6 for a population less than 1 million

No crossing: $\quad Y = (1.9 \times 10^{-2}) \, V^{0.5} \, \exp(-D/100)$

where V is daily traffic flow (in the range 581 - 13356 veh/d) and D is the distance in metres from the nearest intersection (in the range 5 - 150 m).

**Figure 14.4 Marked crosswalks** which do not have indicated pedestrian priority may convey a false sense of security

This study did not consider pedestrian-operated signals, since they are rarely used in the UK. However, an Australian study (Teale, 1984) examined the effects of installing new mid-block pedestrian signals, and found a 26 per cent reduction in casualty accidents, and a 50 per cent reduction in pedestrian accidents.

*Grade separated facilities.* Pedestrian overpasses and underpasses are appropriate when there is high speed and/or high traffic flow, where there is considerable pedestrian delay or a high pedestrian accident problem, or where there is restricted access to the roadway, as with a freeway.

Their effectiveness depends upon pedestrians choosing to use them; Zegeer (1993) quotes US research which indicates that 95 per cent of people will use an overpass if there is no loss of travel time compared with walking across the road at grade, while 'almost nobody' will use it if it takes 50 per cent longer. Usage of underpasses is somewhat less than that of overpasses, probably because of a perceived reduction of security, particularly if there are few other pedestrians using the facility. For maximum effectiveness, approach footpaths should lead the pedestrian into the overpass or underpass, so that pedestrians actually have to go out of their way to avoid using it (Figure 14.5).

**Figure 14.5 Pedestrian underpass**, with approach paths leading pedestrians directly into it.

*Pedestrian malls.* The ultimate in segregation of pedestrian provision is to have a pedestrian-only facility, such as a shopping mall (Figure 14.6). These are in widespread use, usually with a 'civic design' objective, i.e. creating a more pleasant ambience for urban activities such as shopping or recreation. Although rarely if ever provided on safety grounds alone, they may have safety benefits (Zegeer, 1993, p 196). Particular attention needs to be given to the safe operation of any vehicles which are permitted to use the mall, such as delivery vehicles or public transport vehicles, as their presence may be unexpected, and may create unforseen problems.

**Figure 14.6  Pedestrian mall.**

*Integrated facilities*. These differ from malls, in that vehicular use is permitted, with pedestrians and vehicle sharing the road space (Figure 13.1). Vehicular speeds are typically limited to walking pace of about 10 km/h (6 mph). Clear signing is essential to mark the start and end of the shared zone. Typically, this is reinforced by pavement design and texture, and ideally there should be no kerb or other feature which may indicate that part of the road has vehicular priority. Austroads (1995, p 70) suggests that straight untreated sections longer than 25 m (about 80 ft) should be avoided.

*Facilities for the disabled*. In all of the above, particular notice may need to be taken of the mobility and safety needs of people with disabilities - e.g. people in wheelchairs, people with impaired vision or hearing, people who are slow on their feet, etc. There are a range of provisions that can be provided, and increasingly are routinely provided, for such people. These include:

.   the use of tactile surfaces at pedestrian crossings to alert pedestrians to
    the presence of the crossing (Figure 14.7),

.   the use of audible tones at signalized pedestrian crossings, with a
    different pitch and frequency when the pedestrian signal is green,

**Figure 14.7 Tactile surface at pedestrian crossing** for the benefit of
        pedestrians with impaired vision.

379

. the use of ramps at kerbs (also known as kerb cuts or dropped kerbs) so that there is no significant vertical barrier which can impede a wheelchair, pram, etc,

. attention to maintenance of surfaces, so that a smooth, obstruction-free path is available at all times,

. raised guide strips at pedestrian crossings, to provide assistance to people with impaired vision, and

. particular attention may need to be paid to road work and building sites to ensure that an adequate pedestrian facility remains in place while the work proceeds.

*Lighting*. Overhead lighting is provided to enable pedestrians to see hazards or obstacles at night, and to provide a measure of personal security. Streets, footpaths, car parks, pedestrian malls, etc all attract pedestrians at night, and an appropriate level of lighting should be provided. This level may be prescribed in national street lighting codes.

Typically, higher levels of lighting intensity are necessary at pedestrian crossings and refuge islands, outside commercial and retail establishments which trade at night, and at pedestrian underpasses.

*Checklist*

Austroads (1995) has provided a useful checklist for the safety audit of pedestrian schemes (see Chapter 15). However, this may also be usefully applied to an examination of current facilities. Suggested guidelines include:

. check the design in three dimensions,

. ensure that the scheme takes account of the likely range of vehicle speeds,

. ensure that islands are large enough to cater for pedestrians, as well as for the necessary street furniture,

. check that pedestrian routes are continuous,

. avoid mixing different types of pedestrian control in close proximity,

. minimize pedestrian crossing distances,

. where pedestrians are to be deterred from crossing, ensure that fencing is adequate,

. provide refuges where possible on heavily trafficked roads to enable pedestrians to cross the road in stages,

. ensure that pedestrian underpasses are wide, straight, and open,

. ensure that pedestrian lighting is adequate having regard to needs and standards,

. footpaths should be smooth, skid resistant, and kept clear from overhanging foliage,

. ensure pedestrian walk times at signals are adequate for elderly pedestrians,

. provide audio-tactile devices where possible,

. ensure that ramps (dropped kerbs, kerb cuts) are flush with the invert,

. manage parking to maximize sight distances at pedestrian crossings,

. ensure that street furniture does not obstruct the vision of and by pedestrians, especially children,

. ensure that crossings can be identified and negotiated by visually impaired pedestrians, and

. where possible, ensure that islands, refuges, etc are wide enough to accommodate a wheelchair.

*Pedestrians are vulnerable when placed in a situation of potential conflict with a motor vehicle, with the very young, the elderly and people with disabilities or under the influence of alcohol being of particular concern. There are a range of traffic engineering treatments*

*which, when installed appropriately, are likely be effective in reducing pedestrian accidents. Design principles for pedestrian facilities are covered in relevant publications such as those of the Zegeer and Zegeer (1988), the Institution of Highways and Transportation (1987, Chapter 24), and Austroads (1995).*

## Bicyclist safety

*Bicyclists at risk*

Bicycle use varies considerably from country to country, and from city to city. In the US, bicycling is estimated to account for 5-15 per cent of all urban trips (Burden, 1993); in Australia, bicycling accounts for about 2 per cent of work trips and an estimated 7 per cent of all trips (Austroads, 1993c); and in Britain bicycling accounts for 4 per cent of trips (McClintock, 1992, p 7). Usage is much higher in some European continental countries: 29 per cent of trips in the Netherlands, 18 per cent in Denmark, and 11 per cent in Western Germany (McClintock, 1992, p 7). Since bicycle trips tend to be shorter, their contribution to person-kilometres of travel is smaller than these figures imply, with The Netherlands for example having 8 per cent of its person kilometres of travel accommodated on the bicycle. In some developing countries such as China and India, bicycle population and use is far higher and in these countries special facilities are commonly provided for them because they constitute the bulk of road use (Ross Silcock Partnership, 1991, p 84).

Bicyclists are over-represented in casualty accidents. In Britain for example, Harrison, Hall and Harland (1989) have calculated that in 1985 there were 585 casualties per $10^8$ km of travel for bicyclists, compared with 112 casualties per $10^8$ km for all road users. Expressed another way, bicyclists represented 8.5 per cent of injuries, but accounted for only 1.6 per cent of road user kilometres of travel. In Denmark where bicycle usage is very high, bicyclists are still over-represented, with 19 per cent of casualties nationwide being bicyclists, who account for only 8 per cent of person kilometres of travel (Nielsen, 1994). Both these sources also make the important point that bicyclists, along with other vulnerable road users, are significantly under-reported in official road accident statistics. It is also important to note the information presented in Figure 1.1 which showed that per person hour of travel, bicyclists are more than 5 times as likely as car occupants to be killed, while motor cyclists are 30 times as likely to be killed.

Bicyclists most at risk are the young. British statistics (Harrison, Hall and Harland, 1989) indicate that 42 per cent of casualties in bicycle accidents were aged 16 years or less. In the US, 40 per cent of bicycle fatalities are aged 5-14 years; more children are killed as bicyclists or pedestrians in the US than from any other single cause (Burden, 1993).

Burden (1993) has also reported that in the US, there is a significant over-representation of bicycle accidents at night time and in low-light conditions, and that weekends are also over-represented.

*Safety strategies*

Strategies for improving bicyclist safety (McClintock, 1992, p 86; Burden, 1993) include *protection* such as the wearing of helmets, the use of brightly coloured clothing, the use of under-run barriers on trucks, etc; *education* such as bicycle training for child bicyclists and education programs aimed at motor vehicle users with slogans like 'look right, look left, look bike'; *legislation* such as sanctions on speeding, alcohol use, bicyclist conspicuity, compulsory wearing of bicycle helmets, etc; and *changes to the road and traffic environment*, such as traffic calming, the provision of bicyclist facilities, explicit consideration of bicyclist needs at intersections; street lighting; etc. It is this last strategy which is of relevance to this book.

*Bicyclist requirements*

Austroads (1993c) have indicated that there are four basic requirements of bicyclists in relation to the physical facilities they use:

.  a space to ride, particularly adequate lateral clearances,
.  a smooth surface,
.  the ability to maintain speed, i.e. to minimize the need to stop or slow for any reason, and
.  route connectivity and continuity.

These principles are reflected, implicitly or explicitly, in any of the guidelines which have been prepared to assist in the design and provision of bicycle facilities (e.g. Austroads, 1993c; Institution of Highways and

Transportation, 1987, Chapter 25; American Association of State Highway and Transportation Officials, 1991).

*Bicycle facilities*

A useful taxonomy of bicycle facilities for our purposes is:

.   on-street, mixed traffic bicycling
.   on-street bicycle-only lanes
.   on-street shared bus-bicycle lanes
.   bicycle use of road shoulders
.   bicycle paths (within the road reserve or separately)

Features of each which contribute to safety are reviewed below.

*On-street bicycling in mixed traffic.* This is by far the most common arrangement. Bicycles and motor vehicles share the roadspace, with no special provision for the bicyclists (except perhaps at intersections - see below). Provided that traffic flows are moderate and vehicle speeds are not excessive, this arrangement can operate at acceptable levels of safety, even with children. Austroads (1993c, p 17) suggests that mixed traffic arrangements are satisfactory up to about 3000 veh/d, and with traffic speeds of up to around 60 km/h (35 mph).

Once traffic volumes and speeds exceed these values, but a bicycle-only lane is not feasible, Austroads (op cit, p 20) suggests that a wider kerb lane be provided (Figure 14.8). Such an arrangement can be cost-effective for roads with speeds up to about 70 km/h (about 40 mph). A minimum width of 3.7 m (about 12 ft) is suggested for this lane, with a maximum width of 4.5 m (15 ft); lanes with widths in excess of this encourage cars to travel side by side in the lane. Burden (1993) has reported US experience with wide kerbside lanes, and again suggests a lane width of 4.2 - 4.5 m (14-15 ft) with a traffic speed of about 60 km/h (35 mph). In the UK, the recommended width for a kerb lane carrying large numbers of bicycles is 4.25 m (14 ft) (Harrison, Hall and Harland, 1989).

Where the kerb lane is a parking lane, there is the possibility of providing a shared bicycle-car parking lane (Figure 14.9). However, the presence of parked cars represents a hazard to bicyclists, not only because of visibility problems, but also because of the potential for a car occupant to open the car door in front of an approaching bicyclist. For this reason, Austroads (op cit, p 18) recommends a minimum width of the shared bicycle-car parking lane of 4 m (about 13 ft) where speeds are around 60 km/h (35 mph) to 4.5 m (about 15 ft) for speeds of up to about 80 km/h (50 mph). The lane should be clearly marked as a bicycle facility, and this should be supported by regulations which prohibit motor vehicles from travelling in this part of the roadway (except of course for parking).

**Figure 14.8 Wide kerb lane for shared bicycle-vehicle use.**

*On-street bicycle-only lanes.* An exclusive bicycle lane is a lane created by pavement markings and signs indicating that it for bicycle use only (Figure 14.10). It is suitable for roads where speeds exceed 80 km/h (50 mph) and traffic flows exceed about 3000 veh/d (Austroads, 1993c, p 24). Burden (1993) reports from US experience that these 'make the bicyclist more visible (and) give the motorist more entry and exit turning radius, and thus permit improved intersection design.'.

The width of such a lane may vary according to the number of bicyclists, the traffic volume (especially truck volumes), and the feasibility of creating the lane within the space available. Austroads (1993c, p 24) suggests that 1.2 m (4 ft) is the absolute minimum width, although short sections of 1.0 m (3.3 ft) may be provided over a short length at 'squeeze points' (e.g. a road narrowing within a traffic calming scheme). The desirable bicycle lane width is 1.5 m (5 ft), which corresponds to the American experience where 1.2 - 1.8 m (4-6 ft) lanes are provided (Burden, 1993). Austroads (op cit) suggests that the lane width can go to 2.0 m (about 7 ft) where adjacent traffic is moving at 100 km/h (60 mph).

**Figure 14.9  Shared bicycle-car parking lane**

In the UK, contra-flow bicycle lanes are sometimes provided where a one-way street interrupts bicycle route connectivity. These lanes must be clearly marked, and have a width (desirably of 2.0 m (about 7 ft)), although 1.5 m (5 ft) may be satisfactory (Harrison, Hall and Harland, 1989).

The above guidelines are based on experience, and arise from both operational and safety requirements. There is some evidence to support the safety advantages of bicycle lanes. For example, Nielsen (1994) reports that a program of installing bicycle lanes in Denmark showed that these were safer than roads without any bicycle facilities, while Crampton,

Hass-Klau and Thrush (1990) in a comparative study of British and German bicycle safety found 'a noteworthy minority of accidents on cycle lanes .. or shared bus lanes'.

**Figure 14.10    Exclusive bicycle lane**

*On-street shared bus-bicycle lanes.* Where an exclusive bus lane is provided, it may be sensible practice to permit its use by bicyclists, to avoid them being sandwiched between a line of buses and a line of traffic. However, one study observed that this arrangement had the effect of discouraging bus use of the lane! (Crampton, Hass-Klau and Thrush, 1990).

The Institution of Highways and Transportation (1987, p 221) recommends a minimum width of 3.5 - 4.0 m (about 12- 13.5 ft) for a bus lane where there are significant numbers of bicyclists.

One problem with allowing bicycle use of bus lanes is the potential for conflict between bicyclists and bus passengers. In fact, in Denmark, Nielsen (1994) has commented that the safety benefits of bicycle lanes may be 'offset almost entirely by an increase in accidents between bicyclists and pedestrians at bus stops.' He suggests that in this may lead to the need for special treatment to ensure that bicyclists stop and give way to bus passengers at such locations.

*Bicycle use of road shoulders.* As noted in Chapter 12, sealed shoulders on rural roads have safety advantages for motor vehicles. Where they are provided, they are commonly used by bicyclists, and to this end it may be appropriate to consider explicitly the needs of bicyclists when they are installed. Conversely, they may be installed with bicyclists particularly in mind.

The minimum width of seal suggested by Austroads (1993c, p 23) is 1.0 m (about 3 ft) where the traffic speed is less than 60 km/h, rising to a suggested 3.0 m (10 ft) where traffic speeds exceed 100 km/h (60 mph) or there are substantial volumes of heavy trucks.

In recent years, bicyclists have been permitted to use the shoulders of freeways in some jurisdictions, even though vehicle speeds may legally be as high as 110 km/h, and actual speeds of 120 km/h are not uncommon (Austroads, 1993c; Khan, 1995). These require the road agency to provide the bicyclist with 'information, guidance and road conditions which will enable them to use the freeway safely' (Austroads, 1993c, p 44). This includes some signing, especially at on-ramps and off-ramps (Figure 14.11) and at 'squeeze points' where there is insufficient space to provide a full-width shoulder, and the maintenance of a smooth, debris-free sealed shoulder of adequate width (ideally 3.0 m (10 ft)). Experience with these facilities has generally been satisfactory from both an operational and a safety viewpoint.

*Bicycle paths.* Bicycle paths are distinguished by the absence of motor vehicles. They may be provided for the exclusive use of bicyclists, such that other users (pedestrians, equestrians, roller-skaters, etc) are prohibited, or they may be provided as intended joint-use facilities; in practice, whether intended or not, most facilities end up as joint use unless bicycle use is so high as to ensure that it is self-enforcing. Similarly, they may be provided for recreational uses, for commuter purposes, or for either use; the difference is not trivial, since the former will perhaps be appropriately located in pleasant surrounding such as parkland whereas the latter will ideally follow a straighter line, such as alongside a roadway or a railway (Figure 14.12).

**Figure 14.11    Bicycle use of freeway shoulders.**

**Figure 14.12    Bicycle paths** may follow a road, railway, creek, etc.

From a safety viewpoint, shared facilities can create problems, particularly in relation to pedestrian-bicyclist conflicts (Burden, 1993; Harrison, Hall and Harland, 1989). Where possible therefore, shared use facilities should have a longitudinal line to segregate pedestrians from bicyclists (Figure 14.13), and be signed accordingly. This depends upon the width of the path; Harrison, Hall and Harland (op cit) note that 'there seems little point in attempting to segregate tracks narrower than 2.5 m (about 8 ft). Austroads (1993c, p 79) has a desirable minimum width of a shared path of 2.5 m, although allows an absolute minimum of 2.0 m (about 7 ft). It recommends 3.0 m (10 ft) for a path with high pedestrian and/or bicycle flow; these are broadly consistent with UK practice (Harrison, Hall and Harland, op cit).

**Figure 14.13**    **Shared pedestrian-bicycle use**, ideally with separation of pathways.

Paths parallel to a roadway may be appropriate provided that there are few driveways, few intersections, adequate sight distance (especially at intersections with the road network), adequate treatments at squeeze points like bridges, and clear marking and signing (Burden, 1993; McClintock, 1992, p 26).

In all cases, very careful attention must be given to points where the bicycle path crosses a roadway, and to adequate signing at the start and end of shared facilities. Harrison, Hall and Harland (1989) summarize this well: 'Too often, because of the difficulty in continuing a cycle route through a junction, the cycle track simply terminates a few metres before the junction is reached, thus plunging the cyclists back into the main stream of traffic just at the point where they are most in need of assistance.' It is this lack of attention to the problem of the interface between the bicycle facility and the network which caters for motor vehicles that can create a major safety problem for bicycle path networks. McClintock (1992, p 26) for example quotes a Danish study which concluded that 'it is far from guaranteed that cycle paths have a positive effect on cyclists' safety', while Wachtel and Lewiston (1994) using Californian data found that bicyclists on a sidewalk or bicycle path incurred a risk 1.8 times that of bicyclists riding on the roadway.

Because bicycle paths encourage relatively high bicycle speeds (up to 50 km/h (30 mph)), their geometric design is not a trivial task. Attention should be given to things like horizontal curvature, lateral clearance, sight distance, gradient, superelevation, crossfall, drainage, etc. Standards and guidelines for these features are outlined in the various design guides mentioned previously. They are relevant to safety, in that if there is poor or (more importantly) inconsistent design standards, there will be a greater potential for collisions between bicycles, between bicycles and other path users, or between bicycles and fixed objects at the side of the path.

*Intersection treatments*

As noted in the preceding discussion, a key determinant of the safety of any bicycle facility is the attention given to intersections and/or crossings of roadways used by motor vehicles. Problems faced by bicyclists at intersections include (Austroads, 1993c; Burden, 1993; Harrison, Hall and Harland, 1989):

. narrowing of the traffic lane to create a 'squeeze point', often associated with the provision of an extra lane through the intersection for capacity purposes,

. insufficient room between the line of vehicles and the kerb, preventing bicycles from reaching the head of the queue,

. bicyclists may have difficulty in moving from the kerb lane to the median lane in order to execute a right hand turn (for traffic driving on the left - a left hand turn for traffic driving on the right),

. in making a right hand turn (for traffic driving on the left), bicyclists are commonly on the outside of the turning traffic, and may be in potential conflict with opposing right turners,

. motorists may turn left (for traffic driving on the left) across the path of a bicyclist travelling in the kerb lane; bicyclists are generally vulnerable at diverge and merge areas for left turners (right turners for traffic driving on the right),

. unless special detectors are fitted, signal detectors are not sensitive enough to detect a bicycle, with the result that insufficient time may be provided to allow a bicycle to clear the intersection, and

. bicyclists perceive roundabouts to be unsafe, and there is some evidence to support this view (see Chapter 9).

Attention to the specific needs of bicyclists in the design of intersections can alleviate these problems. Methods of doing so are detailed in the various bicycle design guides referred to above. Some good practices are outlined below.

*Priority controlled intersections.* If wide kerbside lanes or bicycle lanes are provided, these should, if possible, be carried through the intersection. Where they cannot be carried through, the lane should be terminated well in advance of the intersection (Austroads, 1993c, p 30 suggests 50 m (about 170 ft)). Left turn slip lanes (for traffic driving on the left) or freeway on/off ramps can be treated with either a continuous bicycle lane or a marked crossing area at right angles to the slip lane. Similarly, special attention may need to be given to locations where service roads are connected to the through roadway, as these are points of conflict between bicyclists and entering/exiting motor vehicles.

*Signalized intersections.* Kerbside approach lanes 4.0 - 4.5 m (about 13-15 ft) wide allow bicyclists to share the lane with motor vehicles. Lanes narrower than that require the bicyclist to occupy the lane; experienced bicyclists will defend their space by positioning themselves in the centre of the lane, but inexperienced riders will be reluctant to do this.

Where a bicycle lane is provided on the approach road, it is desirable to continue this through the intersection. Even where such a lane is not provided, it may be feasible, as an alternative to the wide kerbside lane, to provide a stand-up lane for bicyclists. The suggested minimum width is 1.2 m (4 ft); the adjacent traffic lane may be reduced in width to 2.7 m (9 ft) to allow this to be provided. Another advantage of this arrangement, apart from the priority and safer conditions which it provides for bicyclists, is that it is possible to place a push button on a pedestal at the intersection for use by bicyclists, analogous to that provided for pedestrians.

In Britain, some cities provide 'head start' storage areas for bicycles at the front of the queue of waiting traffic (Figure 14.14) (Wheeler, Leicester and Underwood, 1993; Wheeler, 1992). These are useful where there is very high bicycle flow (in Oxford for example, two-thirds of the vehicles using one intersection with this facility are bicycles), or where there is a significant conflict between bicycles and left turning traffic (for traffic driving on the left). British experience with these has been satisfactory, on both operational and safety grounds.

*Crossings between roads and bicycle paths.* Off-road bicycle paths must be accessible and ideally of reasonable length. This means that they are likely to frequently intersect with roads and streets carrying motor vehicles. All such crossings must be carefully considered from the viewpoint of the bicyclist so as to encourage safe and consistent use. This will require:

. adequate sight distance,
. clear indication of the termination of the bicycle link,
. ideally, a flat approach, or only a slight gradient,
. a right angle intersection, or as close to right angles as possible, and
. effective, but unintrusive, control of bicycle movements.

**Figure 14.14    'Head start' storage area for bicycles at signalised intersection.**

The most common form of crossing is an uncontrolled facility. In many jurisdictions, such a crossing is not a legally-defined intersection or junction, so bicyclists are required to use care when crossing the road and give way to vehicles. This can be assisted by ensuring that there are minimal distractions, such as chicanes or bollards, by attention to detail in the design of ramps (avoiding vertical discontinuities), and where possible providing a refuge island in the centre of the roadway; such a refuge should have a holding rail or post so that bicyclists can remain on their machine while waiting for a gap (Figure 14.15).

Where traffic flows on the road are sufficiently high, a signalized crossing may be provided; in the UK the guideline for provision of such a crossing is 500 veh/h (Harrison, Hall and Harland, 1989). This is analogous to a pedestrian crossing, and in fact there is in Britain the so-called Toucan crossing which is designed as a joint pedestrian-bicyclist facility (Taylor and Wiltshire, 1992).

**Figure 14.15    Refuge island with holding post for bicyclists**.

*Railway crossings*. Bicyclist are subject to the same legal requirements as any other road user at a railway crossing. One particular problem unique to bicyclists however is the risk of getting the bicycle wheel trapped in the rail flange. For this reason, bicycles should be directed to cross a railway crossing at right angles to the rail tracks; this may require some re-orientation of the bicycle path (Burden, 1993).

*Attention to detail*

Finally, there are a number of design features associated with the provision of bicycle facilities which are really just attention to detail in design with the specific needs of bicyclists in mind, with a view to providing safe, convenient operating conditions. These include:

. Ensure that drainage grates cannot trap the wheel of a bicycle, or create alarm for the rider such that a panic swerve results; grates should ideally be inset into the face of the kerb, but where they are in the path of the bicycle, they should be traversable.

. If night-time use of a bicycle facility is expected, consideration must be given to the need for lighting, in the interests of safety and security. Where bicycle paths cross a roadway, adequate lighting, to ensure that the bicyclist is visible to the motorist, is essential.

. Squeeze points, or lane drops, where the lane or roadway becomes narrowed, must be clearly visible to an approaching bicyclist, in time to take appropriate action. In some cases, e.g. at the termination of a bicycle lane, it may be necessary to provide a sign.

. The need for a smooth surface for bicyclists leads to the need for regular maintenance (e.g. potholes, pavement edge drops, pavement cracking, etc) and regular sweeping (for a debris-free surface). It also requires attention to detail in the provision of ancillary devices such as raised reflective pavement markers, rumble strips, etc, and also in relation to re-establishment of a smooth surface after any pavement opening (e.g. to access underground services). These are all relatively simple procedures, but may easily be overlooked as trivial matters; Austroads (1993c) makes the eminently sensible suggestion that 'road maintenance supervisors should ride a bicycle over sections of road commonly used by cyclists'!

. Adequate sight distance needs to be maintained between bicyclists and any facility used by motorists, including private driveways and entry/exit to commercial facilities. Trimming of foliage with this factor in mind may be necessary.

*Traffic calming*

In Chapter 13, a range of traffic calming devices were described. Some of these impact particularly upon bicyclists. Austroads (1993c) makes the following points in relation to the effects of traffic calming on bicyclists:

*Roundabouts*. The small, single lane roundabouts likely to be found on local access streets are designed for low-speed operation, and pose few problems for bicyclists. Larger diameter roundabouts which may be installed on collector roads may have a higher operating speed, but provided that there is only a single lane of circulating roadway, bicyclists will be able to negotiate them with safety. A suggested entry lane width of at between 4.0 m and 5.0 (about 13-17 ft) will provide adequate clearance for bicycles while allowing only single-file vehicle entry.

*Chicanes*. These can create a hazard for bicyclists, since the rider is required to swing out towards the centre of the road and share road space with both same-direction and oncoming traffic. Where space permits, a bypass of the device can be installed (Figure 13.12).

*Humps*. Road humps designed according to well-established principles (see Chapter 13) pose few problems for bicyclists, whether they are of the flat top (plateau) or rounded variety. However, from a bicyclist viewpoint, they should not be located near the bottom of a steep grade, they should extend across the full width of the road so that bicyclists are not squeezed, and they should have a smooth surface. In extreme cases, a bicycle bypass may be provided, as described for chicanes.

*Road closures*. To ensure route connectivity, bicycle (and pedestrian) access should usually be maintained after street closure. Attention to lighting may be required.

*The provision of facilities for bicycles can improve the safety and perceived security of bicycling to the extent that bicycling becomes a more accepted and widely used mode of transport. There is a range of such facilities, including exclusive bicycle facilities, and facilities which may be shared with either pedestrians or motor vehicles. Careful attention to the safety of bicyclists on links or routes, at intersections, and at locations where bicycle paths cross roads is essential.*

# 15  Road safety audit

*Previous chapters have reviewed various aspects of **accident reduction** through the development of remedial measures at sites or locations with a high frequency of accidents.*

*However, as noted in Chapter 2, a complementary approach is to focus on **accident prevention**, that is, to aim to ensure that the road system is safe. One of the key components of this latter approach involves the use of so-called safety checks, or safety audits. These focus on the design of new road and traffic schemes, although sometimes they focus on the existing road system also.*

*Safety audit is well-established in some countries (Great Britain, New Zealand), is becoming established in others (Australia) and is being considered elsewhere (some European Continental countries). In other places it is not practiced at all. There exists, therefore, various sets of guidelines describing road safety audit practices in use. Because these practices tend to reflect local legislation, customs and traditions, details of specific processes and applications will not be presented here. Rather, the overall concept of road safety audit its effectiveness will be discussed[1]. For details of how to conduct an audit, the checklists involved, etc, reference should be made to the local policies and guides which are cited in this chapter.*

## Definition and objectives of road safety audit

In Chapter 2, we noted that road safety engineering includes both remedial and preventative aspects. Although not referring specifically to road safety audit processes, the Transportation Research Board (1987a, p 190) cautions that 'significant improvements in safety are not automatic by-products of (road design) projects; safety must be systematically designed into each project. To do this, highway designers must deliberately seek safety opportunities specific to each project and apply sound safety and traffic engineering principles.' A process which has emerged recently aimed at preventative road safety engineering is the road safety audit.

Road safety audit has been succinctly defined as 'a systematic method of checking the safety aspects of new schemes affecting roads' (Proctor and Belcher, 1993). The Roads and Traffic Authority of New South Wales (1991a) describe it as 'a means of checking the design, implementation and operation of road projects against a set of safety principles as a means of accident prevention and treatment'. Austroads (1994, p 14) note that it 'is a formal examination of an existing or future road or traffic project, or any project which interacts with road users, in which an independent, qualified examiner looks at the project's accident potential and safety performance. The essential elements ... are that it is:

- . a formal process and not an informal check,
- . an independent process,
- . carried out by someone with appropriate experience and training, and
- . restricted to road safety issues.'

The objectives of road safety audit are to identify potential safety problems for road users and others affected by a road project and to ensure that measures to eliminate or reduce the problems are considered. Safety audit aims to:

- . minimize the risk and severity of road accidents that may be affected by the road project at the site or on the nearby network,

- . minimize the need for remedial works after construction,

- . reduce the whole-of-life costs of the project, and

- . improve the awareness of safe design practices by all of those involved in the planning, design, construction and maintenance of roads.

Road safety audit can work in two ways: by removing preventable accident-producing elements (such as inappropriate intersection layouts) at the planning or design stages, or by mitigating the effects of remaining or existing problems by the inclusion of suitable accident-reducing features (such as anti-skid surfacing, guard fencing, traffic control devices, delineation, etc) (Proctor and Belcher, 1993).

In one sense, highway designers and traffic engineers have always practiced a form of safety audit. However what is significant about the recent emergence of the practice is its specific incorporation as a discrete phase, independent of the designer, and the development of defined auditing procedures which are followed within a road or traffic agency. This latter aspect may be incorporated within an overall Quality Management or Quality Assurance process within that agency.

## Use of Road Safety Audit

The concept of road safety audit emerged initially in Britain over the 1980s as one of the key responses to the Government's target of reducing road casualties by one-third by the year 2000 (see Chapter 2). It was given impetus by the preparation of two key publications: a *Road Safety Code of Good Practice* (Local Authorities Association, 1989) and *Guidelines for the Safety Audit of Highways* (Institution of Highways and Transportation, 1990b). Road safety audit was made mandatory for all national trunk roads and motorways (freeways) in the UK in 1991. Revised guidelines were issued in 1994 by the UK Department of Transport (1994a,b).

In the light of the success of the British experience, the process has also been adopted in other places. In New Zealand, the national roads and public transport agency (Transit New Zealand) has embraced road safety audit and began conducting pilot safety audit projects in 1992. From 1993, safety audit was made mandatory for a 20 per cent sample of State highway projects, and a comprehensive road safety audit policy has been prepared (Transit New Zealand, 1993). A pilot program for road safety audit at the local government level commenced in 1994. In Australia, Austroads (the national association of road and traffic agencies) published national guidelines in 1994 (Austroads, 1994), although some states have had safety audit processes in place for several years.

The process is not formally part of road safety practice in the US (Wallen, 1993), although the Federal Highway Administration (1992) has proposed a rule on safety management systems within its Highway Safety Program Guidelines (see Chapter 2) which states that 'the highway safety management system may be further defined as management processes to ensure that all opportunities to improve safety are identified, considered, implemented where appropriate and evaluated'. The Institute of Transportation Engineers (1994) responded to this proposed rule by submitting, among other things, that 'agencies should introduce the concept of the safety audit into their systems'. The Institute also established an Informational Committee charged with responsibility to prepare a report on the development and application of road safety audit (Ogden, 1994b).

The process is being considered in several European continental countries (Proctor and Belcher, 1993). For example, a draft manual on road safety audit has been prepared by Controle de Securite des Infrastructures (1994) in France. Similarly, in developing countries, there has hitherto been very little systematic safety checking of road projects, although Ross, Silcock and Ghee (1992) have noted that the World Bank has begun to show an interest in the area. The British Transport and Road Research Laboratory (Ross Silcock Partnership, 1991) has published a report entitled *Towards Safer Roads in Developing Countries*, which includes a checklist for road safety audit suited to roads in developing countries.

**Application of Road Safety Audit**

Road safety audit may be carried out at any or all of the following five stages:

. feasibility
. draft design
. detailed design
. pre-opening, and
. in-service.

*Stage 1: Feasibility*

As an input to the feasibility stage of a scheme, a safety audit can influence the scope of a project, route choice, selection of design standard, impact on the existing road network, route continuity, provision of interchanges or intersections, access control, number of lanes, route terminals, stage development, etc.

*Stage 2: Draft design*

This audit stage is undertaken on completion of a draft plan or a preliminary design. Typical considerations include horizontal and vertical alignment, sightlines, intersection layouts, lane and shoulder width, pavement crossfall and superelevation, overtaking lanes, provision for parked and stationary vehicles, provision for bicyclists and pedestrians, effects of departures from standards and guidelines, safety during construction, etc. After this stage, as land acquisition becomes finalized, significant changes in road alignment become much harder to achieve.

*Stage 3: Detailed design*

This audit stage is on completion of detailed design, but normally before the preparation of contract documents. Typical considerations include line markings, signing, delineation, lighting, intersection details, clearances to roadside objects, provision for road user groups with special requirements (pedestrians, cyclists, people with disabilities, trucks, buses, etc), temporary traffic management and control during construction, drainage, poles and other roadside objects, landscaping, batters, guard fencing, etc.

*Stage 4: Pre-opening*

Immediately prior to the opening of a scheme to traffic, the audit would involve driving, riding and walking through the project to check that the safety needs of all road users are adequate. This should involve a night-time inspection, and if possible an inspection in both wet and dry conditions. It would canvas similar issues to those raised in Stages 2 and 3, but with a view to assessing their adequacy as actually constructed, taking particular note of variations that might have occurred from the plans in the course of construction.

*Stage 5: In-service*

This stage involves a systematic examination of sections of the existing road network to assess the adequacy of the road, intersections, road furniture, the roadside, etc from an explicit safety viewpoint. This can have two applications - monitoring a new scheme after it is opened to traffic (i.e. in the weeks and months following a stage 4 audit), or a safety audit of an existing road or road network with a view to identifying

403

safety-related deficiencies. The audit of existing roads and road networks is discussed below.

*Use of safety audit*

Although all five of the above stages can be and have been used, in practice the first and last of these stages are less common. The feasibility stage for example is not adopted in UK trunk roads funded by the Department of Transport because 'strategic decisions on matters such as route choice, junction type, standard of provision, and departures from standards should already reflect the best balance of a number of factors including safety' (Department of Transport, 1994b). Similarly, there is not much interest in the UK in the audit of roads in-service, on the grounds that if the road does not have a safety problem as revealed by accident statistics, it is not cost-effective to treat it ahead of another road which does have a demonstrated accident problem. (See Chapter 2 for a more detailed discussion of this issue.)

The road schemes to which a safety audit is applied varies from jurisdiction to jurisdiction. In the UK for example, all work on trunk roads, which are fully funded by the British Government, is subject to audit. Some local authorities such as Kent County Council (1994b) adopt the practice of applying it to all of their works, including traffic management and road maintenance. In New South Wales (Australia) by contrast, both new projects and existing roads are routinely audited; 20 construction projects in each of the Authority's Regions are audited annually, while 20 per cent of the existing road network is also checked annually to identify any deficiencies and determine priorities for treatment.

**Safety audit process**

While each road agency undertaking a road safety audit may have its own audit processes, the key requirements are (Jordan and Barton, 1992):

- management commitment,
- an agreed road safety audit process,
- an independent auditor or audit team,
- a set of checklists,
- training and development of expertise, and
- monitoring and evaluation.

*Commitment*

Whether or not road safety audit lives up to its potential depends largely upon the commitment and endeavours of the organisation and staff involved. It is vital that it be seen as an integral part of an agency's overall program (which is why a relationship to a total quality management process can be important). Otherwise, it runs the risk of being perceived as questioning the competence and professionalism of the designer or road builder. It is important therefore that each individual and group within the agency be involved with the road safety audit process, and share a common goal of using it to promote road safety and accident prevention. The UK Highways Agency (1994) emphasizes the importance of dispelling the notion that auditors are 'outsiders brought in to find things wrong with their work', and instilling the notion that the audit process brings specialist advice to the design team 'in the same way that traffic and geotechnical engineers are brought into scheme design for their specialist knowledge.' Very similar concerns have been expressed in relation to the implementation of safety management systems in the USA by Hall (1993) who was concerned that 'other functional units may believe that the accomplishment of their goals are threatened by the infringement of safety management initiatives into 'their territory'. Thus, care should be taken throughout system implementation to maintain an atmosphere of cooperation and mutual respect among affected functional areas.'

However, over time, one important effect of the road safety audit process is the feedback which it provides to the design engineer in relation to the incorporation of safety into the road design. In fact, the UK County Surveyors' Society (1993b) in their review of UK practice found that 'there was evidence to suggest that the initial thrust of safety audit had already had a beneficial impact on scheme design.' However, the report went on to recommend that 'to maintain and enhance this trend, standard safety checks should now be incorporated in the briefs for and training of both design engineers and development controllers who are seen to be ultimately responsible for the safety of highways.'

*Process*

The road safety audit process must seek to take an overall view of safety. The process aims to reduce the whole life cost of a scheme. Although there will be costs of the audit process, these are worthwhile if offset against the potential for savings elsewhere. The savings may be from timely alteration to plans (it is much cheaper to change a detail on a plan than to replace or remove a feature once installed), from subsequent accident prevention, and from reductions in the costs resulting from litigation. Experience in those jurisdictions where it has been introduced indicates that safety is now a more explicit factor in all levels of road decision making, rather than a minor or implicit consideration as may have been the case previously.

*Organisation*

There are a number of ways in which the safety audit process may be carried out. Some possibilities are detailed in Austroads (1994) and Institution of Highways and Transportation, 1990b, p 9).

There must also be a designated procedure for acting upon the audit report. If a specialist team is used, Austroads (1994) suggests that one of three procedures can be followed: prior agreement to accept the safety audit recommendations, assessment of the audit report by the client (or an independent third party on behalf of the client), or assessment of the audit report by the designer.

An agency developing a road safety audit process will need to determine which of these procedures (or an alternative) to follow, depending upon its own 'culture', expertise and the role of safety auditing within a wider institutional framework, such as quality management. However, whichever method is adopted, the key factors are (Sabey, 1993):

. the audit team must include specialist knowledge of road safety engineering,

. the findings of the audit should be formally documented and reported at each stage of the audit process,

. the reasons for various elements of audit advice should be formally documented,

. the reasons for rejecting any element of advice should be explained to the scheme designer,

. provisions for arbitration should be made, and

. independence of audit must be maintained, and there should be an awareness of possible litigation if there are subsequent failures.

*Checklist*

The actual tasks undertaken by a safety audit team will in many cases involve the use of checklists or prompts. These typically show the sorts of issues and problems which can potentially arise at the relevant stage of the project. Examples are presented as inserts in the guidelines published by the Institution of Highways and Transportation (1990b) and Austroads (1994), for a wide range of applications and project stages. A number of PC-based programs containing checklists or prompts are now coming on the market, and these will help facilitate the audit process.

Importantly, these checklists or prompts are really only a memory prompt. Their advantage is that a formalized checking procedure, using a checklist or something similar, is less likely to overlook problems. However, they cannot be a substitute for expertise, and it is imperative that those responsible for undertaking safety audits have adequate training and experience in road safety engineering (see below). One of the main benefits of checklists is that designers can use them to audit themselves before their work gets to the auditor, thus enhancing quality at an even earlier stage.

It is also vital that the safety audit procedure involves a site visit, at whatever stage it is concerned with, since there will inevitably be factors present and identifiable at the site which are not evident from the plans (Proctor and Belcher, 1993).

Chapters 7 to 14 of this book summarize the safety effects of a wide range of road and traffic factors, and this sort of information is necessary to assist in the development of road safety audit recommendations. Much of this material is helpfully summarized in Table 15.1, which is based upon a useful and extensive overview of road safety engineering principles presented in publication entitled *Road Environment Safety Guidelines* (Roads and Traffic Authority of New South Wales, 1991b).

*Training and development of expertise*

The size of the audit team will vary with the size and complexity of the project to be audited. British experience (Sabey, 1993) is that at the feasibility and/or layout design stage, a three-person team has been found to be suitable, typically comprising a road safety specialist with experience

407

**Table 15.1**
**Summary of road safety engineering**

| Category | Items |
|---|---|
| Accident investigation and prevention | Access to timely and accurate data<br>Awareness of road/ vehicle/ human factors<br>Be aware of pre-crash, in-crash and post-crash countermeasures<br>Look for preventative action as well as remedial treatments |
| Remedial treatments | Must be cost-effective<br>Must target correctable crashes<br>Must be long-lasting |
| Evaluation | Adequate before data is essential<br>Careful selection of control sites<br>Sound statistical approach |
| Roadside safety | Maintain clear recovery areas<br>Shield immovable objects<br>Install frangible structures |
| Road design | Develop clear objectives<br>Provide consistent road geometry<br>Construct safe pavements<br>Create clear zones<br>Reduce, separate or eliminate traffic conflicts<br>Reduce glare and distraction |
| Traffic management | Establish clear objectives<br>Adopt proven or well-founded methods<br>Monitor effectiveness |

**Table 15.1 (Continued)**

| Category | Items |
|---|---|
| Traffic control devices | Select the most appropriate device<br>Consider all users<br>Reduce conflicts and relative speeds |
| Transport and traffic planning | Separate pedestrians and vehicles or modify the road environment<br>Encourage public transport options where appropriate<br>Ensure developments are compatible with the functional hierarchy of roads and land use plans |
| Sign posting | Demonstrate a need for the sign<br>Convey a clear message to all users under all circumstances<br>Ensure that the sign does not create a hazard in itself |
| Delineation | Delineation must be visible under all conditions<br>Special consideration is needed for sub-standard road geometry<br>A high standard of maintenance is essential |
| Work zones | Instruct and guide road users safely through, around or past the work site<br>Provide advance warning of a work zone<br>Take particular care in the installation and maintenance of temporary signs and devices |

Source:    Based on material presented in Roads and Traffic Authority of New South Wales (1991b).

in accident investigation and expertise in safety engineering principles and practice; a highway design engineer; and a person with experience in safety audit who is able to generate discussion and assist in the procedure. At the detailed design stage, it may be necessary to supplement the above team with specialists in particular areas (e.g. traffic control, street lighting, etc) depending on the nature of the scheme. At the pre-opening and in-service stages the inclusion of the police and an engineer who has (or will have) responsibility for the maintenance of the road and its traffic control devices is important. British experience in the counties which have taken road safety audit most seriously is that the safety audit team should comprise staff who are also involved in accident investigation and prevention work, since only in this way can the necessary expertise be developed to identify shortcomings in the design.

As noted above, auditors must have specialist skills in safety audit, and to this end, training is an essential pre-requisite to the introduction of a safety audit process in any jurisdiction. In New Zealand, the development of a national training course is being considered, with a possible aim of linking it to the National Qualifications Authority so that those attending the course can undergo assessment and gain formal accreditation. Similarly, in Britain, a recent extensive review by the County Surveyors' Society (1993b) recommended, amongst other things, that specific training of staff was necessary for the safety audit process to achieve its potential, and that a system of certification be developed.

One of the difficulties which has been faced in the introduction of safety audit is that road designers have come to see safety audit as an unnecessary and undesirable check on their design skills by people with little or no such skill (Sabey, 1993). This perception can act to the detriment of the introduction of safety audit, and it is therefore essential that those doing the safety audit have the respect and support of the design teams. As noted, training is vital here. Having designers alternate from the role of designer of some projects to auditor of others also helps develop a supportive culture. In this way, one of the longer term benefits of safety audit may be its educational effects on road designers and managers, resulting in more safety conscious planning and design.

*Monitoring and evaluation*

A jurisdiction introducing safety audit needs to set up a process of monitoring and evaluation of the process. This involves three aspects (Sabey, 1993):

- procedures, problems encountered, and effectiveness of the system,
- critical appraisal of the checklists and their use, and
- evaluation of costs and resources by scheme type and stage.

## Liability

The Australian guidelines (Austroads, 1994) contain a chapter on legal issues. This will not be summarized here, but its conclusion is relevant:

'No case involving road safety audit has yet come before a court. Therefore the legal implications must be speculative. But the predictions are not guesswork; they are based upon well established principles of tort law.

Safety audits will create a safer road environment. A major aim of litigation in this area of law is to encourage safety, therefore the use of road safety audit will be encouraged by the legal system. But the major focus of the law in this area is the end product - the state of the road itself - and not the method by which an authority achieves this.

Roads can be made safe by a variety of methods - including black spot treatment, periodic inspection, the adoption of higher standards of engineering practice, greater allocation of funds and road safety audits. It is for highway authorities to decide which mix of these is best for any given project, and as an overall policy.

It is obvious that the process of road safety audit can play a vital part in achieving safer roads. Highway authorities that fail to adopt the process run the risk that avoidable defects on the road will not be discovered, and that the defects will cause accidents.'

## Audit of existing roads

As noted above, the safety audit of existing roads has not hitherto been a major component of road safety audit programs, although some guidelines in use in various agencies allow for the inclusion of this stage.

However, a formal program of road safety audit of existing roads can be an important component of the overall audit procedure (Stage 5 as mentioned above). For example, the Australian guidelines (Austroads, 1994) state that the aim of this stage of audit is 'to identify any existing safety deficiencies of design, layout, and street furniture which are not consistent with the road's function. There should be consistency of standards such that the road user's perception of local conditions assists safe behaviour.'

These guidelines suggest a different approach depending upon the length of road. For short lengths (say, less than 30 km (20 miles)), a detailed inspection is suggested, highlighting specific issues and making specific recommendations. For longer lengths (say, in excess of 100 km (about 60 miles)), a 2-part inspection is suggested, the first being a broad assessment of the route highlighting what major problems exist and where they are located. Then only these locations are subject to the more detailed audit, as in the approach suggested for shorter lengths.

The issues and problems identified in an audit of an existing road will vary considerably. Many items will either be related to maintenance of the road, or can be attended to in the course of routine maintenance activities. The benefits of the road safety audit process is therefore to ensure that these items are placed on the maintenance program, and to ensure that works are carried out in accordance with best practice. In this way, Austroads (1994, p 48) notes that 'costs of implementing a Stage 5 audit may therefore be minimal, as any remedial work is part of the on-going maintenance program.'

It is also relevant to note that some agencies attempt to maintain a hazardous roadway inventory, which may be considered as a surrogate for a formal road safety audit. This inventory typically lists the location of identified deficiencies (Zegeer, 1982, p 29). It may be based upon an asset management process which establishes files which can be interrogated to identify the location of specific features (e.g. roadway geometry, roadside furniture, traffic control items, structures, access, etc). It may be augmented by field surveillance and in some cases by public complaint. Increasingly, this process is being driven by concerns about legal liability, as discussed above. A specific example, for the State of Oregon, USA, is described by Hofstetter and Gipson (1993).

**Audit of development projects**

An extension of the road safety audit concept in use in some local authorities is to require that development proposals be audited. These may include, for example, a new commercial development which will generate traffic on an existing road, or a residential development which involves street construction. In a road safety audit context, these would need to be independently audited, and a road safety audit report submitted as part of the development application. This practice is adopted in some UK counties (e.g. Kent County Council, 1994b), and is under consideration in some Australian states.

An audit report of this type might address such things as the safety impact of peak period congestion, the generation of pedestrian and bicyclist movements across existing roads, the safe provision of public transport, vehicular and pedestrian access to the site including driveway locations and type, the adequacy of parking provision from a safety viewpoint, pedestrian-vehicle conflicts on and adjacent to the site, the type and layout of intersections and new road alignments, speeds within the site, and visibility (Austroads, 1994, p 52).

## Effectiveness of road safety audit

Although a relatively recent technique, evidence is emerging that road safety audit is a cost- effective safety measure. In particular, there is evidence that in many cases, existing design and construction processes allow deficient or inappropriate elements of road projects to be implemented. For example, many jurisdictions will have had experience with road safety problems which have arisen within a year or two of the opening of a new project which would have been identified if the project had been subject to safety audit. A formal requirement that a project be subjected to a safety audit will thus very likely lead to improved safety. UK experience suggests that for individual schemes perhaps one-third of accidents have the potential for removal by safety audit.

It should also be noted that the resources that need to be devoted to safety audit are in fact quite small. UK experience (Institution of Highways and Transportation, 1990b) suggests that one safety auditor is required to cover an area experiencing some 2000 casualty accidents per year (although more recent experience suggests that this may be under-estimated by a factor of 2). Australian and New Zealand experience suggests that safety audit adds about 4 per cent to road design costs. However, adopting a whole of life approach, as described above, should mean that the costs of road safety audit are more than recouped from savings elsewhere.

There have been some attempts to quantify the benefits of road safety audit. One highway authority in Scotland (Lothian Regional Council, 1991) has estimated that one-third of future accidents at road improvements are preventable by audit, and that a one per cent accident saving per year - worth approximately one million pounds (approx $US 1.5 million) - is possible across the Region at a resource cost of 70,000 pounds (approx $US 100,000), a benefit:cost ratio of 15:1. In New Zealand, a potential benefit:cost ratio of 20:1 has been estimated for road safety audit procedures (Transit New Zealand, 1993).

Austroads (1994, p 14) summarizes the benefits of road safety audits as follows:

. the likelihood of accidents on the road network can be reduced,
. the severity of accidents can be reduced,
. road safety is given greater prominence in the minds of road designers and traffic engineers,
. the need for costly remedial work is reduced, and
. the total cost of the project to the community, including accidents, disruption and trauma, is reduced.

*Although in its infancy, it is likely that a form of road safety audit will become more common worldwide as agencies seek to minimize the whole of life cost of road projects, and gain a measure of protection from the costs of litigation. Certainly, it can be observed that in those jurisdictions where it has been used, there is enthusiasm for the process based upon a conviction that it is a highly cost-effective road safety measure.*

**Note**

1. This chapter draws on material assembled by an international committee of the Institute of Transportation Engineers, chaired by the author. An abridged report of that committee appeared in an article in the *ITE Journal 65(2)* (Institute of Transportation Engineers, 1995). Any commonality between that article and the material in this chapter is with the kind permission of the Institute of Transportation Engineers, 525 School Street SW, Washington, DC, USA. Fax (+1) 202 863 5486.

# 16 Road safety program appraisal

*In this chapter, we examine the appraisal and implementation of programs involving road safety engineering. As described in the discussion of the various phases of the development of a hazardous road location program, this involves firstly the ranking of sites in priority for treatment and preparation of design plans, etc, and secondly programming and implementing countermeasures.*

## Ranking and project selection

Previous chapters have discussed the identification and investigation phases of the hazardous road location program (Figure 2.3). The culmination of these phases will be a listing of hazardous sites, routes or areas (where hazard has been explicitly defined), and an appreciation of the nature of the safety problems at those sites. Then, in the light of the knowledge about the potential effectiveness of a range of traffic engineering or highway design measures (discussed in Chapters 7 through 14), a judgement can be made about the most suitable measure or measures to be adopted for each site. The remaining question then is, should these measures be implemented, and if so, in what priority order (given that there is rarely sufficient resources to undertake them all immediately)?

More formally, the Institution of Highways and Transportation (1990b, p 25) in its road safety guidelines outlines seven steps to be followed in systematically selecting projects for inclusion in a hazardous road location program:

. determine the range of measures likely to influence the dominant accident types and road features,

. test the measures to ensure that:
  . a decrease in accidents is likely to occur,
  . no future increases are likely in other accident types, and
  . no unacceptable effects are likely on traffic or environment,

. economic assessment of costs and benefits,

. select measures likely to give the greatest benefits,

. public consultation to ensure acceptance by the community affected,

. if necessary, amend proposals, and

. select sites for priority treatment and develop action plans.

In ranking sites and developing a prioritized work program, the use of formal economic appraisal procedures is an invaluable aid; we examine these procedures below. However, it is sensible to apply some prior judgement and common sense to the development of a listing of sites for treatment. For example, with some sites, there may be a clearly defined accident pattern and an obvious solution which the analyst can be very confident about. However, in other cases, the accident pattern may be more diffuse, and/or the appropriate treatment is not so clear. In this latter case, it may be necessary to spend further resources investigating the nature of the problem (e.g. a traffic conflict study - see Chapter 4). The use of sensitivity tests, as discussed below, is also appropriate here. While the former site should presumably be treated (subject to it performing favourably against other candidate sites), the latter should not be forgotten; an interim, low-cost solution may be appropriate.

Often, the road safety engineering works program is complementary to other works programs in the responsible agency. If this is the case, it may be appropriate to either defer the action (e.g. if major road works such as an intersection treatment is planned for the near future), or to apply only a low cost interim solution.

Practical considerations mean that there will likely be a delay between the development of the prioritized program and actual construction. Details of the program should be made known to the engineering construction staff well in advance so that works can be carried out expeditiously. This particularly applies to works which may be influenced by seasonal factors such as weather (e.g. resealing) or traffic flow.

In recent years, it has become both possible and more common to perform a formal appraisal of traffic engineering road safety projects[1]. There are two reasons for this: firstly governments are requiring road and safety agencies to show that investment in such projects is worthwhile, and secondly the data to permit a more rigorous form of appraisal are becoming available. Broadly speaking, such appraisal is of two types:

. a formal economic appraisal in which costs and benefits are calculated and compared, or

. a goals achievement approach (such as the cost-effectiveness approach) whereby projects are ranked, but no attempt is made to assess their economic benefit against their costs.

## Economic appraisal of road safety projects

Economic appraisal is essentially concerned with the economic efficiency of alternative proposals. It compares the economic costs of a proposal with the economic benefits, and indicates not only whether the project is worthwhile (i.e. there is a net economic benefit, such that the community is economically better off by implementing the project than not) but also indicates which is the best project or set of projects to undertake. It consists of six stages:

. identification of relevant benefits and costs,

. valuation of benefits and costs,

. reduction of all future benefits and costs to their equivalent present day values,

. comparison of benefits and costs according to an explicit decision criterion,

417

. sensitivity testing where values are uncertain or risks are high, and

. presentation of results.

In the following discussion, we briefly discuss the meaning of each of these stages in the context of the appraisal of road safety engineering proposals. The treatment is necessarily brief, covering broad principles only, since it is common for each road agency to have its own explicit project appraisal procedures, to varying levels of formality and sophistication[2].

*Benefits and costs*

*Benefits.* The benefits of a road safety engineering program comprise savings in road accident costs which are estimated to result from the construction or introduction of a road safety measure. These may be due to a reduction in costs resulting either from a reduction in the *number* of accidents or a reduction in the *severity* of accidents, or sometimes from both.

In some cases, there will be other consequences of the treatment such as on-going maintenance costs (e.g. maintenance of signs or roadside furniture), and ongoing operation costs (e.g. operation of traffic signals). In some cases (especially with larger projects of which safety benefits are only part), there will be costs related to mobility which result from the measure (e.g. delays to motorists, additional fuel consumption). Where these economic consequences are significant in comparison with the accident savings and project costs, they should be estimated and brought into the calculation.

The net annual benefit (i.e. the savings in accident costs and savings in any other costs, offset by additional ongoing maintenance, operation, or road user costs) then constitute a stream of benefits which are assumed, or need to be calculated, over the evaluation period.

*Costs.* Although there are several ways in which cost can be calculated, the best and most unambiguous definition is that the costs of a project are its initial capital cost, which usually involve only the costs which are incurred up-front as the project is designed and built.

Other cost definitions (such as defining costs as the road agency's expenditure whenever it is incurred) have been used. Whatever definition is used, it must be consistent to avoid double-counting. It is also important to note that criteria based upon dividing one number (e.g. costs) into another (e.g. benefits) will produce different values depending upon the definition of costs and benefits; we address this problem shortly.

*Valuation of costs and benefits*

If we use the recommended definition of cost as just discussed, the valuation of costs is usually straightforward; this is the engineering estimate of the cost of the job.

The valuation of benefits is more difficult, since it involves placing an economic value on accidents and thus of accident savings. This is not the place for detailed exposition of these issues (but see for example Jones-Lee, 1990; Bureau of Transport and Communications Economics, 1992; Steadman and Bryan, 1988; Haight, 1994; Evans, 1994).

As well as the actual valuation of the cost of accidents, the way in which these valuations are expressed is important. Until recently, most jurisdictions used very broad average values, for example the average cost of a rural accident and an urban accident, or the average cost by accident severity. The UK approach to economic evaluation is typical; it is based upon the use of an average cost of accidents by location (rural, urban, motorway) and by severity (fatal, serious, slight).

Recently however, a potentially much more powerful approach has emerged. This is based on the calculation of the average cost of particular accident types. Since the hazardous road location (HRL) process described in the early chapters of this book relies upon an analysis of current accident patterns and a forecast of what will happen to those patterns if a particular remedial treatment is implemented, this method allows the benefits of those treatments to be evaluated directly. That is, knowing the accident types at any site, route, area or mass action program, an estimate can be made of the effect on these accident types of proposed treatments.

This enables a more detailed analysis of the benefits of the treatments to be undertaken, particularly in instances where there may be little effect upon accident frequency, but a significant effect upon accident severity. It also overcomes the problem of having a fatal accident (which is very rare) distorting the analysis because of its high cost. Similarly, the need for such artefacts as 'severity indices' to arbitrarily weight the incidence of different accident severities in order to develop a ranking is no longer necessary.

This approach has been pioneered by Andreassen (1992a,b,c). Andreassen's average standardized costs for nineteen accident type groups, based on 1987-88 data for the state of Victoria, Australia, are shown in Table 16.1 (Andreassen, 1992b, Table B1). Although these particular values are specific to Victoria because they relate to reported accidents in that state, they are probably broadly indicative of the costs of these accident types anywhere, at least relatively. It should be noted that the valuations are actual valuations in every instance, calculated according to the methodology used elsewhere in Australia (Steadman and Bryan, 1988) which in turn is similar to current international practice. However, average costs per accident will be somewhat different in different countries since the cost structure will vary.

*Discounting*

Future cash flows need to be reduced to equivalent present-day values, because the value of a dollar in the future is less than the value of a dollar today. This is referred to as discounting. There are two situations relevant to the present analysis:

The present worth, P, of a single sum of $S, n years in the future, at a discount rate of i% per annum is

$$P = \frac{S}{(1 + i)^n}$$

Similarly, the present worth, P, of a stream of annual sums of $R, at the end of each year for n years in the future, at a discount rate of i % per year is

$$P = R \frac{(1 + i)^n - 1}{i (1 + i)^n}$$

Present worth factors for single sums and uniform series are presented in any source text on economic appraisal, but they are not difficult to calculate using the relevant equation.

**Table 16.1**
**Costs[2] by accident type**

| Accident type[1] | | Urban | Rural |
|---|---|---|---|
| **One-vehicle accident types** | | $ | $ |
| 001-003 | pedestrian crossing road | 79,300 | 148,800 |
| 605 | permanent obstruction | 56,000 | 89,800 |
| 609 | hit animal | 18,100 | 22,700 |
| 701-702 | off road, on straight | 30,700 | 54,400 |
| 703-704 | off road, on straight, hit object | 55,200 | 88,900 |
| 705 | out of control on straight | 31,200 | 53,900 |
| 801-802 | off road, on curve | 44,400 | 84,100 |
| 803-804 | off road, on curve, hit object | 69,500 | 107,200 |
| 805 | out of control on curve | 32,900 | 56,600 |
| **Two-vehicle accident types** | | | |
| 101-109 | intersection, adjacent approaches | 38,500 | 90,300 |
| 201 | head on | 86,800 | 186,400 |
| 202-206 | opposing vehicles turning | 46,800 | 85,000 |
| 301-303 | rear end | 26,400 | 58,200 |
| 305-307 | lane change | 22,100 | 81,600 |
| 308-309 | parallel lanes, turning | 25,300 | 68,400 |
| 207,304 | U-turn | 38,700 | 81,500 |
| 407 | vehicle leaving driveway | 31,900 | 69,700 |
| 503,506 | overtaking, same direction | 21,600 | 55,300 |
| 601 | hit parked vehicle | 21,700 | 42,200 |

1. accident type code: refer Figures 4.1 and 4.2.
2. in Australian dollars (1987-88).

Source: Andreassen (1992b).

The discount rate appropriate to this form of economic appraisal is a matter of some controversy. However, for present purposes, we may simply note that any agency undertaking formal economic evaluation procedures will have explicit discount rates to use. Often, these are prescribed by another arm of government (a Treasury or Department of Finance) in order that economic appraisals undertaken by different agencies are consistent. Currently, values of 4 - 7 per cent are in common use; these are real values, i.e. the nominal value minus the rate of inflation.

The appraisal period, i.e. the period of time over which future benefit streams are discounted, needs to be carefully assessed. At one extreme, a short appraisal period may be used, during which it is reasonable to assume that traffic and other conditions remain unchanged, and therefore there is some confidence in the inputs to the appraisal process. However, this may under-estimate the benefits (or perhaps costs) because benefits and costs beyond the evaluation period will not be included. On the other hand, a longer period can be used (eventually running out to the life of the project - perhaps 20 years or more). If this is done, it is necessary to make estimates of future traffic flows and other conditions, as these affect accident frequencies, operating costs, and so on.

Typically, for traffic engineering works, an appraisal period of around 5 years is used, although a longer period is appropriate if traffic is expected to be reasonably stable. One decision criterion (the first year rate of return - see below) implicitly uses only a one year appraisal period. Longer time periods would usually be used for major construction projects, perhaps 10-20 years.

*Decision criteria*

Having calculated the present value of the future stream of benefits and costs, these are used to calculate an index which is used to assess the worth of the treatment, and perhaps to rank it against other candidate projects. In general, five such criteria are in use for the economic appraisal of projects:

. net present value (NPV),
. benefit:cost ratio (BCR),
. internal rate of return (IRR),
. payback period, and

. first year rate of return (FYROR).

*Net present value*. With this method, the streams of current and future benefits and costs are discounted to their present value, and then subtracted one from the other to determine a resulting net present value. In mathematical terms,

$$NPV_{xni} = PVB_{xni} - PVC_{xni}$$

where $NPV_{xni}$ = the net present value of alternative x, for an n-year period and discount rate i,

$PVB_{xni}$ and $PVC_{xni}$ = present value of the benefits and costs respectively, for the corresponding x, n and i.

Application of the present worth factors (see above) reduces this to:

$$NPV_{xni} - \sum_{t-0}^{n} \frac{B_{xt} - C_{xt}}{(1+i)^t}$$

where $B_{xt}$ and $C_{xt}$ are respectively the benefits and costs of alternative x during year t (Wohl and Hendrickson, 1984, p 171).

The net present value must be determined for each alternative. All alternatives which have a positive NPV can be regarded as economically worthwhile, i.e. the community is better off to undertake them than not to undertake them.

All else being equal (i.e. if there are no capital, social, political, environmental or other reasons for doing otherwise), the alternative with the highest NPV will be the best of the alternative solutions to the project in question. This is a major methodological advantage of the NPV method compared with the other methods to be discussed below. With the others, it is necessary to perform pair-wise comparisons of alternatives to ensure that the marginal benefits outweigh the marginal increment in cost. This is not necessary with the NPV method, because if the NPV increases when moving from a lower cost alternative to a higher cost one, then the marginal increase in benefit must increase also, otherwise the NPV would not have increased. Moreover, the NPV method is applicable where there is a budget constraint and the aim is to select the most worthwhile set of projects. In this case, the solution is to 'combine those projects whose total initial costs are less than or equal to the budget constraint but whose combined total net value is the largest' (Wohl and Hendrickson, 1984, p 173).

The NPV method is straightforward, and will ensure that the best economic alternative - i.e. the one which maximizes economic efficiency - is chosen. Wohl and Hendrickson (1984, p 173) say that 'in sum, there is no more easily applied, unambiguous, complete and less tedious benefit-cost method than this one'. Similarly, Meyer and Miller (1984, p 406) say that the NPV method 'provides the most useful information to decision makers and is thus recommended for use in efficiency evaluation.'

*Benefit:cost ratio.* This method uses the same measures of benefits and costs as those used in the NPV method above, but instead of calculating an aggregate value for each alternative, the BCR method calculates a ratio of benefits against costs. That is, the benefit:cost ratio is calculated from:

$$BCR_{xni} = \frac{PVB_{xni}}{PVC_{xni}}$$

As with the NPV approach, a positive benefit:cost ratio indicates that the alternative is worthwhile, but again it says nothing in itself about whether that project should be undertaken.

The benefit:cost ratio itself must *not* be used to rank alternatives. Rather, ranking involves a pair-wise comparison of all alternatives with a BCR greater than 1 to determine the marginal benefit obtained for a marginal increment in cost. This process proceeds by first eliminating all alternatives with a BCR of less than one, and then listing the remainder in order of ascending cost. The marginal benefit:cost ratio is then determined by pair-wise comparison of alternatives, starting with the lowest and second lowest cost alternatives (Wohl and Hendrickson, 1984, p 174). That is:

$$IBCR_{x/x+1,n,i} = \frac{PVB_{x+1,n,i} - PVB_{x,n,i}}{PVC_{x+1,n,i} - PVC_{x,n,i}}$$

where:  IBCR = incremental benefit:cost ratio
x and x+1 are respectively the lowest cost and next to lowest cost alternatives
x/x+1 means alternative x as compared to alternative x+1

If IBCR is larger than one, then alternative x+1 is to be preferred, since the marginal benefit exceeds the marginal cost; alternative x is eliminated from comparison. Conversely, if the IBCR is less than one, alternative x+1 is eliminated.

The pair-wise comparison continues until all but one alternative is eliminated. This is the most economically worthwhile of all the alternatives considered.

A major problem with the BCR is that it can give ambiguous and misleading results, depending upon how benefits and costs are defined. This is particularly a problem in road safety evaluation, where benefits are usually considered as reductions in costs. For example, we suggested above that costs are the initial investments only, and that benefits are net consequences of that investment. Reductions in maintenance thus appear as a benefit, i.e. in the numerator. However, we also noted that in some applications, maintenance would be regarded as a cost, and thus reductions in maintenance (suitably discounted) would appear in the denominator. Commenting on this, Stopher and Meyburg (1974, p 94) note that moving such items from the numerator to the denominator 'will radically change the benefit:cost ratio computed ... there is no clear rule as to which is the correct way of handling such items.' It might be noted that this problem does not arise with the NPV method.

In summary, the BCR approach is more cumbersome than the NPV approach, and may produce ambiguous and misleading results. For this reason, it is less satisfactory than the NPV approach, and its use is not recommended.

*Internal rate of return.* The IRR method involves determining the discount rate for which the present value of the benefits equals the present value of the costs (i.e. it is the discount rate which produces a zero NPV). In mathematical terms, IRR is the value of i where:

$$PVB_{xnr} - PVC_{xnr}$$

or

$$\sum_{t-0}^{n} \frac{B_{xt}}{(1+r_x)^t} - \sum_{t-0}^{n} \frac{C_{xt}}{(1+r_x)^t}$$

where the variables are as previously defined.

For the purposes of screening alternatives (i.e. determining whether they are economically worthwhile), the IRR (r) is compared with the test discount rate (i), i.e. the discount rate which is used to calculate the present value of costs and benefits in the NPV and BCR methods. If the IRR equals or exceeds the test discount rate, the alternative is worthwhile.

However, the IRR can give misleading or ambiguous results when used to rank projects. As with the BCR method, what is required is the incremental IRR, by pair-wise comparison of all alternatives with an acceptable rate of return, starting with the lowest cost. The task is to compute r(x/x+1), the 'discount rate for which the extra discounted benefits (of x+1 over x) are just equal to the extra discounted costs (of x+1 over x)'. (Wohl and Hendrickson, 1984, p 179). That is, determine r such that:

$$PVB_{x+1,n,r(x/x+1)} - PVB_{x,n,r(x/x+1)} = PVC_{x+1,n,r(x/x+1)} - PVC_{x,n,r(x/x+1)}$$

This is a non-trivial computational task if the project is of any size and complexity.

The IRR has the advantage that it can be compared with yields from investments, and is thus readily understood by decision-makers. However, it has some problems. It can be difficult to compute, especially when attempting to rank alternatives. It can give misleading results, since it may give undue weight to short term effects. Under some circumstances (e.g. when a project incurs net costs initially, then has a period where it shows net benefits, then reverts to net costs), there may be more than one value of IRR which satisfies the above equations. Finally, it may sometimes be impossible to calculate a value of IRR. For these reasons, it is not recommended for use.

*Payback period.* The payback period is the number of years required to recover the original investment in a project. This approach has had little use in road or traffic project evaluation, but has been used elsewhere, especially in situations of high future uncertainty.

It is not a rigorous economic evaluation criterion, since it does not discount future benefits and costs, and it ignores benefits and costs beyond the payback time horizon.

It is therefore concluded that this method is not suitable for road evaluation purposes, and should not be used.

*First year rate of return.* This method merely compares the benefits expected to accrue in the first year, and compares them with the project costs. As such, it is not a rigorous evaluation criteria at all, since it ignores any benefits or costs after the first year. Its use in situations of very high uncertainty may be justified, but for most situations it does not give a valid basis for decision making on economic terms. In effect, it is really an index which provides a crude means of ranking projects, rather than a rigorous economic evaluation technique.

This method is commonly used in the UK for road safety engineering projects, and its use in this application has been defended on the grounds that estimation of benefits beyond the first year is difficult, and that in any case, very high first year rates of return (often in excess of 100 per cent) are found, so the use of more sophisticated decision criteria is not necessary.

*Conclusion.* To repeat the point made earlier, the net present value method is recommended as the best of the five techniques for economic analysis. It is subject to the least ambiguity, it produces information which is readily understood, is least likely to be affected by assumptions (especially definitions of benefits and costs), and is easiest to calculate, both as a value in itself, and as a means of comparing alternatives.

*Sensitivity test*

An appraisal should always be subject to a sensitivity test to assess how robust the result is to changes in the assumptions used in calculating it. In particular, a range of expected accident reductions should be assessed, since one can never be certain as to what the actual outcome will be; using a low and a high estimate of possible and realistic outcomes is always good practice. If the outcome is favourable even if a pessimistic forecast is used, we can be confident that the project is worthwhile. Conversely, if the outcome is unfavourable even with optimistic assumptions, we can be confident that the project is unlikely to be worthwhile. The middle ground - favourable under optimistic assumptions and unfavourable under pessimistic assumptions - requires us to do more work to try and get a better forecast.

*Presentation of the results*

The final phase of the appraisal process involves the presentation of the results of the analysis to the decision-making body. Tabular or graphical presentations, highlighting the economic benefits, the accident savings, and the expected performance against accident reduction targets are all useful devices. Actual practice will depend upon customs and conventions within the agency concerned, and few generalizations can be made.

## Goals achievement approach to project appraisal

This is an alternative to the economic appraisal approach described above. In essence, it aims to show the extent to which alternative proposals achieve a range of pre-set goals. The goals may be both quantifiable (e.g. economic) and non-quantifiable (e.g. social and environmental). The essence of evaluation is to present the decision-maker with information about the consequences of alternative courses of action.

The focus of these techniques involves the development of a table which shows the extent to which each alternative achieves the prescribed goals or objectives. Typically, the presentation is of the form shown in Figure 16.1, where one axis lists the measures which are to be used to assess the various goals, (these may be called criteria, or measures of effectiveness), and the other lists the alternatives. The entries in the cells are the values of each measure for each alternative, in 'natural' units (i.e. no attempt is made to reduce the measures to common terms, such as dollars).

| Criteria | Unit | Alternative | | | |
|---|---|---|---|---|---|
| | | A | B | C | D |
| **Safety Factors** | | | | | |
| Total accidents | number | | | | |
| Casualty accidents | number | | | | |
| Accident costs | $ | | | | |
| **Economic Factors** | | | | | |
| Capital cost | $ | | | | |
| Maintenance cost | $ | | | | |
| Vehicle operating cost | $ | | | | |
| Accident costs | $ | | | | |
| **Accessibility Factors** | | | | | |
| Car travel | person-hour | | | | |
| Public transport travel | person-hour | | | | |
| Truck travel | truck-hour | | | | |
| Cyclist travel | cycle trips | | | | |
| **Energy Factors** | | | | | |
| Fuel consumed | litres | | | | |
| **Environmental Factors** | | | | | |
| Emissions (by type) | ppm | | | | |
| Noise (houses above x dBa) | number | | | | |

**Figure 16.1 Typical evaluation matrix.**

In the context of road safety engineering, two specific approach within this generic form are relevant, namely the goals achievement matrix, and the cost-effectiveness approach.

*Goals achievement matrix*

This approach takes a matrix of the form shown in Figure 16.1, with the purpose of determining the extent to which each alternative will meet objectives which have been set in advance, and which are measured in terms of the listed criteria (Hill, 1968). In general these objectives are the benefits to be derived, and it is the likely success or failure in doing so (rather than the costs involved) on which the alternatives are assessed.

A modification of this approach is to use a simple assessment scale to determine whether the alternative contributes towards goal achievement (+), whether it detracts from it (-), or has no effect (0). Again, weights may be introduced for each criterion, and an overall index calculated. For example, Cambridgeshire County Council in the UK uses a weighting scale to reach an overall assessment of the 'score' of a proposed project based on:

.   accidents (number and severity),
.   congestion,
.   cyclist and pedestrian convenience and safety,
.   environmental effects of traffic on residences, schools and shopping centres, and
.   environmental effects of the project (trees, open space, signing, etc).

The advantage of these techniques is that they assist the decision-maker to make decisions in situations where there are disparate objectives, which cannot readily be converted to a single measure of effectiveness, such as dollars.

*Cost effectiveness*

The cost effectiveness approach to decision-making fits into this general category of goals assessment, because it is essentially concerned with determining the extent to which each of a number of alternatives contributes to the attainment of prescribed objectives. It is most applicable where:

. there is a fixed budget, and the aim is to achieve maximum results from that expenditure, or

. there is a specified objective, and the aim is to determine the cheapest way of achieving it.

Where it (and all other goals assessment techniques) differs from economic evaluation techniques is that it says nothing about how *worthwhile* the objective is; there is no measure of worth or value about the objectives or the results of the analysis. Therefore, the cost effectiveness approach has relevance to road safety project appraisal only to the extent that it assists in screening and ranking alternatives which are essentially similar in nature, and which can be assessed with respect to a single objective, such as reduction in the number of accidents. For example, if an agency has a simply-expressed goal of reducing the number of accidents in total (or perhaps reducing the number of casualty accidents, or fatal accidents), then the economic benefits or other impacts of remedial schemes are essentially irrelevant to that goal. A cost-effectiveness approach which simply lists the expected accident reduction from each of various alternative schemes would therefore be appropriate to that goal, as it would indicate to the decision-maker the set of treatments which are expected to have the maximum potential to reduce accident frequency.

**Worked examples**

*Example 1*

Consider the installation of a roundabout in a local street. Assume that we have data on accidents, including accident type according to an accident type code (Figure 4.1 and 4.2), and that the accident costs by accident type are as shown in Table 16.1. The following parameters apply:

capital cost: $20,000
change in vehicle operating cost: assumed zero
current accident rate: average of one adjacent-approaches accident per year (type 101 - refer to Figures 4.1 and 4.2)
assumed effect of roundabout on accidents: 50-80 per cent reduction

appraisal period: 10 years
discount rate: 4 per cent per annum

*Solution.* We must first assume that there will be no change in the traffic flow through the intersection over the appraisal period; if this were not so, we would need to calculate what the likely future annual accident rate would be in the 'do nothing case'. But if it is in a local street, we could reasonably assume that if there is a history of one adjacent-approaches accident every year, that this will continue in the future in the 'do nothing' case.

Therefore, in the 'do nothing' case, we have an annual accident cost of $38,500 for accident type 101 (based on Table 16.1). The roundabout is expected to eliminate between and 50 and 80 per cent of these accidents (Table 7.2). We need to assume that there will be no other effects of the roundabout, i.e. that it will not introduce accident types which are not there at present. Therefore the annual benefit of the roundabout is between $19,250 and $30,800 per year.

Using a discount rate of 4 per cent per annum, we calculate that the present worth of an annual sum of $1 per year over 10 years at 4 per cent is 8.11.

Therefore the benefit of the project is $156,100 (low estimate) to $249,800 (high estimate).

Hence, the NPV is in the range of about $136,000 to $230,000, and the BCR is in the range 7.8 to 12.5.

*Example 2*

This example is based on Andreassen (1992a, p 5), and refers to the post-evaluation of a traffic signal installation program. New traffic signals were installed at 41 intersections. Accident data were analysed for two years before and after the installation at each site. The only significant changes in accident types were a reduction of adjacent approaches accidents (accident type 101 in Table 16.1) from 6.54 per site per year to 1.88, and an increase in opposing vehicles-turning accidents (accident type 202) from 0.71 per site per year to 1.82. To evaluate the program, assume the following:

capital cost: $60,000 per intersection
operating cost: $6,000 per intersection per year
appraisal period: 5 years
discount rate: 7 per cent per annum

*Solution.* We first assume that the same level of accidents would occur each year for the next five years if the signals were not installed.

The average cost of accident types 101 and 202 (based on Table 16.1) are $38,500 and $46,800 respectively. Therefore, the annual benefit of the program is (6.54-1.88)x$38,500 - (1.82-0.71)x$46,800 = $127,500 per intersection per year.

The present value of a sum of $1 per year for 5 years at 7 per cent is 4.10. Therefore the benefit of the signalization at one intersection is 4.10 ($127,500 - $6,000) = $498,000. Hence the NPV of the project is $438,000, and the BCR is 8.3.

Note that we have taken the benefit as the net annual return from the investment (i.e. safety benefits minus operating costs), and the cost as the initial up front investment. If we had defined costs as the outlay by the road authority, as is sometimes done, then the benefit would be $522,700 (4.1 x $127,500), and the costs would be $84,600 ($60,000 + 4.1 x $6,000). This would give an NPV of $438,000 and a BCR of 6.2.

Note that the NPV is identical whichever way we choose to define our costs and benefits, whereas the BCR will change. This is a major advantage of the NPV method

## Checklist

Economic appraisal of proposals is likely to be increasingly required of road safety engineering projects. A useful checklist has been provided by Andreassen (1992a, p 11):

. I have identified the project costs in terms of capital, maintenance and operating costs,

. I have carefully chosen an appraisal period,

. I have chosen a discount rate,

. I have thought about and defined the effects on various accident types,

. I have differentiated between the effects of this treatment on accident frequency and on casualty outcomes,

. I have used local studies to estimate the effects of this treatment on the frequency of accident types and included this in my report,

. I have made an estimate based on studies from other localities or countries of the effects of this treatment on the frequency of accident types and included this in my report,

. I have identified the accident type or types in which this treatment is likely to have its greatest effect on casualty outcomes, and

. I have identified other accident types in which this treatment may have some effect on the casualty outcome.


**Notes**

1. The term *appraisal* is used here to refer to the analysis of measures before they have been undertaken. By contrast, the word *evaluation* is used to refer to the analysis of measures after implementation; see Chapter 17. It is acknowledged that the word *evaluation* is sometimes used generically to refer to either process, but the terminology used here is consistent with current practice.

2. For a more detailed exposition on this topic, refer to such sources as Wohl and Hendrickson (1984), Meyer and Miller (1984), or Stopher and Meyburg (1976). More advanced treatment is presented in Sudgen and Williams (1978), Heggie (1972), and Pearce and Nash (1981).

# 17 Monitoring and program evaluation

*Throughout this book, the need to base road safety engineering treatments upon a sound scientific basis has been stressed. For this approach to be productive and useful, the analyst must have a firm basis for believing that a particular treatment is likely to be effective or not effective. This in turn implies the need firstly for systematic observation of the effect of various treatments which affect road safety, and secondly a statistical analysis of those observations so that robust conclusions can be drawn from an analysis of the data. These two requirements, of monitoring and evaluation, are considered in this chapter.*

## The need for monitoring

Monitoring may be most simply defined as the systematic collection of data about the performance of road safety treatments after their implementation. It is only in this way that the effectiveness of treatments can be assessed. Post-implementation monitoring is therefore essential to ascertain the effects (positive or negative) of a treatment and thus improve the accuracy and confidence of predictions of that treatment's effectiveness in subsequent applications.

In addition to the development of skills and knowledge, monitoring is important to ensure that a particular scheme or treatment has not led to a significant *increase* in accidents; the road safety engineer has a duty to ensure that the public does not experience additional hazard as a result of treatments, and this duty carries with it an implied need to monitor what happens when a scheme is introduced.

It can also be argued that there is a professional responsibility to share the results of experience with one's professional peers, so that knowledge

435

and skills can be mutually developed. This may be achieved through publications and conferences and the like, but it may also be attempted in a more systematic way, as for example through the MOLASSES (Monitoring of Local Authority Safety Schemes) program initiated by the UK County Surveyors' Society and now administered by the Transport Research Laboratory, or through the US Local Technical Assistance Program (LTAP) technology transfer centres established in each state with Federal funding (albeit that safety is only a minor part of this program).

More formally, the Institution of Highways and Transportation (1990c, p 58) defines the purposes of monitoring as follows:

. assess the effects of accident occurrence in relation to safety objectives,

. assess the effects on the distribution of traffic and speeds of motor vehicles,

. call attention to any unintended effects on traffic movements or accident occurrence,

. assess the effects of the scheme on the local environment, and

. learn of public response to the scheme in terms of its acceptability in general and people's concerns about safety in particular.

The County Surveyors' Society (1991) suggests that monitoring of a site should be undertaken in three ways. The first is to pay careful attention to a site immediately after treatment to 'in case things go badly wrong.' The second is to assess the effects over a longer time period, say three years, to attempt to determine the influence of the treatment on accidents or other performance measures. However, it notes that this requires careful statistical analysis to attempt to correct for external factors (see below), and in any case the accident frequencies may be so low that any observed changes in accidents may not be statistically significant. The third approach therefore is to focus upon the accident types which the treatment was intended to correct, and assess whether these have in fact declined.

This implies that monitoring and evaluation are only meaningful if there has been a clear statement of the objectives of the treatment, a prediction of its effects, and a logical link between the treatment and its effects. Monitoring therefore reinforces the rigour that should apply to all accident investigation and prevention work.

Furthermore, the performance indicators may relate not only to accidents, but also to other changes which may follow the treatment. Ward and Allsop (1982) suggest that road safety schemes potentially affect the following parameters, and thus some or all of them may need to be monitored:

. the number and type of accidents,
. the severity of accidents,
. the distribution of accidents over the road network,
. traffic flows and travel times,
. turning movements and delays at intersections,
. access times and distances within residential areas,
. routes taken by motorists, cyclists and pedestrians, and
. operations of buses.

A comprehensive monitoring exercise should ideally include all of these effects, since without a knowledge of what has happened to (say) traffic volumes, information about what has happened to accidents may be misleading or meaningless.

One difficulty with monitoring accidents alone is that because accidents are comparatively rare events, it may take a very long time for a statistically reliable sample to accrue. This can be partially overcome by the use of proxy measures, such as the traffic conflicts technique (see Chapter 4) or indirect measures such as insurance company claims records, emergency service records (e.g. ambulance, hospital admissions), or tow truck records.

Finally, it should be acknowledged that the resources devoted to monitoring in most agencies are very limited. There is an understandable inclination to direct resources into the development and implementation of schemes which have been prioritized and shown to have a potential for accident reduction, rather than into monitoring exercises.

Therefore, we need to acknowledge that our understanding of the safety effectiveness of road safety engineering treatments (and other road safety measures for that matter) is limited, and in many cases rests on shaky foundations. This point is lucidly and comprehensively argued by Hauer (1988), who says that 'the level of safety built into roads is largely unpremeditated. Standards and practices have evolved without a foundation of knowledge. At times the safety consequences of engineering decisions are not known, at others some knowledge exists but is not used.'

## Monitoring techniques

### *Experimental design*

The essence of monitoring is to measure, for each of our performance indicators, what is actually happening in the real world, and then, in an evaluation phase, to attempt to compare that with what we expect would have happened if the treatment had not been introduced. There are several experimental design challenges in doing this, including:

.   There may be changes in the road environment, such as a change in speed limit, change in traffic flow, change in abutting land uses, or change in traffic control (other than the safety-related change whose effect is to be monitored). All of these are possible at a site over a 3-5 year time period, and virtually certain over an area or route. It is therefore impossible to conduct a rigorous scientific study where every possible influence is controlled.

.   Because accidents are rare and randomly occurring events, there will be fluctuations year by year which have nothing to do with the treatment being analysed. Data for short time periods (say one year) are therefore highly unreliable. These random year by year fluctuations, while not necessarily biasing the result of a monitoring exercise, introduce variability which must be accounted for in the statistical analysis. A particular problem is that of so-called regression to the mean (see below).

.   It is necessary to monitor all significant factors which could possibly affect the outcome, otherwise the outcome may be wrongly attributed to the treatment. If the variation in the treatment (e.g. a speed limit) varies systematically with another variable (e.g. design standard), it may not be possible to isolate the effects of one from the other. However, if only one is measured, it is likely that all of the change will be attributed to it.

. As a variation on the previous point, if the two variables which are systematically related are in fact both measured, then it will not be possible to reliably isolate their independent effects. This is particularly a problem if multiple linear regression techniques are used, since these require that the various independent variables are not correlated one with another.

. Statistical correlation does not necessarily imply logical correlation. For example, Haight (1981) quotes a case where the law giving pedestrians the right of way over vehicles was considerably strengthened in 1977, and the number of pedestrian deaths dropped from 365 in 1977 to 268 in 1983. However, the new law was not enforced and thus had no effect on behaviour, so the improvement in the pedestrian situation could not have been a result of the change in the law and must have been due to some other factor. This underlines the importance of ensuring a linkage between the treatment being monitored and the change in the performance measure.

. Seasonal factors must be taken into account. Some factors which may affect road safety vary in a systematic way throughout the day (e.g. natural light, street lighting), and others throughout the year (rain, hours of daylight, perhaps traffic flow). The selection of factors such as control sites and before-and-after periods must take these variations into account. It would be incorrect to compare the summer (before) accident record with the winter (after) accident record if one was trying to assess the effect of skid-resistant pavements, for example.

. Accident reporting levels may change over time, and there may be inconsistencies in the accident data which need to be considered. For example, the definitions attached to specific pieces of data (e.g. severity) may change over time, or the requirement to report accidents (e.g. property-damage only accidents) may be changed. The analyst needs to be aware of these changes and correct for them, since they can severely impact upon the analysis, e.g. in before-and-after studies.

. There may be a long term trend in accident occurrence, and thus changes over time in the number or rate of accidents at a site may merely reflect global trends. For his reason, it is usually necessary to use some form of control group and compare accidents at the test site with those at the control site (see below).

It is necessary to take these sorts of factors explicitly into account in the evaluation of the effect of a road safety treatment or program. There are basically four ways in which this can be done:

. controlled experimentation, in which all other factors are held constant except the factor whose effect is being investigated; this approach is rarely if ever applicable in road safety engineering because in the real world it is not possible to hold everything constant, and it will not be discussed further,

. before and after studies,

. comparisons using control sites, and

. time trend comparisons.

*Before and after studies*

The simplest method is to compare the accident record at the site before and after the implementation of the change. This is also the least satisfactory method, because of the lack of control of extraneous factors such as those mentioned above. For example, over the decade of the eighties, several countries experienced a very substantial reduction in total casualty accidents (see Chapter 1). If a treatment installed in the middle of the decade was evaluated using, say, 3-5 before and after periods, it would quite possibly have shown a significant reduction in accidents in the 'after' period compared with the 'before' period. However, in reality, this may have merely reflected nationwide trends, and had very little to do with the conditions at the site. Nevertheless, this method is sometimes used. It essentially involves:

. determining in advance the relevant objectives (e.g. accident types intended to be affected) and the corresponding evaluation criteria (e.g. accident frequency, accident rate),

. monitoring the site or area to obtain numerical values of these criteria before the treatment and again after the treatment,

. comparing the 'before' and 'after' results, and

. considering whether there are other plausible explanations for the changes, and correcting them if possible.

Note that in any before and after study, we will usually be relying on pre-existing data for the before period; it would be very rare indeed that implementation was delayed just so that adequate 'before' data for a site could be collected! This underlines the need for systematic, on-going data collection, so that the effect of changes in the system can be monitored routinely.

The above description of the process highlights the importance of determining in advance what the evaluation criteria are to be. While unexpected results may appear, and indeed the data should be examined carefully to ensure that undesirable effects have not occurred, the prime criterion is whether the treatment has had the desired effect or not. To this end, it is necessary to distinguish accidents by type, and perhaps by time of day (e.g. a lighting scheme), by weather conditions (e.g. skid resistant pavement treatment), etc. It is often helpful to prepare collision diagrams for the site or area before and after the treatment, as there may be new or relocated accident patterns evident.

If sample surveys are undertaken (e.g. to obtain a measure of traffic flow or turning volumes), the observation period should ideally cover several days to gain a representative sample.

The statistical analysis of the data should be carefully undertaken, having regard to the accuracy of the data (see below). It will often be helpful to consider more than just the change in accidents expressed, say, as annual average accident frequency of the particular accident type. It may also be useful to consider changes in the 85 percentile values, the variance, skew, etc.

While monitoring of the site or area should commence immediately after implementation (to detect any unexpected accident or operational problems), for any formal before-and-after comparisons to be statistically valid, a reasonable period of time must elapse to enable a sufficiently large sample to be obtained. While one year may be considered the minimum evaluation period, three years is generally regarded as a reasonable period for trends to be established and a large enough data set to be obtained. Nicholson (1987) has recommended five years from the viewpoint of statistical confidence.

These periods should exclude the period while work was in progress, and in fact, it may be sensible to omit data from the period immediately following implementation, while the system is 'settling down'. Exclusion of data for the year in which construction activity took place is often a useful practice.

*Comparisons using control sites*

As mentioned above, a major drawback with the simple before-and-after approach is that it takes no account of trends or changes across the network as a whole. This can be overcome through the use of control sites. There are two variations of this method, the first using control groups which are randomly determined, and the second using selected comparison groups (Council, et al, 1980).

The first method involves a controlled experiment, whereby several candidate sites for a particular treatment are identified in advance. They are then randomly split into two groups; all sites in the first group are treated, and no sites in the second group are treated. The purpose therefore is to attempt to make the control and treatment groups equal on all factors except for the execution of the treatment. The two groups do not have to be of equal size, but must satisfy sample size requirements (see below).

This method has considerable power as an investigation tool. However, it is of limited validity for most applications faced by a road safety engineer, because there will rarely be the opportunity to conduct a controlled experiment of this nature.

Therefore, the second variation mentioned above is of more relevance. This involves a before-and-after study, as discussed in the previous section, but the results for the before and after period at the treated site(s) are compared with the results for the control site(s). The process therefore involves:

.   determining in advance the relevant objectives (e.g. accident types intended to be affected) and the corresponding evaluation criteria (e.g. accident frequency, accident rate),

.   identifying a control site or (preferably) a set of control sites where no remedial works have been or are intended to be introduced,

.   monitoring both the treated site(s) and the control site(s) to obtain numerical values of these criteria before the treatment and again after the treatment,

.  comparing the 'before' and 'after' results at both the treated and control sites, and

.  considering whether there are other plausible explanations for the changes, and correcting for them if possible.

Selection of the control sites is obviously of key importance. Ideally, they would be randomly selected. However, this is rarely possible, unless a large number of control sites can be identified and a random selection made from these (Andreassen, 1989, p 34). The control sites should satisfy the following criteria (Ward and Allsop, 1982; Institution of Highways and Transportation, 1990c; National Association of Australian State Road Authorities, 1988a; Council, et al, 1980; Benekohal and Hashmi, 1992):

.  be similar to the treated sites in general characteristics (e.g. network configuration, geometric standard, land use, socio-economic characteristics, enforcement practices, etc),

.  be geographically close,

.  have the same or similar traffic flows,

.  not be affected by the treatment at the test site,

.  not be treated in any way themselves for the period of the before-and-after study, and

.  have accident records and other data (if applicable) which are consistent in both collection criteria and coding covering the period of the study.

Typical control sites (depending upon the nature of the treatment being examined) include an adjacent section of rural highway, a nearby network of urban streets, other similar nearby intersections, or an adjacent town.

The before and after periods for both the test sites and the control sites must, of course, be the same. It is not, however, essential that the before period be of the same duration as the after period.

While there are useful statistical tests which can and should be conducted (see below), a useful exploratory device is to simply graph the number of 'before' accidents against the number of 'after' accidents at a site, for both the test sites and control sites (County Surveyors' Society, 1991). Obviously, if there no change in the number of accidents (or whatever criterion might be used) between the before and after periods, all points would lie on a 45 degree line passing through the origin. The extent to which there is a change in accidents in the after period is indicted by the departure from the 45 degree line. If therefore there is a noticeable tendency for points representing the treated sites to be well below the 45 degree line compared with the control sites, this suggests that the treatment is having a positive effect (Figure 17.1).

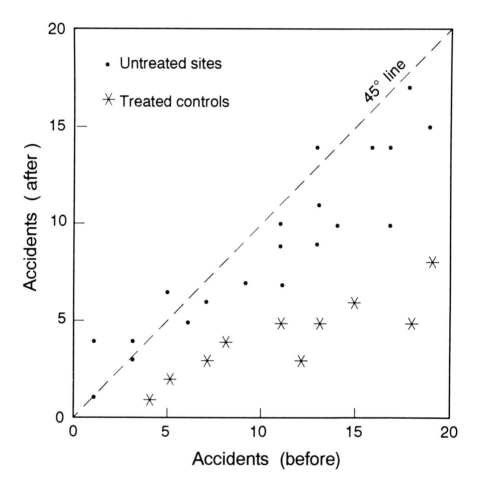

**Figure 17.1 Comparison of accident data before and after treatment**

## Time trend comparisons

This method, which usually involves the development of a model for estimating the trend in accidents over time, is an alternative method of accounting for time-dependent changes without using control sites. It involves:

. determining in advance the relevant objectives (e.g. accident types intended to be affected) and the corresponding evaluation criteria (e.g. accident frequency, accident rate),

. obtaining data on each of the criteria for an extended period of time, both before and after implementation of the treatment,

. developing a model based on the 'before' period,

. comparing projections based upon the model for the 'after' period with the measured criteria for that period, and

. considering whether there are other plausible explanations for the changes, and correcting for them if possible.

This method is useful in some aspects of road safety where a substantial countermeasure has been introduced at a given point in time (e.g. seat belt legislation, drink driving laws) (Andreassen, 1989; Hutchinson and Mayne, 1977). It's application to road safety engineering is more limited, since it is difficult if not impossible to control for all the variables in a real-world analysis. As a result, it is very difficult to isolate the effect of a specific treatment from many other factors which could plausibly have had an influence.

Ward and Allsop (1982) note that the analytical power of this approach has been much extended by the development of log-linear models and standardized computer packages such as GLIM (Generalized Linear Interactive Modelling) for estimating the models by maximum-likelihood techniques. Examples of applications of these methods to road safety engineering are reported in Dalby and Ward (1981), Institution of Highways and Transportation (1990c), and Benekohal and Hashmi (1992).

445

## Analysis of accident statistics

The previous discussion in this chapter has emphasized the role of statistical analysis in the evaluation process. It is necessary therefore to discuss the statistical techniques which any road safety engineer may need to use, and the pitfalls to be aware of in performing such analyses.

This subject is a complex though important one, and we will not attempt a comprehensive review here. The reason for the relatively simple exposition is a practical one - the extent and accuracy of the data which is generally available to the road safety engineer are such that more sophisticated analyses are not possible. This, together with the rather limited grasp of statistical theory which most road safety engineers can command, mean that the discussion here is targeted to what such a person might reasonably be expected to undertake in the course of their professional duties. (Nevertheless, some familiarity with statistical concepts is assumed in the following discussion.)

That having been said, it must also be acknowledged that if a more comprehensive analysis is to be undertaken and the data exist to support it, there are a wide range of statistical techniques which can be brought to bear. These are summarized in Table 17.1. The reader is referred to standard texts on statistical analysis. Both National Association of Australian State Road Authorities (1988a) and Organisation for Economic Cooperation and Development (1981b) contain useful summaries of the application of such techniques. For an interesting discussion on the use of statistical inference in matters related to road safety, see Hauer (1983).

As can be seen from Table 17.1, the three main applications of statistical testing in this area are:

. comparison of *accident frequencies*, for which a chi-squared test is suitable, or a paired t-test if the distribution of accidents can be assumed to follow a normal distribution,

. comparison of *accident rates*, for which a paired t-test is suitable, and

. comparison of *proportions*, for which a z-test is suitable.

**Table 17.1**
**Guide to statistical tests**

| Evaluation Design | Criterion | Test(s) or Procedures |
|---|---|---|
| Before and after | frequencies | $\chi^2$ for Poisson<br>paired t-test (if<br>    normally assumed) |
| | rates | paired t-test |
| | proportions | z-test for proportions |
| | variances | F-test |
| | distribution shifts | RIDIT<br>Kolmogorov-Smirnov |
| Before and after with randomized controls, comparison groups, or with correction for regression to the mean | frequencies | $\chi^2$ for Poisson<br>    frequency<br>Paired t-test for<br>    before/ after within<br>    group<br>t-test for group vs<br>    group<br>Analysis of covariance<br>Median test (categorical<br>    data)<br>Mann-Whitney<br>    (categorical data) |
| | proportions | z-test for proportions |
| | rates | Paired t-test for<br>    before/ after within<br>    group<br>t-test for group vs<br>    group<br>Analysis of covariance |
| | variances | F-test |
| | distribution shifts | F-test<br>Kolmogorov-Smirnov |

(Sources for Table 15.1: Council, et al (1980); National Association of Australian State Road Authorities (1988a).)

In addition, there is a very simple test which we can use to calculate *probabilities*, namely the Poisson distribution. This has been discussed in Chapter 5, in relation to determining whether a particular accident frequency is within the bounds of what might be considered normal year by year fluctuations.

### Chi-squared test

As discussed above, it is very common in road safety engineering to have to undertake a before-and-after evaluation, that is:

. given a set of accident data for a site (or route or area) before and after a remedial treatment, is the difference in the accident frequency statistically significant?

. or, given accident data for a test site and a control site, is there any difference between the before-and-after accident frequency at the test site compared with the control site?

For both of these situations, the chi-squared test is appropriate and has been widely used (Taylor and Young, 1988, p 112). (For examples of its application to various road safety applications see for example Jordan and Young, 1982; Andreassend, Hoque and Young, 1984; Fairlie and Taylor, 1990). The chi-squared test is based upon a *contingency table* - a table showing both the observed values of a set of data (O), and their corresponding expected values (E). The chi-squared statistic is then given by:

$$\chi^2 = \sum_{i=1}^{n} \sum_{j=1}^{m} \frac{(O_{ij} - E_{ij})^2}{E_{ij}}$$

where    $O_{ij}$ is the observed value in column j and row i of the contingency table,

                $E_{ij}$ is the expected value in column j and row i of the contingency table,

m is the number of columns, and
n is the number of rows

Clearly, the smaller the value of chi-squared as calculated from the above formula, the closer the 'observed' and the 'expected' values, until of course we get to the point where the observed and the expected values are identical, in which case, chi-squared is zero. Hence, we can use tables which show the probability that the 'expected' values and the 'observed' values are drawn from the same sample, with a small value indicating that there is a high probability that there is no difference between the 'observed' and the 'expected' chi-squared distributions. These tables also require us to know the number of degrees of freedom in the contingency table, and this is given by:

degrees of freedom $= (n-1)(m-1)$

These tables may be found in any good statistics text book or published tables of statistics (e.g Taylor and Young, 1988, p 342). A worked example of the chi-squared test is presented below:

*Worked example of chi-squared: simple before and after comparison.* This example is taken from National Association of Australian State Road Authorities (1988a, page 61). In this case, we are given a set of data showing the number of accidents at six sites, for a two year before period and a one year after period:

| Site | 1 | 2 | 3 | 4 | 5 | 6 | Total |
|--------|----|----|----|----|----|---|-------|
| Before | 10 | 10 | 12 | 14 | 18 | 12 | 76 |
| After | 10 | 8 | 6 | 6 | 9 | 6 | 45 |

The first implicit assumption we have to make is that all intersections are similar, so that we can combine the data to perform our test. If this is not so (e.g. if some are roundabouts, some are signalized intersections and some are uncontrolled intersections) it would not be valid to combine the data. A cursory examination of the above data shows that the average number of accidents in the 'before' period was 38 per year (76/2), and in the 'after' period, this had increased to 45. The question is: is this difference significant?

Our null hypothesis (i.e. the hypothesis we set out to prove) is that the two sets of data are drawn from the same sample so there is no significant difference between them. In this case, our best estimate of the 'expected' number of accidents in the after period at any site is the simple arithmetic average of the number of accidents in the before and after periods (Tanner, 1958). Remembering that we have two years of 'before' data, the annual average number of accidents at site 1 (for example) in the 'before' period is 5 accidents per year, and in the 'after' period is 10 accidents per year, giving an 'expected' average annual accident frequency of 0.5(5 + 10) = 7.5 accidents per year.

Doing this calculation for all six sites, we end up with the following contingency table:

| Site | 1 | 2 | 3 | 4 | 5 | 6 |
|------|-----|-----|-----|-----|-----|-----|
| Observed (after) | 10 | 8 | 6 | 6 | 9 | 6 |
| Expected | 7.5 | 6.5 | 6.0 | 6.5 | 9.0 | 6.0 |

The chi-squared statistic, using the above formula, is therefore:

$$(10\text{-}7.5)^2/7.5 + (8\text{-}6.5)^2/6.5 + (6\text{-}6)^2/6 + (6\text{-}6.5)^2/6.5 + (9\text{-}9)^2/9 + (6\text{-}6)^2/8 = 1.217$$

This statistic of 1.217 is then used to assess the probability that the two sets of data (the observed and the expected) are drawn from the same distribution. We first need to calculate the number of degrees of freedom $(n\text{-}1)(m\text{-}1)$; in this case $n=2$ (number of rows: one row for observed, one for expected) and $m=6$ (number of sites). Therefore, there are 5 degrees of freedom.

Using a table such as that presented in Taylor and Young (1988, p 342), we find that for 5 degrees of freedom, a chi-squared value of 1.217 indicates that there is between 90 and 95 per cent probability that the two sets of data are drawn from the same distribution. (The 95 per cent level is given by chi-squared of 1.145 and the 90 per cent level by 1.610).

We can be confident therefore that the two data sets are similar, and that the difference in the number of accidents at the six sites before and after the treatment is not statistically significant (at the 90 per cent level).

*Worked example of chi-squared: use of control area data.* The second worked example is for analysis of accidents within an area, using a control area.

The following table shows the number of accidents experienced in a local traffic area before and after the introduction of a set of traffic calming devices. To assess whether the reduction in accidents is statistically significant, a control area was used; the control area was similar in as many respects as possible to the treated area, and all before and after periods of time were the same. The 'observed' data were as follows:

|  | Treated area | Control area | Total |
|---|---|---|---|
| Before | 24 | 32 | 56 |
| After | 11 | 30 | 41 |
| Total | 35 | 62 | 97 |

As before, our null hypothesis is that the two sets of before and after data are drawn from the same distribution. Therefore our best estimate of the 'expected' values is to use the marginal totals and calculate the individual entries by proportion (Taylor and Young, 1988, p 112; Tanner, 1958). For example, 56/97 of the accidents occurred in the before period, and 35 accidents occurred in the treated area. Therefore our best estimate of the expected number of accidents in the treated area before the treatment is 56/97 of 35 = 20.21. Applying this reasoning to all entries, we get the following table showing the 'expected' number of accidents:

|  | Treated area | Control area | Total |
|---|---|---|---|
| Before | 20.21 | 35.79 | 56.00 |
| After | 14.79 | 26.21 | 41.00 |
| Total | 35.00 | 62.00 | 97.00 |

The chi-squared statistic, using the above formula, is therefore:

$(24-20.21)^2/20.21 + (32-35.79)^2/35.79 + (11-14.79)^2/14.79$
$+ (30-26.21)^2/26.21 = 2.63$

451

In this case there is one degree of freedom (n=2 and m=2), and examination of a table of chi-squared values indicates that there is around a 10 per cent probability that these data are drawn from the same distribution (chi-squared for one degree of freedom and probability of 10 per cent = 2.71). We could therefore be reasonably confident that the null hypothesis can be rejected, that is we could state that the two distributions are different, and therefore the effect of the treatments in the treated area was significant.

## Paired t-test

The paired t-test is an alternative to the chi-squared test where it can be assumed that the distribution of accidents across sites follows a normal distribution (Taylor and Young, 1988). It is also applicable where we wish to compare accident rates. That is, if we have the same questions as posed above for the chi-squared test, but the evaluation criterion is an accident rate not an accident frequency. The t-statistic is calculated as:

$$t = \frac{\overline{X_B} - \overline{X_A}}{\frac{S_D}{\sqrt{N}}}$$

where:

$$S_D^2 = S_A + S_B^2 - 2 \left[ \frac{1}{N-1} \sum_{i=1}^{N} (X_{Bi} - \overline{X_B})(X_{Ai} - \overline{X_A}) \right]$$

$\overline{X_B}$ and $\overline{X_A}$ = before and after sample means respectively

$S_B$ and $S_A$ = before and after standard deviations respectively

$N$ = number of locations.

The t-statistic so-calculated may then be compared with a set of critical values tabulated in any statistics text, for the chosen level of significance and degrees of freedom (where the latter equals the number of locations minus 1).

*Worked example of paired t-test for accident rates.* This example is taken from National Association of Australian State Road Authorities (1988a, page 62). In this case, we wish to evaluate the effectiveness of improved pavement delineation on accident rates. We have before and after data for six locations (accidents per 100 km per year), as follows:

| Site | 1 | 2 | 3 | 4 | 5 | 6 | Total | Mean |
|------|-----|------|------|------|------|------|-------|-------|
| Before | 7.0 | 14.1 | 19.0 | 20.6 | 30.2 | 41.1 | 132.0 | 22.00 |
| After | 7.3 | 8.5 | 14.2 | 17.5 | 18.5 | 30.1 | 96.1 | 16.02 |

The null hypothesis that we aim to test is that the two sets of data are drawn from the same distribution, and there is no statistically significant difference between them. For the t-test, we must assume that the distributions are approximately normal with means (x) and standard deviations (s) as follows:

$x_B$ = 22.00
$x_A$ = 16.02
$s_B^2$ = 146.08
$s_A^2$ = 68.50
n = 6
degrees of freedom = (6-1) = 5

Using these values, $s_D$ = 4.65 and hence we calculate t = 3.15.
Comparing t = 3.15 with the critical value of t for a significance level of 5 per cent and 5 degrees of freedom, (2.02), we reject the null hypothesis and hence conclude that the new delineation is effective.

## Z-test

The z-test can be used either for proportions or frequencies (Table 17.1). It is useful in testing whether the proportion of a parameter found in a test case (e.g. the proportion of accidents which result in death, the proportion involving pedestrians, the proportion at night time, etc) is the same as that found in the population as a whole. For a large sample (over 30 data points in both the test and control group), the z-statistic is calculated from:

$$z = \frac{p_1 - p_2}{\sqrt{p(1-p)\left(\dfrac{1}{N_1} + \dfrac{1}{N_2}\right)}}$$

where:

$p_1 = x_1 / N_1$

$p_2 = x_2 / N_2$

$p = (x_1 + x_2) / (N_1 + N_2)$

$x_1$ = number of occurrences in sample group 1, out of a total possible $N_1$ occurrences, i.e. $x_1/N_1$ is the proportion of occurrences for sample group 1 (and similarly for sample group 2)

The test then is that if the z-statistic so-calculated is greater than a critical value, the difference in proportions is statistically significant. For a simple 2-way comparison (e.g. between a test group and a control group), some critical z-values are:

for differences significant at the 10 per cent level: 1.28
for differences significant at the 5 per cent level: 1.64
for differences significant at the 1 per cent level: 2.33

*Worked example of Z-test for proportions.* Suppose that over a road network, we have had 1000 reported accidents, and that 300 (30 per cent) of these occur on wet roads. At one site (not included in the network), our accident data show that of the last 40 accidents, 22 (55 per cent) have been on wet roads. Is this site significantly different from the rest?

For this situation, we have:

$x_1 = 300$ and $N_1 = 1000$
$x_2 = 22$ and $N_2 = 40$
hence $p = 0.309$

and the z-statistic is calculated as 3.35

This is significant at greater than the 1 per cent level, so we could confidently say that the site is statistically significantly different from the others.

## Methodological issues

In applying and using the statistical techniques discussed above for the purposes of road safety evaluation, the analyst needs to be aware of some issues which may need to be addressed. These are essentially methodological in nature, since they affect the way in which the evaluation is performed and interpreted. There are four important issues of this nature:

. regression to the mean,
. accident migration,
. risk compensation, and
. sample size determination.

### *Regression to the mean*

Over a period of years, if there are no changes in the physical or traffic characteristics at a site, accidents at that site per unit of time (say, annually) will tend to fluctuate about a mean value due to the random nature of accident occurrence. Because sites are commonly selected for treatment on the basis of their ranking in numbers of accidents compared to all other sites, there is a high possibility that sites will be chosen when their accident count is higher than the long term average. Even without treatment, the accident rate at these sites is likely to experience a lower rate (i.e. regress to the mean) in the year following selection.

This aspect of accident experience is a matter of concern in the post-implementation evaluation of a safety treatment, because to the extent that the phenomenon is present, the impact of the treatment will be exaggerated. Wright and Boyle (1987) assert that regression to the mean can over-state the effect of a treatment by 5-30 per cent. To the extent that our knowledge about the safety effects of treatments is built up from the results of just these sorts of studies, there is therefore (unless we correct for it) a tendency to overstate the effectiveness of road and traffic engineering treatments. This is sometimes called 'bias by selection' (Hauer, 1980). There is a responsibility therefore for the analyst to separate the real gains from the particular treatment from the changes due to regression to the mean.

The problem can be substantially minimized by increasing the number of years of data used in the site selection process (Nicholson, 1987). However, this does not solve the problem entirely, nor is it always expedient to wait for several years before conducting an evaluation exercise.

Some of the theoretical issues involved in the estimation of the regression-to-the mean effect are quite complex; these are discussed by Wright and Boyle (1987). Depending upon the needs of the analysis and the adequacy of the data, there are several methods which can be adopted in an attempt to correct for the phenomenon. These are comprehensively reviewed by Wright, Abbess and Jarrett (1988). However, as an indication of the complexity and practical difficulties of taking this phenomenon into account, it is interesting to note that the authors of this paper stated that 'we would like to draw attention to the fact that none of the methods referred to ... have been tested against real data in a controlled experiment.'

To correct for the regression to the mean phenomenon, the essence of the task is to attempt to estimate the *true* underlying accident rate. There are two common approaches to this: to model the accident situation in order to estimate the true underlying accident rate and then base the evaluation on the model not the raw accident data, or to adjust the data to correct for biases using assumptions about the statistical distribution of accidents year by year.

The former approach is typified by the multi-variate modelling approach developed by Hauer (1983, 1992) which extends the Empirical Bayes model to allow what Hauer refers to as 'unsafety' to be estimated when a large reference population does not exist. The model can be simply described as follows:

If $x_B$ and $x_A$ are respectively the accident frequencies observed before and after treatment at a site which prior to treatment had an underlying mean accident frequency m, then the treatment effect, t is given by:

$$t = x_A \, / \, m$$

and the regression to the mean effect, r, by:

$$r = m \,/\, x_B$$

If regression to the mean effects are ignored, it is assumed that $m = x_B$. However, rather than using data only for the study site itself to estimate m, the Empirical Bayes approach uses an expression of the form:

$$m = a + bx_B$$

If accident frequencies have been observed during the before period at a group of sites similar to the study site, then the sample mean and variance can be calculated for this group of sites, and a and b estimated from:

$$a - \frac{\bar{x}^2}{s^2} \qquad b - \frac{s^2 - \bar{x}}{s^2}$$

While there are variations on the way in which a and b may be estimated (see for example Mountain, Fawaz and Sineng, 1992a,b) the essence of the approach is the development of an equation such as this to estimate the underlying accident rate. Data to estimate the model are drawn from a sample population in the 'before' period, such as a set of control sites.

The alternative approach, which is probably simpler to apply in an everyday application, is that described (for a single site) by Abbess, Jarrett and Wright (1981):

Accident data must be assembled for all sites similar to the site under study, for the same time period. Then, using the full data base, the mean number of accidents a and the variance of accidents *var (a)* is calculated. The regression to the mean effect, R (in per cent), is then given by:

$$R = \left[ \frac{(S_o + S)n}{(n_o + n)S} - 1 \right] . \ 100$$

where    S = the number of accidents observed at the particular site during a period of n years,

$$S_o = a^2 / (\text{var}(a) - a)$$

$$n_o = a / (\text{var }(a) - a)$$

$S_o$ and $n_o$ are the estimates of the parameters of the statistical distribution showing the underlying true accident rates, i.e. the probability distribution of the accident rate before any data become available. This assumes that a particular site with a given accident history should behave in the same way as the set of all similar sites with the same accident history.

*Worked example of correction for regression to the mean.* Suppose that we have a site where there have been 90 accidents over the previous 5 years (an average of 18 accidents per year). The site has been treated, and in the following period, it has shown an average of 14 accidents per year.

To correct for regression to the mean, we need data for sites which are, as far as possible, similar to the site under study. We use data for these sites to estimate the parameters of the statistical distribution of accidents at the test site.

Suppose that over the previous five years, the number of accidents at the comparison sites had been 15, 15, 16, 17 and 19 accidents per year. This produces a mean (a) of 16.4 accidents per year and a variance *var (a)* of 2.80.

Thus, the values for entry in the above equations are:

n = 5 (years)
S = 90 (accidents)
$S_o$ = -19.78
$n_o$ = - 1.21

giving a value of R of 0.09.

That is, we would expect that in the after period, accidents at the test site, even if we did nothing, would reduce by 9 per cent, i.e. to 16.38 per year. It is this value of 16.38 which must then be compared with the actual 'after' performance of 14 accidents per year to determine whether there has been a significant change in the accident frequency.

*Accident migration*

The hypothesis here is that accidents may increase at sites surrounding the treated site due to changes in trip pattern or drivers' assessment of risk. Boyle and Wright (1984) for example found in a sample of sites in London that accidents at the treated sites fell by 22 per cent but accidents in the surrounding streets increased by 10 per cent. To the extent that this phenomenon exists, the effect of a remedial measure is not to reduce accidents, but to relocate them.

This observation is sometimes explained in behavioural terms, as a manifestation of risk compensation (see below), but Maher (1987) has developed a statistical explanation, showing that there is a spatial correlation between accident frequencies at adjacent or nearby sites, and therefore the use of neighbouring sites as control sites leads to bias. However, this study and further work by Mountain and Fawaz (1992) indicated that this did not fully explain the apparent increase in accidents at adjacent sites, and concluded that the accident migration effect was 'large enough to be considered of practical significance', but indicated that more work was needed to quantify the effect. Interestingly, they noted a tendency for the effect to disperse over time: in the first year, the migration tended to be within 200 m (about 700 ft) of the treated site, and in the second year effects were evident over 500 m (about 1700 ft) of the treated site, and that 'the migration effect may well extend beyond 500 m from the treated site two years after treatment.'

It is not normal in accident evaluation to make a correction to the results to account for accident migration. Wright and Boyle (1987) conclude that 'it would appear that the existence (or otherwise) of accident migration ... remains an open question.'

*Risk compensation*

Road users are not passive participants in the road system. They adjust their behaviour according to the way in which they perceive the road system. One factor which may affect behaviour is the perception of risk; if the road is perceived as being more hazardous then drivers may respond accordingly, for example by reducing speed in icy conditions (Wright and Boyle, 1987).

The notion of risk compensation in relation to accident evaluation postulates that some of the additional level of safety provided as a result of road safety treatments is 'used up' by drivers behaving in a more risky fashion. Indeed, accident migration, as described above, has been ascribed, in part, to this cause (e.g. Boyle and Wright, 1984).

To make sense of this notion in the context of road safety engineering, it is necessary to distinguish between *objective risk* (as measured for example in accident studies) and perceived or *subjective risk* (which is what affects behaviour). A road safety treatment may:

. reduce the objective risk while increasing the subjective risk (e.g. a set of traffic signals both alerts drivers to the hazard presented by the intersection, while moderating the hazard by separating conflicting streams of traffic),

. increase subjective risk alone (e.g. a warning sign depends entirely for its effectiveness on driver response),

. reduce the objective risk without any change in the subjective risk (e.g. skid resistant pavements are not usually discernible to the driver), or

. reduce both objective risk and subjective risk (e.g. improved road geometry, improved sight distance at intersections, grade separations, etc).

Logically, it is only in this last category that risk compensation, if it occurs at all, could be a factor, since in the other cases there is either no change in the subjective risk, or an increase in it. However, provided that the reduction in objective risk is at least as great as the reduction in subjective risk, the treatment will still produce a positive outcome (Rumar, 1982). Wong and Nicholson (1992) for example, found that while vehicle speeds increased after an improvement in road alignment, the levels of side friction demanded by drivers declined significantly, indicating that the level of safety had indeed been increased by the realignment: 'the ultimate test of the effect of the realignment is whether the actual margin of safety has improved, and the results of this study show clearly that it has. What risk compensation, if any, has occurred has been insufficient to completely undermine the intended goal of the realignments, namely a reduction in the likelihood of accidents at the curves.'

This carries with it the implication that any road design change which reduces the subjective risk should also reduce objective risk to at least the same extent, otherwise the road user will have a tendency to respond inappropriately. In particular, care should be taken in situations where sight distance is increased, since this will possibly lead to an increase in approach speeds, and if the geometry and/or traffic control at the site does not support these higher speeds, it is possible that the situation could become more, not less, hazardous. Or to put it in the words used above, the subjective risk has been reduced to a greater extent than the objective risk.

However, the notion of risk compensation, and more particularly its extent, is not universally acknowledged. Haight (1986) for example, while acknowledging that subjective or perceived risk influences driver behaviour, questions the extent to which this is significant compared with other factors:

'Beginning with the need (or at least desire) for mobility, and proceeding on through such motivations as vanity, thrift, boredom, haste, and so forth, we can distinguish a complex of factors which can affect driving style. In the context of such diverse motivations, it would appear that conscious evaluation of risk is either a quite insignificant factor, particularly when we bear in mind that the risk (either as a probability or an expectation) is itself extremely small. There are undoubtedly exceptions to such a conclusion ... but it would be showing remarkable insensitivity to road user patterns in industrialized countries to believe that this is often the case.'

A radical extension of the accident compensation hypothesis is to assert that there is full and complete compensation for any road safety measure, such that every measure produces exactly zero result, and that all potential safety benefits are converted to performance benefits such as higher speed. This is referred to as *risk homeostasis* (Adams, 1985; Wilde, 1982, 1986; Evans, 1986, 1991). Haight (1986) dismisses this argument by saying that it is either meaningless, since it is incapable of being tested or 'simply false ... (and) in my view, a sufficient argument against the validity of risk homeostasis is provided by the incoherence of its 'theoretical' formulation'. Other commentators have also been dismissive: Evans (1986) says that 'there is no convincing evidence supporting it and much evidence refuting it', while Wright and Boyle (1987) state that they 'believe that risk compensation probably occurs ... but not homeostatic.'

*Sample size determination*

The final methodological issue is the important one of sample size determination. This is of fundamental importance, since apparent differences in accident frequency (or any other parameter for that matter) are illusory unless the sample is sufficiently large for the difference to be statistically significant, i.e. have a high probability that it is not the result of chance fluctuations.

Most road safety engineering programs result in only modest changes in accidents at any given site over a given time period (e.g. one year). The smaller the change, the larger is the sample necessary to determine statistical significance. This means that in evaluating a countermeasure, the analyst must use either a longer time period, or a larger number of sites.

The sample size required depends on (National Association of Australian State Road Authorities, 1988a, p 45):

. the effect that the analyst seeks to detect, e.g. whether the treatment is expected to decrease accidents by 10 per cent, 20 per cent, 50 per cent or whatever,

. the probability of detecting a real effect, and

. the level of significance of the test.

All feasible combinations of these three factors will produce a multitude of outcomes. However, for simplicity, Table 17.2 indicates the minimum sample size needed in order to determine the probability of detecting a real effect at a level of significance of 5 per cent and 10 per cent, where the 'before' and 'after' periods are of equal duration, for various sample sizes and detection levels. The sample sizes necessary for other situations are presented in sources such as Council, et al, (1980), National Association of Australian State Road Authorities (1988a) and Nicholas Clark and Associates (1979).

For example, with equal duration of before and after measurement periods, if we measured 125 accidents in the before period and 75 in the after period (ratio of after:before of 0.6; total accidents measured, 200) then we can be 99 per cent certain that the reduction in accidents is statistically significant at the 10 per cent level (or 97.5 per cent certain at the 5 per cent level).

**Table 17.2**
**Sample sizes for various probabilities and confidence levels**

| Total number of accidents observed | Ratio of accident frequency after: before | Level of significance | |
|---|---|---|---|
| | | 5% | 10% |
| 50 | 0.9 | .101 | .181 |
| | 0.8 | .194 | .309 |
| | 0.7 | .342 | .486 |
| | 0.6 | .550 | .692 |
| | 0.5 | .775 | .873 |
| 100 | 0.9 | .131 | .225 |
| | 0.8 | .296 | .432 |
| | 0.7 | .548 | .638 |
| | 0.6 | .811 | .896 |
| | 0.5 | .963 | .985 |
| 200 | 0.9 | .184 | .295 |
| | 0.8 | .431 | .614 |
| | 0.7 | .806 | .891 |
| | 0.6 | .975 | .990 |
| | 0.5 | 1.0 | 1.0 |
| 500 | 0.9 | .320 | .458 |
| | 0.8 | .801 | .887 |
| | 0.7 | .990 | .996 |
| | 0.6 | 1.0 | 1.0 |
| | 0.5 | 1.0 | 1.0 |

Source: Nicholas Clark and Associates (1979).

This example indicates that the answer to the question 'how big a sample do I need?' is not straightforward, since it depends upon the interaction of these three factors. A 10 per cent confidence level is probably acceptable in many instances; 5 per cent is obviously more desirable.

Table 17.2 may be used to determine the confidence that can be placed on any measured change in accident frequencies believed to result from a remedial program where the before and after periods are of equal duration.

# 18 References

Abbess CR, Jarrett DF and Wright CC (1981) Accidents at blackspots: Estimating the effectiveness of remedial measures, with special reference to the regression to the mean effect. *Traffic Engineering and Control 22(10)*, pp 535-542.

Adam V and Shah SC (1974) Evaluation of open-graded plant mix seal surfaces for correction of slippery pavements. *Transportation Research Record 523*. pp 88-96.

Adams J (1985) *Risk and Freedom: The Record of Road Safety Regulation*. (Transport Publishing Projects, Cardiff, Wales).

Allot and Lomax Consulting Engineers (1991) *Cyclists and roundabouts: A review of the literature*. 32 p. (Cyclists' Touring Club, London).

American Association of State Highway and Transportation Officials (1989) *Roadside Design Guide*. (AASHTO, Washington, DC).

American Association of State Highway and Transportation Officials (1990) *A Policy on Geometric Design of Highways and Streets 1990*. 1044 p. (AASHTO, Washington, DC).

American Association of State Highway and Transportation Officials (1991) *Guide for the Development of Bicycle Facilities*. 45 p. (AASHTO, Washington, DC).

American National Standards Institute (1989) *ANSI D-16.1 Manual on Classification of Motor Vehicle Traffic Accidents, 5th edition*. (ANSI, Washington, DC).

Andreassen (1985a) Traffic accidents and advertising signs. *Australian Road Research 15(2)*, pp 103-105.

Andreassen DC (1985b) Linking deaths with vehicles and population. *Traffic Engineering and Control 26(11)*, pp 547-549.

465

Andreassen DC (1989) Strategies for safety problems. *ARRB Research Report ARR 163.* 101 p. (Australian Road Research Board, Melbourne).

Andreassen DC (1991) Population and registered vehicle data vs road deaths. *Accident Analysis and Prevention 23(5)*, pp 343-352.

Andreassen DC (1992a) A guide to the use of road accident cost data in project evaluation and planning. *ARRB Research Report ARR 226.* 16 p. (Australian Road Research Board, Melbourne).

Andreassen DC (1992b) Costs for accident types and casualty classes. *ARRB Research Report ARR 227.* 36 p. (Australian Road Research Board, Melbourne).

Andreassen DC (1992c) Trucks, semi-trailers and motor cycles: Accident costs for project planning and evaluation. *ARRB Research Report ARR 232.* 23 p. (Australian Road Research Board, Melbourne).

Andreassen DC (1994) Model guidelines for road accident data and accident types: Version 2.1. *ARRB Technical Manual ATM 29.* 46 p. (Australian Road Research Board, Melbourne).

Andreassend DC, Hoque MM and Young W (1984) Pedestrian accidents by road class. *Proc 12th Australian Road Research Board Conference 12(6)*, pp 58-71.

Andreassen DC and Hoque MM (1986) LATM and road safety: Accidents in road classes in Melbourne. *Proc 13th Australian Road Research Board Conference 13(9)*, pp 7-24.

Andreassend DC (1983) The use of accident data in problem identification, in Andreassend DC and Gipps PG (eds) *Traffic Accident Evaluation.* (Monash University, Melbourne, Australia).

Anon (1988a) 65 mph limit is taking its toll. *Status Report 23 (8)*, p 1.

Anon (1988b) Rumble strips alert drivers, save lives and money. *TR News 135*, pp 20-21.

Appleyard D (1981) *Livable Streets.* (University of California Press, Berkeley, CA, USA).

Armour M (1984) The relationship between shoulder design and accident rates on rural highways. *Proc 12th Australian Road Research Board Conference 12(5)*, pp 49-62.

Armour M and Cinquegrana C (1990) Victorian study of single vehicle rural accidents. *Proc 15th Australian Road Research Board Conference, 15 (7)*, pp 79-91.

Armstrong HB, Black JA, Lukovich T, Sheffield D and Westerman HL (1992) Environmental adaptation of the main street in rural towns: Towards guidelines. *FORS Report CR 110*. 74 p plus appendices. (Federal Office of Road Safety, Canberra, Australia).

Australian Road Research Board (1988) *Accidents and Road Type*. (leaflet) (ARRB, Melbourne).

Austroads (1993a) *Guide to Traffic Engineering Practice. Part 6, Roundabouts*. 86 p. (Austroads, Sydney, Australia).

Austroads (1993b) *Guide to Traffic Engineering Practice. Part 7, Traffic Signals*. 128 p. (Austroads, Sydney, Australia).

Austroads (1993c) *Guide to Traffic Engineering Practice. Part 14, Bicycles*. 124 p. (Austroads, Sydney, Australia).

Austroads (1994) *Road Safety Audits*. 100 p. (Austroads, Sydney, Australia).

Austroads (1995) *Guide to Traffic Engineering Practice. Part 13, Pedestrians*. 90 p. (Austroads, Sydney, Australia).

Axia (1986) *Attitudes of Heavy Vehicle Drivers to other Road Users*. (Traffic Authority of New South Wales, Sydney, Australia).

Axup DR (1993) Enforcement, in *The Traffic Safety Toolbox: A Primer on Traffic Safety*, pp 215-224. (Institute of Transportation Engineers, Washington, DC).

Ballard AJ (1983) Current state of truck escape-ramp technology. *Transportation Research Record 923*, pp 35-42.

Barjonet P, Benjamin T and Wittink R (eds) (1994) *European drivers and traffic safety*. (Presses des Ponts et Chaussees, Paris).

Barton EV (1989) Performance and design of intersections, in Ogden and Bennett DW (eds) *Traffic Engineering Practice (4th edition)*, pp 290-325. (Monash University, Melbourne, Australia).

Bayley JM and Uber CB (1990) A comprehensive program to improve road safety at railway level crossings. *Proc 15th Australian Road Research Board Conference 15(7)*, pp 217-234.

Benekohal RF and Hashmi AM (1992) Procedures for estimating accident reductions on two-lane highways. *ASCE Journal of Transportation Engineering 118(1)*, pp 111-129.

Bennett GT (1966) Accidents at heavily trafficked rural 3-way junctions. *J Institution of Highway Engineers 13(2)*, pp 29-37.

Bennett GT and Marland J (1978) Road accidents in traditionally-designed residential estates. *Supplementary Report SR 394*. 38 p. (Transport and Road Research Laboratory, Crowthorne, UK).

Berg WD, Knoblauch K and Hucke W (1982) Causal factors in railroad-highway grade crossing accidents. *Transportation Research Record 847*, pp 47-54.

Bhatnagar YS (1994) Observations on the use of chevron alignment markers. *Proc 17th Australian Road Research Board Conference 17(5)*, pp 65-81.

Bhesania RP (1991) Impact of mast-mounted signal heads on accident reduction. *ITE Journal 61(10)*, pp 25-30.

Bissell HH (1993) Traffic control devices: Delineation, in *The Traffic Safety Toolbox: A Primer on Traffic Safety*, pp 85-90. (Institute of Transportation Engineers, Washington, DC).

Bligh P, Sicking DL and Ross HE (1987) Development of guardrail to bridge rail transition. *Research Report 461-1F*. (Texas Transportation Institute, College Station).

Bowman BL (1987) Analysis of railroad-highway crossing active advance warning devices. *Transportation Research Record 1114*, pp 141-151.

Bowman BL and Coleman JA (1990) Grade severity rating system. *ITE Journal, 60(7)*, pp 19-24.

Box PC (1972) Comparison of accidents and illumination. *Highway Research Record 416*, pp 1-9.

Box PC and Oppenlander JC (1976) *Manual of Traffic Engineering Studies*. 233 p. (Institute of Transportation Engineers, Washington, DC).

Boyle AJ and Wright CC (1984) Accident migration after remedial treatment at accident blackspots. *Traffic Engineering and Control 25(5)*, pp 260-267

Bray JS (1993) A realistic safety management system. *Transportation Research Circular 416: Issues Surrounding Highway and Roadside Safety Management*, pp 21-29. (Transportation Research Board, Washington, DC).

Brindle RE (1989) SOD the distributor! *Multi-Disciplinary Engineering Transactions GE13(2)*, pp 99-112. (Institution of Engineers, Australia, Canberra).

Brindle RE (1992) Local street management in Australia: Is it 'traffic calming'? *Accident Analysis and Prevention 24(1)*, pp 29-38.

Brindle RE (1986a) The 'difficult distributor': The problem of traffic routes in residential areas. *Australian Planner 2(4)*, pp 14-20.

Brindle RE (1986b) The relationship between traffic management, speed and safety in neighbourhoods. *Proc 13th Australian Road Research Board Conference 13(9)*, pp 90-102.

Bronstad ME and Michie JD (1981) Multiple service level highway bridge railing selection procedures. *National Cooperative Highway Research Program Report 239.* (Transportation Research Board, Washington, DC).

Bronstad ME, Ray MH, Mayer JB and McDevitt CF (1987) Guardrail-bridge rail transition evaluations. *Transportation Research Record 1133*, pp 7-16.

Brownfield J (1993) Road safety plans: Guidance on best practice. *Proceedings PTRC Summer Annual Meeting, Seminar C*, pp 261-284. (Planning and Transportation Research and Computation, London).

Bryden JE (1993) Work zone traffic management, in *The Traffic Safety Toolbox: A Primer on Traffic Safety*, pp 179-186. (Institute of Transportation Engineers, Washington, DC).

Bryer TE (1993) Safety management, in *The Traffic Safety Toolbox: A Primer on Traffic Safety*, pp 11-24. (Institute of Transportation Engineers, Washington, DC).

Buchanan CD (Chairman) (1963) *Traffic in Towns: Report of the Working Group.* 263 p. (Her Majesty's Stationery Office, London).

Bui B, Cameron M and Foong CW (1991) *Effect of Right Turn Phases at Signalised Intersections. Part 1, Safety Performance.* 80 p. (Monash University Accident Research Centre, Melbourne, Australia).

Bui B, Corben B, Leeming A and Brierley R (1991) *Survey of Drivers Involved in Crashes at Signalised Intersections in the Melbourne Metropolitan Area.* 33 p. (Monash University Accident Research Centre, Melbourne, Australia).

Burden D (1993) Bicycling element, in *The Traffic Safety Toolbox: A Primer on Traffic Safety*, pp 203-214. (Institute of Transportation Engineers, Washington, DC).

Bureau of Transport and Communications Economics (1992) Social cost of transport accidents in Australia. *BTCE Report 79.* 119 p. (Australian Government Publishing Service, Canberra).

Bureau of Transport and Communications Economics (1993) Cost effectiveness of black spot treatments: A pilot study. *BTCE Working Paper 9.* 37 p. (Department of Transport and Communications, Canberra, Australia).

Bureau of Transport and Communications Economics (1994) *Costs of Road Crashes in Australia.* 2 p. (BTCE, Canberra, Australia).

Bureau of Transport and Communications Economics (1995) Evaluation of the black spot program. *BTCE Report 90.* 317 p. (Australian Government Publishing Service, Canberra).

Burns JC, Meyer WE, Hayhoe GF and Ivey DL (1984) Pavement Edges, in *State of the Art Report: The Influence of Roadway Surface Discontinuities on Safety*, pp 17-23. (Transportation Research Board, Washington, DC).

Burrough P (1991) *Procedure for the Road Safety Audit of Trunk Road Schemes.* 10 p. (UK Department of Transport, London).

Cairney PT (1983) An analysis of casualty accidents at urban intersections in Victoria and their relationship to traffic control devices. *Internal Report AIR 394-1.* 25 p. (Australian Road Research Board, Melbourne).

Cairney PT (1984) Australian road users' understanding of traffic control devices. *Proc. 11th Australian Road Research Board Conference 11(5)*, pp 206-216.

Cairney PT (1986) Major-minor intersections and junctions - a greater problem than we think? *Proc 13th Australian Road Research Board Conference 13(9)*, pp 78-79.

Cairney PT (1988) Safety at traffic signals. *ARRB Internal Report AIR 394-10.* 21 p. (Australian Road Research Board, Melbourne).

Cairney PT and Catchpole JE (1991) Road user behaviours which contribute to accidents at urban signalised intersections. *ARRB Research Report ARR 197.* 69 p. (Australian Road Research Board, Melbourne).

Cameron MH and Newstead S (1993) Evaluation of mass media publicity as support for enforcement. *Proc Australasian Drink-Drive Conference.* pp 21-43. (VicRoads, Melbourne, Australia).

Cantilli EJ (1982) Transportation safety, in Homburger WS, Keefer LE and McGrath WR (eds) *Transportation and Traffic Engineering Handbook (2nd edition)*, pp 555-584. (Prentice Hall, Englewood Cliffs, NJ, for the Institute of Transportation Engineers, Washington, DC).

Carney JF (ed) *Effectiveness of Highway Safety Improvements.* 295 p. (American Society of Civil Engineers, New York).

Carstens OMJ, Tight MR, Southwell MY and Plows B (1989) *Urban Accidents: Why Do They Happen?* 68 p. (Automobile Association Foundation for Road Safety Research, Basingstoke, UK).

Carthy T, Packham D, Salter D and Silcock D (1995) *Risk and Safety on the Roads: The Older Pedestrian*. 103 p. (AA Foundation for Road Safety Research, Basingstoke, UK).

Chadda HS and Carter EC (1983) Multi-way stop signs: Have we gone too far? *ITE Journal 53(5)*, pp 19-21.

Chang GL and Paniati JF (1990) Effects of 65 mph speed limit on traffic safety. *Journal of Transportation Engineering 116 (2)*, pp 213-226.

Chapman RA (1973) The concept of exposure. *Accident Analysis and Prevention 5*, pp 95-110.

Chatfield BV (1987) System-wide safety improvements: An approach to safety consistency:. *National Cooperative Highway Research Program Synthesis of Highway Practice 132*. (Transportation Research Board, Washington, DC).

Chira-Chivala T and Mak KK (1986) Identification of accident factors on highway segments: A method and applications. *Transportation Research Record 1068*, pp 52-58.

Cirillo JA (1992) *Safety Effectiveness of Highway Design Features. Volume 1, Access Control*. 9 p. (Federal Highway Administration, Washington, DC).

Cirillo JA (1993) Roadside safety, in Institute of Transportation Engineers *The Traffic Safety Toolbox: A Primer on Traffic Safety*, pp 149-156. (ITE, Washington, DC).

Cirillo JA and Council FM (1986) Highway safety: Twenty years later. *Transportation Research Record 1068*, pp 90-95.

Clark JE (1985) High speeds and volumes on residential streets: An analysis of physical street characteristics as causes in Sacramento, California. *Compendium of Technical papers, 55th Annual Meeting*. pp 93-96. (Institute of Transportation Engineers, Washington, DC).

Cleveland DE (1987) The effect of resurfacing on highway safety, in *State of the Art Report Number 6: Relationship Between Safety and Key Highway Features*, pp 78-95. (Transportation Research Board, Washington, DC).

Cole BL (1972) Visual aspects of road engineering. *Proc. 6th Australian Road Research Board Conference 6(1)*, pp 102-148.

Cole BL and Jenkins SE (1980) The nature and measurement of conspicuity. *Proc. 10th Australian Road Research Board Conference 10(4)*, pp 99-107.

Cole BL and Jenkins SE (1982) Conspicuity of traffic control devices. *Australian Road Research 12(4)*, pp 223-238.

Colwill DM and Daines ME (1987) Development of spray-reducing macadam road surfacings in the United Kingdom. *Transportation Research Record 1115*, pp 196-202.

Controle de Securite des Infrastructures (1994) *Vade-Mecum.* (CSI, Paris).

Corben BF (1989) *Crashes at Traffic Signals: Guidelines for a traffic Engineering Safety program of Replacing Selected intersection Signals with Roundabouts.* 10 p. (Monash University Accident Research Centre, Melbourne, Australia).

Corben BF, Ambrose C and Foong CW (1990) Evaluation of accident black spot treatments. *Report No. 11.* 16 p. (Monash University Accident Research Centre, Melbourne, Australia).

Corben BF and Cunningham JA (1989) Traffic engineering treatment of hazardous locations, in Ogden KW and Bennett DW (eds) *Traffic Engineering Practice (4th edition)*, pp 271-289. (Monash University, Melbourne, Australia).

Corben BF and Foong CW (1990) Pro-active traffic engineering safety study: Final Report, Part 2, Right turn against crashes at traffic signals. *Report No. 14.* 15 p. (Monash University Accident Research Centre, Melbourne, Australia).

Council FM and Hall WL (1989) Large truck safety: An analysis of North Carolina accident data. *Proc 33rd Conference, American Association for Automotive Medicine*, pp 91-110.

Council FM, Reinfurt DW, Campbell BJ, Roediger FL, Carroll CL, Dutt AK and Dunham JR (1980) Accident research manual. *Report FHWA RD-80-016.* (Federal Highway Administration, Washington, DC).

Council FM, Stewart JR and Rodgman EA (1987) *Development of Exposure Measures for Highway Safety Analysis.* 114 p. (Highway Safety Research Centre, University of North Carolina, Chapel Hill, USA).

County Surveyors' Society (1987) *Small and Mini Roundabouts.* (CSS, Chelmsford, UK).

County Surveyors Society (1989a) *Automated Traffic Signals Installation.* (CSS, Ipswich, UK).

County Surveyors' Society (1989b) *Carriageway Definition.* (CSS, Ipswich, UK).

County Surveyors' Society (1991) *Monitoring the Effectiveness of Remedial Measures.* 9 p. (CSS, London).

County Surveyors' Society (1993a) *Accidents at Signalised Roundabouts*. 7 p. (CSS, Ipswich, UK).

County Surveyor's Society (1993b) *The Current State of Road Safety Audit in Great Britain*. 19 p. (CSS, London).

County Surveyors' Society (1994) *Traffic Calming in Practice*. (Landor Publishing, London).

Crampton G, Hass-Klau C and Thrush J (1990) Bicycle safety in German and English towns. *Proceedings PTRC Summer Annual Meeting, Seminar G*, pp 225-236. (Planning and Transportation Research and Computation, London).

Craus J, Livneh M and Ishai I (1991) Effect of pavement and shoulder condition on highway accidents. *Transportation Research Record 1318*, pp 51-57.

Croft PG (1980) An assessment of 'running the red signal' as a traffic safety problem, in Hulsher FR (ed) *Driver Observance of Traffic Light Signals*. (Traffic Authority of NSW, Sydney, Australia).

Crowley JD and Denman OS (1992) Site-specific issues: Application or misapplication of highway safety appurtenances. *Transportation Research Record 1367*, pp 84-91.

Cumming RW (1964) The analysis of skills in driving. *Australian Road Research 1(9)*, pp 4-14.

Cumming RW and Croft PG (1973) Human information processing under varying task demand. *Ergonomics 16(5)*, pp 581-586.

Cunard RA (1993) Traffic control devices: Signs, in *The Traffic Safety Toolbox: A Primer on Traffic Safety*, pp 53-62. (Institute of Transportation Engineers, Washington, DC).

Daines ME (1992) Trials of porous asphalt and rolled asphalt on the A38 at Burton. *Research Report 323*. (Transport and Road Research Laboratory, Crowthorne, UK).

Dalby E and Ward H (1981) Application of low cost road accident countermeasures according to an area-wide strategy. *Traffic Engineering and Control 22(11)*, pp 567-575.

Daly PN, McGrath F and van Emst AB (1991) Accidents at pedestrian crossing facilities. *Contractor Report CR 57*. 52 p. (Transport Research Laboratory, Crowthorne, UK).

Datta TK and Dutta U (1990) Traffic signal installation and accident experience. *ITE Journal 60(9)*, pp 39-42.

473

Davies H and Winnett M (1993) Why do pedestrian accidents happen? *Proceedings PTRC Summer Annual Meeting, Seminar C*, pp 315-324. (Planning and Transportation Research and Computation, London).

Davies R and Barrell J (1993) Bypass demonstration project: Contrasting features of the six towns. *Proceedings PTRC Summer Annual Meeting, Seminar C*, pp 85-94. (Planning and Transportation Research and Computation, London).

Deacon JA, Zegeer CV and Deen RC (1975) Identification of hazardous rural road locations. *Transportation Research Record 543*, pp 16-33.

Department of Industry, Technology and Commerce (Australia) (1990) *Australian Model Code for Residential Development*. (Australian Government Publishing Service, Canberra).

Department of Transport (UK) (1985) Safety fences and barriers. *Departmental Standard TD 19/85*. (DOT, London).

Department of Transport (UK) (1986) *Accident Investigation Manual*. (2 vols). (DOT, London).

Department of Transport (UK) (1987) *Inter-Departmental Review of Road Safety. Road Safety: The Next Steps*. 48 p. (DOT, London).

Department of Transport (UK) (1991) 20 mph speed limit zones. *Traffic Advisory Leaflet 7/93*. 4 p. (DOT, London).

Department of Transport (UK) (1992) *Killing Speed and Saving Lives*. 19 p. (DOT, London).

Department of Transport (UK) (1993a) Traffic calming special authorisations. *Traffic Advisory Leaflet 3/93*. 4 p. (DOT, London).

Department of Transport (UK) (1993b) Traffic calming regulations. *Traffic Advisory Leaflet 7/93*. 6 p. (DOT, London).

Department of Transport (UK) (1993c) Rumble devices. *Traffic Advisory Leaflet 11/93*. 4 p. (DOT, London).

Department of Transport (UK) (1993d) The Geometric Design of Roundabouts. *Departmental Standard TD 16/93*. (DOT, London).

Department of Transport (UK) (1993e) Bypass Demonstration Project. 8 p. (DOT, London).

Department of Transport (UK) (1994a) *Design Manual for Roads and Bridges. Highway Advice Note HA42/94: Road Safety Audits*. (DOT, London).

Department of Transport (UK) (1994b) *Design Manual for Roads and Bridges. Departmental Standard HD 19/94: Road Safety Audits*. (DOT, London).

Department of Transport (UK) (1994c) VISP - A summary. *Traffic Advisory Leaflet 1/94*. 6 p. (DOT, London).

Department of Transportation (US) (1991) Action plan: Effective highway accident countermeasures. *Publication No. FHWA-SA-91-016*. 29 p. (US DOT, Washington, DC).

Devon County Council (1992) *Traffic Calming Guidelines*. (DCC, Exeter, UK).

Devon County Council (1994) *Traffic Calming: Practice Notes*. 14 p. (DCC, Exeter, UK).

Dewar R (1993) Traffic control devices, highway safety and human factors. *Transportation Research Circular 414: Human Factors Research in Highway Safety*, pp 12-20. (Transportation Research Board, Washington, DC).

Donald D (1995) Making traffic signs work: An overview of design and testing procedures. *ARRB Special Report 52*. 51 p. (Australian Road Research Board, Melbourne).

Donaldson GA (1986) Safety of large trucks and the geometric design of two-lane two-way roads. *Transportation Research Record 1052*, pp 10-14.

Drummond AE (1989) An overview of novice driver performance issues: A literature review. *MUARC Report No 9*. (Monash University Accident Research Centre, Melbourne, Australia).

Dunlap DF, Fancher PS, Scott RE, McAdam CC and Segal L (1978) Influence of combined highway grade and horizontal alignment on skidding. *National Cooperative Highway Research Program Report 184*. 33 p. (Washington, DC).

Eck RW and Sabra ZA (1985) Active advance warning signs at high-speed signalised intersections: A survey of practice. *Transportation Research Record 1010*, pp 62-64.

Ells JG and Dewar RE (1979) Rapid comprehension of verbal and symbolic traffic sign messages. *Human Factors 21(2)*, pp 161-168.

Emerson JW and West LB (1986) Shoulder rumble strips at narrow bridges. in Carney JF (ed) *Effectiveness of Highway Safety Improvements*, pp 207-217. (American Society of Civil Engineers, New York).

Engel U and Thomsen LK (1992) Safety effects of speed reducing measures in danish residential areas. *Accident Analysis and Prevention 24(1)*, pp 17-28.

Epstein JA and Hunter LL (1984) The legal implications of frangible poles. *Report CR 31*, 211 p. (Federal Office of Road Safety, Canberra, Australia).

Ercoli L and Negri L (1985) A proposal for the standardisation of road accident reports. *Evaluation 85: Proceedings of an International Meeting on the Evaluation of Local Traffic Safety Measures, Vol 3.* pp 769-786. (Organisme National de Securite Routiere, Paris).

Evans AW (1994) Evaluating public transport and road safety measures. *Accident Analysis and prevention 26(4)*, pp 411-428.

Evans L (1986) Risk homeostasis theory and traffic accident data. *Risk Analysis 6(1)*, pp 81-94.

Evans L (1991) *Traffic Safety and the Driver*. 404 p. (van Norstrad Reinhold, New York).

Evans L and Wasielewski P (1983) Risky driving related to driver and vehicle characteristics. *Accident Analysis and Prevention 15(2)*, pp 121-136.

Fairlie RB and Taylor MAP (1990) Evaluating the safety benefits of local area traffic management. *Proc 15th Australian Road Research Board Conference 15(7)*, pp 141-166.

Fambro DB, Heathington KW and Richards SH (1989) Evaluation of two active traffic control devices for use at railroad-highway grade crossings. *Transportation Research Record 1244*, pp 52-62.

Fancher PS (1986) Sight distance problems related to large trucks. *Transportation Research Record 1052*, pp 29-35.

Faure A and de Neuville A (1992) Safety in urban areas: The French program 'safer city, accident-free districts'. *Accident Analysis and Prevention 24(1)*, pp 39-44.

Federal Highway Administration (1982) Synthesis of safety research related to traffic control and road way elements (2 volumes). *Report FHWA-TS-82-233*. (FHWA, Washington, DC).

Federal Highway Administration (1986) *Guide for Monitoring and Enhancing Safety on the National Truck Network*. (FHWA, Washington, DC).

Federal Highway Administration (1991a) *Proc Safety Management System Workshop: Managing Mobility Safely*. 15 p plus appendices. (FHWA, Washington, DC).

Federal Highway Administration (1991b) *Management Approach to Highway Safety: A Compilation of Good Practice*. 8 p. (FHWA, Washington, DC).

Federal Highway Administration (1992). *FHWA/FTA Docket 92/14: Proposed Rule for Safety Management System.* (FHWA, Washington, DC).

Federal Office of Road Safety (1992) *The National Road Safety Strategy.* 24 p. (FORS, Canberra, Australia).

Fildes BN and Lee SJ (1993) The Speed Review: Road environment, behaviour, speed limits, enforcement and crashes. *FORS Report CR 127.* 146 p. (Federal Office of Road Safety, Canberra, Australia).

Forbes TW (1972) *Human Factors in Highway Traffic Safety Research.* 419 p. (Wiley, New York).

Forrester JW (1969) *Urban Dynamics.* 285 p. (MIT Press, Cambridge, MA, USA).

Foyster MJ and Thompson M (1986) The effects of road lighting improvements in Westminster on road accidents. *Proceedings PTRC Summer Annual Meeting, Seminar P.* (Planning and Transportation Research and Computation, London).

Freedman M, Staplin LK, Gilfillan DP and Byrnes AM (1988) Noticeability requirements for delineation on non-illuminated highways. *Report No FHWA-RD-88-028.* 96 p. (Federal Highway Administration, Washington, DC).

Fujitsuka T (1991) From community streets to 'road-pia'. *The Wheel Extended 73.* pp 3-8. (Toyota Motor Corporation, Tokyo).

Gaberty MJ and Barbaresso JC (1987) A case study of the accident impacts of flashing signal operations along roadways. *ITE Journal 57(7),* pp 27-28.

Garber NJ and Hoel LA (1988) *Traffic and Highway Engineering.* 959 p. (West Publishing Co., St. Paul, MN, USA).

Garber S and Graham JD (1990) The effect of the new 65 mph speed limit on rural highway fatalities: A state-by-state analysis. *Accident Analysis and Prevention 22(2),* pp 137-149.

Garder P (1989) Pedestrian safety at traffic signals: A study carried out with the help of a traffic conflicts technique. *Accident Analysis and Prevention 21(5),* pp 435-444.

Gazis D, Herman R and Marududin A (1960) The problem of the amber signal light in traffic flow. *Traffic Engineering 30(1),* pp 19-26.

Geoffroy DN (1993a) Infrastructure maintenance: Pavements, in *The Traffic Safety Toolbox: A Primer on Traffic Safety,* pp 157-164. (Institute of Transportation Engineers, Washington, DC).

Geoffroy DN (1993b) A management perspective on developing and implementing safety management systems. *Transportation Research Circular 416: Issues Surrounding Highway and Roadside Safety Management*, pp 8-16. (Transportation Research Board, Washington, DC).

Geoplan Town Planning (1990) Neighbourhood safety and amenity. *FORS Report CR 98*. 91 p plus appendices. (Federal Office of Road Safety, Canberra, Australia).

Glauz WD and Migletz DJ (1980) Application of traffic conflict analysis at intersections. *National Cooperative Highway Research Program Report 219*. 109 p. (Washington, DC).

Glennon JC (1987a) Effect of pavement/ shoulder drop-offs on highway safety. *State of the Art Report 6: Relationship Between Safety and Key Highway Features*, pp 36-47. (Transportation Research Board, Washington, DC).

Glennon JC (1987b) Effect of alignment on highway safety, in *State of the Art Report Number 6: Relationship Between Safety and Key Highway Features*, pp 48-63. (Transportation Research Board, Washington, DC).

Glennon JC (1987c) Effect of sight distance on highway safety, in *State of the Art Report Number 6: Relationship Between Safety and Key Highway Features*, pp 64-77. (Transportation Research Board, Washington, DC).

Glennon JC (1993) Geometric design: Sight distance, in *The Traffic Safety Toolbox: A Primer on Traffic Safety*, pp 109-122. (Institute of Transportation Engineers, Washington, DC).

Glennon J and Azzeh JA (1976) Access control on arterial highways. *ASCE Transportation Engineering Journal 76(1)*, pp 75-90.

Good MC and Baxter GI (1985) Evaluation of short range roadway delineation. *ARRB Internal Report 381-1*, (Australian Road Research Board, Melbourne).

Good MC, Fox JC and Joubert PN (1987) An in-depth study of accidents involving collisions with utility poles. *Accident Analysis and Prevention 19(5)*, pp 397-413.

Graham JL (1988) Design considerations for trucks in work zones, in Smith BL and Mason JM (eds) *Accommodation of Trucks on the Highway: Safety in Design*, pp 74-88. (American Society of Civil Engineers, New York).

Graham JL and Harwood DW (1983) Effectiveness of clear recovery zones. *Transportation Research Record 923*, pp 72-86.

Grayson GB (1975) The Hampshire child pedestrian accident study. *Laboratory Report LR 668.* (Transport and Road Research Laboratory, Crowthorne, UK).

Greenberg FM (1995) Pedestrian signal usage in the central business district of medium-sized cities. *ITE Journal 65(4),* pp 15-18.

Griffin LI (1984) How effective are crash cushions in reducing death and injury? *Public Roads 47(4),* pp 132-134.

Gunnarsson SO (1993) Traffic planning, in Institute of Transportation Engineers *The Traffic Safety Toolbox: A Primer on Traffic Safety,* pp 25-44. (ITE, Washington, DC).

Haddon W (1980) Advances in the epidemiology of injuries as a basis for public policy. *Public Health Reports 95(5),* pp 411-421.

Hagan B and Amamoo SE (1988) Residential street management in South Australia. *ITE Journal 60(3),* pp 35-41.

Haight FA (1981) Pedestrian safety in the Unites States: Some recent trends. *Accident Analysis and Prevention 13(1),* pp 43-55.

Haight FA (1983) Some theoretical aspects of road safety, in Andreassend DC and Gipps PG (eds) *Traffic Accident Evaluation.* (Monash University, Melbourne, Australia).

Haight FA (1985) Conceptual pitfalls in traffic safety evaluation. *Evaluation 85: Proceedings of an International Meeting on the Evaluation of Local Traffic Safety Measures, Vol 1.* pp 32-42. (Organisme National de Securite Routiere, Paris).

Haight (1986) Risk, especially risk of traffic accident. *Accident Analysis and Prevention 18(5),* pp 359-366.

Haight FA (1987) Some underlying issues in traffic safety. *ITS Review 10(2),* pp 4-8.

Haight FA (1994) Problems in estimating comparative costs of safety and mobility. *Journal of Transport Economics and Policy 28(1),* pp 7-30.

Hakkert AS and Malalel D (1978) The effect of traffic signals on road accidents with special reference to the introduction of a blinking green phase. *Traffic Engineering and Control 19(6),* 212-215.

Hall Rd (1986) Accidents at 4-arm single carriageway urban traffic signals. *Contractor Report CR 65.* 107 p. (Transport and Road Research Laboratory, Crowthorne, UK).

Harris S (1986) Linking road accident data to other files. *Proceedings PTRC Summer Annual Meeting, Seminar P.* (Planning and Transportation Research and Computation, London).

479

Harrison JH, Hall RD and Harland DG (1989) Literature review of accident analysis methodologies and cycle facilities. *Contractor Report CR 163.* 39 p. (Transport and Road Research Laboratory, Crowthorne, UK).

Harwood DW (1993) Use of rumble strips to enhance safety. *National Cooperative Highway Research Program: Synthesis of Highway Practice 191.* 42 p. (Transportation Research Board, Washington, DC).

Harwood DW and Hoban CJ (1987) Low cost operational and safety improvements for two lane roads *Report FHWA-IP-87-2.* (Federal Highway Administration, Washington, DC).

Harwood DW, St John AD and Warren DL (1985) Operational and safety effectiveness of passing lanes on two-lane highways *Transportation Research Record 1026,* pp 31-39.

Hass-Klau C (1990) The theory and practice of traffic calming: Can Britain learn from the German experience. *Rees Jeffries Road Fund, Transport and Society Discussion Paper 10.* (Transport Studies Unit, University of Oxford).

Hauer E (1980) Selection for treatment as a source of bias in before-and-after studies. *Traffic Engineering and Control 21(8/9),* pp 419-421.

Hauer E (1983) Reflections on methods of statistical inference in research on the effects of safety countermeasures. *Accident Analysis and Prevention 15(4),* pp 275-285.

Hauer E (1988) A case for science-based road safety design and management, in Stammer RE (ed) *Highway Safety: At the Crossroads,* pp 241-278. (American Society of Civil Engineers, New York).

Hauer E (1992) Empirical Bayes approach to the estimation of "unsafety": The multivariate regression method. *Accident Analysis and Prevention 24(5),* pp 457-477.

Hauer E (1993) Overview, in *The Traffic Safety Toolbox: A Primer on Traffic Safety,* pp 1-10. (Institute of Transportation Engineers, Washington, DC).

Hauer E, Ng CN and Lovell J (1988) Estimation of safety at signalised intersections. *Transportation Research Record 1185,* pp 48-61.

Hawley L, Henson C, Hulse A and Brindle R (1993) Towards traffic calming: A practitioner's manual of implemented local area traffic management and blackspot devices. *Report CR 126.* (Federal Office of Road Safety, Canberra, Australia).

Heathington KW, Fambro DB, and Richards SH (1989) Field evaluation of a four-quadrant gate system for use at railroad-highway grade crossings. *Transportation Research Record 1244*, pp 39-51.

Hedman KO (1990) Road design and safety. *VTI Rapport 351A*, pp 225-238. (Swedish Road and Traffic Research Institute, Linkoping, Sweden).

Heggie IG (1972). Transport Engineering Economics. (McGraw Hill, London).

Helliar-Symons RD (1981) Yellow bar experimental carriageway markings: Accident study. *Laboratory Report LR 1010.* 17 p. (Transport and Road Research Laboratory, Crowthorne, UK).

Helliar-Symons RD and Lynam DA (1989) Accident reduction and prevention programmes in highway authorities. *Research Report RR 187.* (Transport Research Laboratory, Crowthorne, UK).

Herrstedt L (1992) Traffic calming design: A speed management method. *Accident Analysis and Prevention 24(1)*, pp 3-16.

Highways Agency (1994) *Trunk Road Safety Audits.* 10 p. (HA, London).

Hill M (1968). A goals-achievement matrix for evaluating alternative plans. *Journal of the American Institute of Planners 34(1)*, pp 19-29.

Hillier JA and Wardrop JG (1966) Effect of grade and curvature on accidents on the London-Birmingham motorway. *Traffic Engineering and Control 17(10),* pp 617-621.

Himus A (1990) Sea change in safety fencing. *Highways 59 (1959)*, pp 12-14.

Ho YS (1991) Vehicle skidding in injury road accidents. *Road Accidents Great Britain 1990*, pp 46-49. (Department of Transport, London).

Hoban CJ (1982) The two and a half lane road. *Proc 11th Australian Road Research Board Conference 11(4)*, pp 59-67.

Hoban CJ (1988) Selecting appropriate geometric standards for rural road improvements. *Compendium of Technical papers, 58th Annual Meeting.* pp 332-340. (Institute of Transportation Engineers, Washington, DC).

Hocherman I, Hakkert AS and Bar-Ziv J (1990) Safety of one-way urban streets. *Transportation Research Record 1270*, pp 22-27.

Hodge GA, Daley KF and Nguyen TN (1986) Signal coordination in regional areas of Melbourne - a road safety evaluation. *Proc 13th Australian Road Research Board Conference, 13(9)*, pp 178-190.

Hofstetter DKH and Gipson J (1993) Roadside rating scales. *Transportation Research Circular 416: Issues Surrounding Highway and Roadside Safety Management*, pp 39-48. (Transportation Research Board, Washington, DC).

Homburger WS, Deakin EA, Bosselmann PC, Smith DT and Beukers B (1989) *Residential Street Design and Traffic Control*. 152 p. (Prentice Hall, Englewood Cliffs, NJ, for the Institute of Transportation Engineers, Washington, DC).

Homburger WS, Keefer LE and McGrath WR (eds) (1990) *Transportation and Traffic Engineering Handbook (2nd edition)*. 883 p. (Prentice Hall, Englewood Cliffs, NJ, for the Institute of Transportation Engineers, Washington, DC).

Hoque MM and Sanderson JT (1988) Road Safety Countermeasures for Rural Roads. *Report TS88/3*. 40 p. (Royal Automobile Club of Victoria).

Hosking JR and Woodford GC (1976) Measurement of skidding resistance: Guide to the use of SCRIM. *Laboratory Report LR 737*. (Transport and Road Research Laboratory, Crowthorne, UK).

Howie DJ and Oulton G (1989) *Crashes at Traffic Signals*. (Monash University Accident Research Centre, Melbourne, Australia).

Hughes BP (1991) *Accident Prediction at Traffic Signals*. 55 p. (Main Roads Department, WA, Perth).

Hulbert S (1982) Human factors in transportation, in Homburger WS, Keefer LE and McGrath WR (eds) *Transportation and Traffic Engineering Handbook (2nd edition)*, pp 209-234. (Prentice Hall, Englewood Cliffs, NJ, for the Institute of Transportation Engineers, Washington, DC).

Hulsher FR (1984) The problem of stopping drivers after the termination of the green signal at traffic lights. *Traffic Engineering and Control 25(3)*, pp 110-116.

Hummer JE (1994a) Traffic accident studies, in Robertson HD, Hummer JE and Nelson DC (eds) *Manual of Traffic Engineering Studies*. pp 191-218. (Prentice Hall, Englewood Cliffs, NJ, for the Institute of Transportation Engineers, Washington, DC).

Hummer JE (1994b) Traffic conflict studies, in Robertson HD, Hummer JE and Nelson DC (eds) *Manual of Traffic Engineering Studies*. pp 219-235. (Prentice Hall, Englewood Cliffs, NJ, for the Institute of Transportation Engineers, Washington, DC).

Hummer EJ, Montgomery RE and Sinha K (1990) Motorists understanding of and preferences for left-turn signals. *Transportation Research Record 1281*, pp 136-147.

Hunt J (1993) Pedestrian crossings: Changing the balance of priorities. *Proceedings PTRC Summer Annual Meeting, Seminar C*, pp 325-336. (Planning and Transportation Research and Computation, London).

Hutchinson BG (1988) Geometric, capacity and safety impacts of large trucks in urban areas. *Proc Roads and Traffic Association of Canada Annual Meeting*, pp D3-D32.

Hutchinson TP and Mayne AJ (1977) The year to year variability in the numbers of road accidents. *Traffic Engineering and Control 18(9)*, pp 432-433.

Institute for Road Safety Research (1985) *Reclassification and Reconstruction of Urban Roads in The Netherlands* (IRSR, SWOV, The Netherlands).

Institute for Road Safety Research (1986) Safety barriers for motorways. *Report R-86-24*. (IRSR, SWOV, The Netherlands).

Institute of Transportation Engineers (1990) *Guidelines for Parking Facility Location and Design.* 32 p. (ITE, Washington, DC).

Institute of Transportation Engineers (1993a) *The Traffic Safety Toolbox: A Primer on Traffic Safety.* 258 p. (ITE, Washington, DC).

Institute of Transportation Engineers (1993b) Guidelines for the design and application of speed humps. *ITE Journal 63(5)*, pp 11-17.

Institute of Transportation Engineers (1994) ITE supports expansion of highway safety program guidelines. *ITE Journal 64(4)*, p 9.

Institute of Transportation Engineers (1995) Road safety audit: A new tool for accident prevention. *ITE Journal 65(2)*, pp 15-22.

Institution of Highways and Transportation (1987) *Roads and Traffic in Urban Areas.* 418 p. (IHT, London).

Institution of Highways and Transportation (1990a) *Highway Safety Guidelines: Accident Reduction and Prevention.* 36 p. (IHT, London).

Institution of Highways and Transportation (1990b) *Guidelines for the Safety Audit of Highways.* 40 p. (IHT, London).

Institution of Highways and Transportation (1990c) *Guidelines for Urban Safety Management.* 124 p. (IHT, London).

Ivey DL and Griffin LI (1976) Driver-vehicle reaction to road surface discontinuities. *Proc. 16th Congress of the International Federation of the Societies of Automotive Engineers.* (Tokyo, Japan).

Ivey DL and Morgan JR (1986) Timber pole safety by design. *Transportation Research Record 1065*, pp 1-11.

Ivey DL and Mounce JM (1984) Water accumulations, in *State of the Art Report: The Influence of Roadway Surface Discontinuities on Safety*. pp 24-34. (Transportation Research Board, Washington, DC).

Ivey DL, Olson RM, Walton NE, Weaver GD and Furr LW (1979) Safety at narrow bridge sites. *National Cooperative Highway Research Program Report 203*. (Transportation Research Board, Washington, DC).

Ivey DL and Sicking DL (1986) Influence of pavement edge and shoulder characteristics on vehicle handling and safety. *Transportation Research Record 1084*, pp 30-39.

Jackson J (1981) Safety measures: The contribution of carriageway markings. *The Highway Engineer 28(2), pp 2-5.*

Jackson LE (1986) Truck accident studies. *Transportation Research Record 1052*, pp 137-145.

James HF (1991) Under-reporting of road traffic accidents. *Traffic Engineering and Control 32(12)*, pp 573-583.

Janssen STMC (1991) Road safety in urban districts: Final results of accident studies in the Dutch demonstration projects of the 1970s. *Traffic Engineering and Control 32(6)*, pp 292-296.

Jarvis JR (1992) An investigation of road humps for use on bus routes: Final report. *ARRB Research Report ARR 222.* (Australian Road Research Board, Melbourne).

Jarvis JR (1994) *Heavy Vehicle Braking Behaviour.* 269 p plus appendices. PhD thesis, Department of Civil Engineering. (Monash University, Melbourne, Australia).

Jarvis JR and Hoban CJ (1988) VLimits: An expert system for speed zone determination in Victoria. *ARRB Research Report ARR 155.* 46 p. (Australian Road Research Board, Melbourne).

Jarvis JR and Mullen EF (1977) Roadside hazards - the institutional problem. *Proc Joint ARRB/DOT Fixed Roadside Hazards Symposium*, pp 1-5. (Australian Road Research Board, Melbourne).

Jennings BE and Demetsky MJ (1985) Evaluation of curve delineation signs. *Transportation Research Record 1010*, pp 53-61.

Johnson HD (1980) Cross-over accidents on all-purpose dual carriageways. *Supplementary Report 617*, 9 p. (Transport and Road Research Laboratory, Crowthorne, UK).

Johnston AW and Cole BL (1976) Investigations of distraction by irrelevant information. *Australian Road Research 6(3),* pp 3-23.

Johnston IR (1982) Modifying driver behaviour on rural road curves. *Proc 11th Australian Road Research Board Conference 11(4),* pp 115-134.

Johnston IR (1983) The effects of roadway delineation on curve negotiation by both sober and drinking drivers. *ARRB Research Report ARR 128,* (Australian Road Research Board, Melbourne).

Johnston N, McDonald N and Fuller R (1994) *Aviation Psychology in Practice.* 363 p. (Avebury Technical, Aldershot, UK).

Jones-Lee MW (1990) The value of transport safety. *Oxford Review of Economic Policy 6,* pp 39-60.

Jordan PW (1985) Pedestrians and cyclists at roundabouts. *Proc 3rd National Local Government Engineers Conference,* pp 196-205. (Institution of Engineers, Australia, Canberra).

Jordan PW and Barton EV (1992) Road safety audit: What is it and why do we need it? *Proc 16th Australian Road Research Board Conference, 16(4).* pp 67-80.

Jordan PW and Young W (1982) The incidence of alcohol amongst injured pedestrians. *Proc 11th Australian Road Research Board Conference 11(5),* pp 131-143.

Kahlberg VP (1991) The effects of reflector posts on driving behaviour and accidents. *Proceedings PTRC Summer Annual Meeting, Seminar K ,* pp 181-192. (Planning and Transportation Research and Computation, London).

Kent County Council (1994a) *Traffic calming: A Code of Practice.* 96 p. (KCC, Maidstone, UK).

Kent County Council (1994b) *Safety Practice Note No. 3: Safety Audit.* 17 p. (KCC, Maidstone, UK).

Khan AM and Bacchus A (1995) *Bicycle Use of Highway Shoulders.* Paper presented at 1995 Annual Meeting of the Transportation Research Board, Washington, DC.

Khisty CJ (1990) *Transportation Engineering: An Introduction.* 671 p. (Prentice Hall, Englewood Cliffs, NJ, USA).

Kihlberg JA and Tharp KJ (1968) Accident rates as related to design elements of rural highways. *National Cooperative Highway Research Program Report 47,* (Highway Research Board, Washington, DC).

King GF, Abramson P, Cohen JW and Wilkinson MR (1978) Seven experimental designs addressing problems of safety and capacity on two-lane rural highways. Vol 2, Experimental design to develop and evaluate dynamic aids for narrow bridges. *Report no DOT-TSC-FHWA-78-2, II*, (Federal Highway Administration, Washington, DC).

Kjemtrup K and Herrstedt L (1992) Speed management and traffic calming in urban areas in Europe: An historical view. *Accident Analysis and Prevention 24(1)*, pp 57-68.

Klyne MO (1988) Geometric design of local street roundabouts and S-bend slow points for speed regulation. *Proc 14th Australian Road Research Board Conference 14(2)*, pp 56-67.

Knasbasis S, Zegeer CV and Cynecki MJ (1982) Effects of pedestrian signals on safety, operations and pedestrian behaviour. *Transportation Research Record 847*, pp 78-86.

Kneebone DC (1964) Advisory speed signs and their effect on traffic. *Proc 2nd Australian Road Research Board Conference 2(1)*, pp 524-538.

Konecni VJ, Ebbesen EB and Konecni DK (1976) Decision processes and risk taking in traffic: Driver response to the onset of the yellow light. *Journal of Applied Psychology 61(3)*, pp 359-367.

Krammes RA (1993) Geometric design: Cross section and alignment, in in *The Traffic Safety Toolbox: A Primer on Traffic Safety*, pp 99-108. (Institute of Transportation Engineers, Washington, DC).

Kuciemba SR and Cirillo JA (1992) *Safety Effectiveness of Highway Design Features. Volume 5, Intersections.* 8 p. (Federal Highway Administration, Washington, DC).

Kumar A and Cunningham JA (1992) Proactive skid resistance programs - do they have a place? *Proc International Road Federation/Australian Road Federation Asia-Pacific Conference.*

Laker IB (1988) High containment barriers. *Transportation Research Circular 341*, pp 45-59. (Transportation Research Board, Washington, DC).

Landles JR (1980) Accident remedial measures. *Proceedings PTRC Summer Annual Meeting, Seminar R*, pp 147-162. (Planning and Transportation Research and Computation, London).

Langan J (1992) The collection, collation and analysis of personal injury accident data. *Road Accidents Great Britain 1991*, pp 29-32. (Department of Transport, London).

Langley JD (1988) The need to discontinue the use of the term 'accident' when referring to unintentional injury events. *Accident Analysis and Prevention 20(1)*, pp 1-8.

Lave C and Elias P (1994) Did the 65 mph speed limit save lives? *Accident Analysis and Prevention 26(1)*, pp 49-62.

Lawson SD (1989) *Traffic Collisions in an Urban Area of Great Britain.* 70 p. (Automobile Association Foundation for Road Safety Research, Basingstoke, UK).

Lawson SD (1990) *Accidents to Young Pedestrians: Distributions, circumstances, consequences and scope for countermeasures.* 163 p. (AA Foundation for Road Safety Research, Basingstoke, UK).

Lawson SD (1992) Automatic surveillance and red-light running: Potential for camera use and accident reduction at high-risk light-controlled junctions. *Traffic Engineering and Control 33(1)*, pp 10-12.

Lay MG (1986) *Handbook of Road Technology (2 vols).* 712 p plus appendices. (Gordon and Breach, London).

Lay MG (1988) Roads and Road Safety - New Approaches. *Proc Workshop on New Approaches to Road Safety.* (Monash University Accident Research Centre, Melbourne, Australia).

Layfield RE and Maycock G (1986) Pedal cyclists at roundabouts. *Traffic Engineering and Control 27(6)*, pp 343-349.

Lipinski ME, Meador GC, Gilbronson AL, Traylor ML, Berg WD, Anderson CL and Wertman RH (1970) Summary of current status of knowledge on rural intersection illumination. *Highway Research Record 336*, pp 33-62.

Local Authorities Associations (1989) *Road Safety Code of Good Practice.* (Association of County Councils, London).

London Accident Analysis Unit (1994) Accidents involving parked vehicles in Greater London. *Fact Sheet Number 55.* 15 p. (LAAU, London Research Centre, London).

Lothian Regional Council (1991) *Notes of in-house Training Course on Road Safety Audit.* (Edinburgh, Scotland).

Lum HS and Hughes WE (1990) Edgeline widths and traffic accidents. *Public Roads 54 (1)*, pp 153-158.

Lum HS and Parker MR (1982) Intersection control and accident experience in rural Michigan. *Public Roads 46(3)*, pp 102-105.

Lum HS and Stockton WR (1982) Stop sign versus yield sign. *Transportation Research Record 881.* pp 29-33.

Lumenfeld H (1988) Accommodation of large trucks: Traffic control issues, in Smith BL and Mason JM (eds) *Accommodation of Trucks on the Highway: Safety in Design*, pp 89-103. (American Society of Civil Engineers, New York).

Lumenfeld H and Alexander GJ (1984) Human factors in highway design and operations. *ASCE Journal of Transportation Engineering 110(2)*, pp 149-158.

Lynam DA, Mackie AM and Davies CH (1988) Urban safety project: Design and Implementation of Schemes. *Research Report RR153*. 25 p. (Transport and Road Research Laboratory, Crowthorne, UK).

MacDonald WA and Hoffman ER (1978) Information coding on turn restriction traffic signs. *Proc. 9th Australian Road Research Board Conference, 9(5)*, pp 371-382.

Mackie AM, Ward HA and Walker RT (1990) Urban safety project: Overall evaluation of area-wide schemes. *Research Report RR 153*. 26 p. (Transport Research Laboratory, Crowthorne, UK).

Maher MJ (1987) Accident migration: A statistical explanation? *Traffic Engineering and Control 28(9)*, pp 480-483.

Maher MJ and Mountain LJ (1988) The identification of accident blackspots: A comparison of current methods. *Accident Analysis and Prevention 20(2)*, pp 143-151.

Mak KK (1987) Effect of bridge width on highway safety, in *State of the Art Report Number 6: Relationship Between Safety and Key Highway Features*, pp 22-35. (Transportation Research Board, Washington, DC).

Mak KK and Sicking DL (1990) Rollover caused by concrete safety-shaped barrier. *Transportation Research Record 1258*, pp 71-81.

Malalel D and Zaidel DM (1985) Safety evaluation of a flashing green light in a traffic signal. *Traffic Engineering and Control 26(2)*, pp 79-81.

Maycock G and Hall RD (1984) Accidents at 4-arm roundabouts. *Laboratory Report LR 1120*. 61 p. (Transport and Road Research Laboratory, Crowthorne, UK).

McBean PA (1982) The influence of road geometry at a sample of accident sites. *Laboratory Report LR 1053*. 16 p. (Transport and Road Research Laboratory, Crowthorne, UK).

McClintock H (ed) *The Bicycle and City Traffic*. 217 p. (Belhaven Press, London).

McCluskey J (1987) *Parking: A Handbook of Environmental Design*. (Spon, London).

McCormick EJ and Sanders MS (1982) *Human Factors in Engineering and Design (Fifth edition).* 615 p. (McGraw Hill, New York).

McCoy PT, Ramanujam M, Moussavi M and Ballard JL (1990) Safety comparison of types of parking on urban streets in Nebraska. *Transportation Research Record 1270*, pp 28-39.

McCoy TA, McCoy PT, Haden RJ and Singh VA (1991) Safety evaluation of converting on-street parking from parallel to angle. *Transportation Research Record 1327*, pp 36-41.

McDevitt CF (1988) Upgrading transitions from approach guardrails to bridge rails. *Proc Roads and Transportation Association of Canada Conference 1(E), pp E3-24.* (RTAC, Ottawa).

McGee HW and Blakenship MR (1989) Guidelines for converting Stop to Yield control at intersections. *National Cooperative Highway Research Program Report 320*, 49 p. (Transportation Research Board, Washington, DC).

McGuigan DRD (1981) The use of relationships between road accidents and traffic flow in 'black spot' identification. *Traffic Engineering and Control 22(9)*, pp 448-453.

McGuigan DRD (1982) Non-junction accident rates and their use in 'black spot' identification. *Traffic Engineering and Control 23(2)*, pp 60-65.

McGuigan DRD (1991) Pre-evaluation: Estimating the potential benefits of treatment. *Proc County Surveyors' Society/ Universities Transport Studies Group Joint Seminar on the Evaluation of Road Safety Schemes.* 7 p. (CSS, London).

McGuigan DRD, McBride A and Ryall M (1994) A GIS for road safety in Lothian: Getting it right. *Proceedings PTRC Summer Annual Meeting, Seminar N*, pp 11-29. (Planning and Transportation Research and Computation, London).

McLean AJ, Anderson RWG, Farmer MJB, Lee BH and Brooks CG (1994) Vehicle travel speeds and the incidence of fatal pedestrian collisions. *FORS Report CR 146*. 82 p. (Federal Office of Road Safety, Canberra, Australia).

McLean JR (1985) Accident-width relationship for single-carriageway rural highways. *Australian Road Research 15(4)*, pp 271-275.

McLean JR (1989) *Two-Lane Highway Traffic Operations: Theory and Practice.* 408 p. (Gordon and Breach, New York).

McShane WR and Roess RP (1990) *Traffic Engineering.* 658 p. (Prentice Hall, Englewood Cliffs, NJ, USA).

Meyer MD and Miller EJ (1984). Urban Transportation Planning: A Decision-Oriented Approach. 524 p. (McGraw Hill, New York).

Michie JD (1986) Large vehicles and roadside safety considerations. *Transportation Research Record 1052*, pp 90-95.

Miller TR (1992) Benefit/cost analysis of lane marking. *Transportation Research Record 1334*, pp 38-45.

Ministry of Transport (New Zealand) (1993) *Targets for Road Safety, New Edition, 1993.* (Wellington, NZ).

Moore SE and Lowrie PR (1976) Further on the effects of coordinated traffic signal systems on accidents. *Proc 8th Australian Road Research Board Conference, 8(5),* pp 26.10 26.17.

Moses PJ (1985) Cats eyes cost effective. *Western Roads (October),* pp 1-3.

Moses PJ (1986) Edge lines and single vehicle crashes. *Western Roads (April),* pp 6-8.

Mountain L and Fawaz B (1992) The effects of engineering measures on safety at adjacent sites. *Traffic Engineering and Control 33(1),* pp 15-22.

Mountain L, Fawaz B and Sineng L (1992a) The assessment of changes in accident frequencies at treated intersections: A comparison of four methods. *Traffic Engineering and Control 33(2),* pp 85-87.

Mountain L, Fawaz B and Sineng L (1992b) The assessment of changes in accident frequencies on link segments: A comparison of four methods. *Traffic Engineering and Control 33(7/8),* pp 429-431.

Munden JW (1967) The relationship between a driver's speed and his accident rate. *Laboratory Report LR 88.* (Road Research Laboratory, Crowthorne, UK).

Naatanen R and Summala H (1976) *Road User Behaviour and Traffic Accidents.* (North Holland, Amsterdam).

Nairn RJ and Partners (1987) A review of the cost-effectiveness of road safety measures. *Report 10/87.* (Road Safety Division, Department of Transport, Adelaide).

National Association of Australian State Road Authorities (1984) *Grade Separated Interchanges: A Design Guide.* 72 p. (NAASRA, Sydney).

National Association of Australian State Road Authorities (1987) *Safety Barriers.* 29 p. (NAASRA, Sydney).

National Association of Australian State Road Authorities (1988a) *Guide to Traffic Engineering Practice: Part 4, Road Crashes.* 74 p. (NAASRA, Sydney).

National Association of Australian State Road Authorities (1988b) *Guide to Traffic Engineering Practice: Part 5, Intersections at Grade.* 67 p. (NAASRA, Sydney).

National Association of Australian State Road Authorities (1988c) *Guide to Traffic Engineering Practice: Part 10, Local Area Traffic Management.* 48 p. (NAASRA, Sydney).

National Association of Australian State Road Authorities (1988d) *Guide to Traffic Engineering Practice. Part 11. Parking.* 42 p. (NAASRA, Sydney).

National Association of Australian State Road Authorities (1988e) *Guide to Traffic Engineering Practice. Part 9. Arterial Road Traffic Management.* 46 p. (NAASRA, Sydney).

National Association of Australian State Road Authorities (1988f) *Guide to Traffic Engineering Practice. Part 8. Traffic Control Devices.* 37 p. (NAASRA, Sydney).

National Association of Australian State Road Authorities (1989) *Guide to the Geometric Design of Rural Roads.* 62 p. (NAASRA, Sydney).

National Highway Traffic Safety Administration (1992) *NHTSA Docket 90-07: Critical Automated Data Reporting Elements.* (NHTSA, Washington, DC).

National Highway Traffic Safety Administration (1994) Highway safety program guidelines. Number 10. Traffic records. *NHTSA Docket 93-21: Amendments to Highway Safety Program Guidelines.* (NHTSA, Washington, DC).

Nedas ND, Balcar GP and Macy PR (1982) Road markings as an alcohol countermeasure for highway safety: Field study of standard and wide edgelines. *Transportation Research Record 847,* pp 43-47.

Neuman TR (1985) Intersection channelisation design guide. *National Cooperative Highway Research Program Report 279.* 153 p. (Transportation Research Board, Washington, DC).

Neuman TR (1993) Geometric design: Urban intersections, in *The Traffic Safety Toolbox: A Primer on Traffic Safety,* pp 123-134. (Institute of Transportation Engineers, Washington, DC).

Neuman TR and Glennon JC (1983) Cost effectiveness of improvements to stopping sight distance safety problems. *Transportation Research Record 923,* pp 26-34.

Neuman TR, Glennon JC and Saag JB (1983) Accident analyses for highway curves. *Transportation Research Board 923,* pp 54-57.

Newman P and Kenworthy J (1991) *Towards a more sustainable Canberra.* (Institute for Science and Technology, Murdoch University, Perth, Australia).

Nguyen T, Hodge G and Hall K (1987) *The Road Safety Effectiveness of Traffic Signal Installation at 4-leg Intersections in Victoria.* (Victorian Ministry of Transport, Melbourne, Australia).

Nicholas Clark and Associates (1979) Study design for the evaluation of the effectiveness of MITERS-type projects. *Report CR 8.* (Office of Road Safety, Canberra, Australia).

Nicholson AJ (1987) The estimation of accident rates and countermeasure effectiveness. *Traffic Engineering and Control 28(10)*, pp 518-523.

Nicholson AJ (1990) *Identification of Hazardous Sites, Routes and Areas.* Paper presented at Road Hazards Conference Training Workshop, Wollongong, 25-29 June. 10 p. (Roads and Traffic Authority of New South Wales, Sydney, Australia).

Nielsen MA (1994) Safety of cyclists in urban areas. *Proceedings PTRC Summer Annual Meeting, Seminar J*, pp 113-123. (Planning and Transportation Research and Computation, London).

Niessner CW (1984) Raised pavement markers at hazardous locations. *Report No FHWA-TS-84-215.* (Federal Highway Administration, Washington, DC).

O'Day J (1993) Accident data quality. *National Cooperative Highway Research Program. Synthesis of Highway Practice 192.* 48 p. (Transportation Research Board, Washington, DC).

Ogden KW (1989) *Crashes at Bridges and Culverts.* (Monash University Accident Research Centre, Melbourne, Australia).

Ogden KW (1990) Human factors in traffic engineering. *ITE Journal 60(8)*, pp 41-46.

Ogden KW (1992) *Urban Goods Movement: A Guide to Policy and Planning.* 397 p. (Ashgate, London).

Ogden KW (1993) *Benefit/cost Analysis of Road Trauma Countermeasures: Rural Road and Traffic Engineering Programs.* 32 p. (Monash University Accident Research Centre, Melbourne, Australia).

Ogden KW (1994a) Traffic engineering road safety: A practitioner's guide. *Report CR 145*, 109 p. (Federal office of Road Safety, Canberra, Australia).

Ogden KW (chair) (1994b) *Committee 4S-7: Informational Report, Road Safety Audit.* 22 p. (Institute of Transportation Engineers, Washington, DC).

Ogden KW and Bennett DW (1989) *Traffic Engineering Practice (4th edition).* 479 p. (Monash University, Melbourne, Australia).

Ogden KW and Howie DJ (1990) Pro-active traffic safety: A study of bridges and culverts. *Proc 15th Australian Road Research Board Conference 15(7)*, pp 23-44.

Ogden KW and Newstead S (1994a) Analysis of crash patterns at Victorian signalised intersections. *Report No. 60.* 42 p plus appendices. (Monash University Accident Research Centre, Melbourne, Australia).

Ogden KW, Newstead SV, Ryan PK and Gantzer S (1994b) Factors affecting crashes at signalised intersections. 30 p. *Report no. 62. (Monash University Accident Research Centre, Melbourne, Australia).*

Ogden KW, Patton TA and Clark NF (1973) A review of railway crossings in relation to road safety. *Expert Group on Road Safety Report NR/10.* 107 p. (Department of Transport (Australia), Canberra).

Ogden KW and Pearson RA (1991) A review of road and traffic factors in truck accidents: Australian truck safety study task 1. *ARRB Research Report ARR 201.* 68 p. (Australian Road Research Board, Melbourne).

Oglesby CH (1985) Consistency on design for low volume rural roads. *ASCE Journal of Transportation Engineering 111(5)*, pp 510-519.

Organisation for Economic Cooperation and Development (1976) *Hazardous road locations: Identification and counter-measures.* 108 p. (OECD, Paris).

Organisation for Economic Cooperation and Development (1979) *Traffic Safety in Residential Areas.* 109 p. (OECD, Paris).

Organisation for Economic Cooperation and Development (1981a) *Proc Symposium on the Effects of Speed Limits on Traffic accidents and Transport Energy Use: Conclusions and Recommendations.* (OECD, Paris).

Organisation for Economic Cooperation and Development (1981b) *Methods for Evaluating Road Safety Measures.* 108 p. (OECD, Paris).

Organisation for Economic Cooperation and Development (1984) *Integrated Road Safety Programs.* 95 p. (OECD, Paris).

Organisation for Economic Cooperation and Development (1986) *OECD Road Safety Research: A Synthesis*. 106 p. (OECD, Paris).

Organisation for Economic Cooperation and Development (1988) *Transporting Hazardous Goods by Road*. 144 p. (OECD, Paris).

Organisation for Economic Cooperation and Development (1989) *Traffic Management and Safety at Highway Work Zones*. 145 p. (OECD, Paris).

Organisation for Economic Cooperation and Development (1994) *Targeted Road Safety Programs*. 114 p. (OECD, Paris).

Pak Poy and Kneebone Pty Ltd (1988) Road safety benefits from rural road improvements. *FORS Report CR 71*. 171 p. (Federal Office of Road Safety, Canberra, Australia).

Parsonson PS (1993) Traffic control devices: Signals, in *The Traffic Safety Toolbox: A Primer on Traffic Safety*, pp 71-84. (Institute of Transportation Engineers, Washington, DC).

Pearce DW and Nash CA (1981). The Social Appraisal of Projects. (McMillan, London).

Pickering D, Hall RD and Grimmer M (1986) Accidents at rural T-junctions. *Research Report RR 65*. 39 p. (Transport and Road Research Laboratory, Crowthorne, UK).

Pigman JG, Agent KR and Creasey T (1985) Analysis of crashes involving crash cushions. *Transportation Research Record 1024*, pp 80-91.

Polus A (1985) Driver behaviour and accident records at unsignalised urban intersections. *Accident Analysis and Prevention 17(1)*, pp 25-32.

Proctor S (1990) Reducing the risks. *Surveyor* (August).

Proctor (1991a) Accident reduction through area-wide traffic schemes. *Traffic Engineering and Control 32(12)*, pp 566-573.

Proctor S (1991b) Taking the calmer approach. *Surveyor* (December). pp 1-4.

Proctor S and Belcher M (1990) The development of roadside crash cushions in the UK. *Traffic Engineering and Control 31(8/9)*, pp 460-465.

Proctor S and Belcher M (1993) The use of road safety audits in Great Britain. *Traffic Engineering and Control 34(2)*, pp 61-65.

Queensland Transport (1993) *A Guide to the Traffic Accident Remedial Program*. 45 p plus appendices. (Queensland Transport, Brisbane, Australia).

Radwan AE and Sinha KC (1978) Effect of national speed limit on the severity of heavy truck accidents. *Traffic Quarterly 32 (2)*, pp 319-328.

Reason J (1990) *Human Error*. 302 p. (Cambridge University Press, Cambridge).

Richards SH and Heathington KW (1988) Motorist understanding of railroad-highway grade crossings and associated traffic laws. *Transportation Research Record 1160*, pp 52-59.

Roads and Traffic Authority of New South Wales (1989) *Towards Guidelines for Retail Centres Along Traffic Routes*. 27 p. (RTA, Sydney, Australia).

Roads and Traffic Authority of New South Wales (1991a) *Road Safety Audits*. 17 p plus appendices. (RTA, Sydney, Australia).

Roads and Traffic Authority of NSW (1991b) *Road Environment Safety Guidelines*. 67 p. (RTA, Sydney, Australia).

Roads and Traffic Authority of NSW (1992) *Road Safety 2000: The Strategic Plan for Road Safety in NSW 1990s and Beyond*. 27 p. (RTA, Sydney, Australia).

Roads and Traffic Authority of New South Wales (1995) *Procedures for Road-based Countermeasures*. (RTA, Sydney, Australia).

Roe PG, Webster DC and West G (1991) The relation between surface texture of roads and accidents. *Research Report RR 296*. 18 p. (Transport Research Laboratory, Crowthorne, UK).

Rogness RO, Fambro DB and Turner DS (1982) Before-after accident analysis for two shoulder upgrading alternatives. *Transportation Research Record 855*, pp 41-47.

Rolls GWP, Hall RD, Ingham R and McDonald M (1991) *Accident Risk and Behavioural Patterns of Younger Drivers*. 115 p. (Automobile Association Foundation for Road Safety Research, Basingstoke, UK).

Rosenbaum MJ (1983) A review of research related to the safety of stop versus yield sign traffic control. *Public Roads 47(3)*, pp 77-83.

Ross A, Silcock DT and Ghee C (1992) Safety audit: An international overview. *Paper presented at 1992 Annual Meeting*. pp 1-8. (Institute of Transportation Engineers, Washington, DC).

Ross HE and Sicking DL (1986) Selection of performance levels for longitudinal barriers, in Carney JF (ed) *Effectiveness of Highway Safety Improvements*, pp 231-241. (American Society of Civil Engineers, New York).

Ross HE, Sicking DL, Zimmer RA and Michie JD (1993) Recommended procedures for the safety performance evaluation of highway features. *National Cooperative Highway Research Program Report 350.* 132 p. (Transportation Research Board, Washington, DC).

Ross Silcock Partnership (1991) *Towards Safer Roads in Developing Countries.* 220 p. (Transport and Road Research Laboratory, Crowthorne, UK).

Roy Jorgensen and Associates (1978) Cost and safety effectiveness of highway design elements. *National Cooperative Highway Research Program Report 197.* (Transportation Research Board, Washington DC).

Royal Dutch Touring Club ANWB (1977) *Woonerf.* (ANWB, The Hague).

Royal Society for the Prevention of Accidents (1994) *Road Safety Engineering Manual.* (RoSPA, Birmingham, UK).

Rumar K (1982) The human factor in road safety. *Proc 11th Australian Road Research Board Conference 11(1),* pp 65-80.

Russell PO (1993) Traffic control devices: Markings, in *The Traffic Safety Toolbox: A Primer on Traffic Safety,* pp 63-70. (Institute of Transportation Engineers, Washington, DC).

Sabey BE (1980) Road safety and value for money. *Supplementary Report SR 581.* 16 p. (Transport and Road Research Laboratory, Crowthorne, UK).

Sabey BE (1993) Safety audit procedures and practice. *Traffex '93.* (Planning and Transportation Research and Computation, London).

Sabey BE and Johnson HD (1973) Lighting accidents: Before and after studies on trunk road sites. *Laboratory Report LR 586.* 15 p. (Transport and Road Research Laboratory, Crowthorne, UK).

Sabey BE and Storie VJ (1968) Skidding in personal accidents in Great Britain in 1965 and 1968. *Laboratory Report LR 173.* (Road Research Laboratory, Crowthorne, UK).

Sabey BE and Taylor H (1980) The known risks we run: The highway. *Supplementary Report SR 567.* 24 p. (Transport and Road Research Laboratory, Crowthorne, UK).

Sandberg U (1980) Efficiency of spray protectors. *VTI Rapport 199A.* (Swedish Road and Traffic Research Institute, Linkoping, Sweden).

Sanders JH (1976) Driver performance in countermeasure development at railroad-highway grade crossings. *Transportation Research Record 562,* pp 28-37.

Sanderson JT and Cameron MH (1986) Identification of hazardous road locations. *Proc 13th Australian Road Research Board Conference 13(9)*, pp 133-147.

Satterthwaite SP (1981) A survey of research into relationships between traffic accidents and traffic volumes. *Supplementary Report SR 692*. 43 p. (Transport and Road Research Laboratory, Crowthorne, UK).

Schlackman W and Winstone P (1988) *Motoring and the Older Driver*. 40 p. (Automobile Association Foundation for Road Safety Research, Basingstoke, UK).

Schnull R and Lange J (1992) Speed reduction on through roads in Nordrhein-Westfalen. *Accident Analysis and Prevention 24(1)*, pp 67-74.

Schoppert DW and Hoyt DW (1968) Factors influencing safety at highway-rail grade crossings. *National Cooperative Highway Research Program Report 50*. 113 p. (Transportation Research Board, Washington, DC).

Schreuder DA (1991) Practical determination of tunnel entrance lighting needs. *Transportation Research Record 1327*, pp 8-13.

Schwab RN and Capelle DG (1980) Is delineation needed? *ITE Journal, 50(5)*, pp 21-28.

Scott PP (1980) The relationship between road lighting quality and accident frequency. *Laboratory Report LR 929*. 19 p. (Transport and Road Research Laboratory, Crowthorne, UK).

Shinar D (1978) *Psychology on the Road*. 212 p. (Wiley, New York).

Shinar D and Raz S (1982) Driver response to different railroad crossing protection systems. *Ergonomics 25(9)*, pp 801-808.

Short M, Woelfl G and Chang CI (1982) Effects of traffic signal installation on accidents. *Accident Analysis and Prevention 14(3)*, pp 135-145.

Sicking DL and Ross HE (1986) Benefit-cost analysis of roadside safety alternatives. *Transportation Research Record 1065*, pp 98-105.

Silcock DT and Smyth AW (1984) The methods used by British highway authorities to identify accident blackspots. *Traffic Engineering and Control 25(11)*, pp 542-545.

Silcock DT and Worsley GM (1982) Relationships between accident rates, road characteristics and traffic on two urban roads. *Transport Operations Research Group Research Report 40*. 57 p. (University of Newcastle upon Tyne, UK).

Simmonds AG (1987) The effect of measures designed to reduce right turning accidents at signalised junctions. *Report ATWP 84.* (London Accident Analysis Unit, London).

Simpson D and Brown M (1988) A review of recent Department of Transport accident-based studies. *Journal of the Institution of Highways and Transportation 35(2)*, pp 26-28.

Skinner RE (1986) RRR design standards: Cost-effectiveness issues, in Carney JF (ed) *Effectiveness of Highway Safety Improvements*, pp 41-50. (American Society of Civil Engineers, New York).

Smith BL (1986) Existing design standards. *Transportation Research Record 1052*, pp 23-29.

Smith BL and Mason JM (eds) (1988) *Accommodation of Trucks on the Highway: Safety in Design.* 192 p (American Society of Civil Engineers, New York).

Solomon D (1964) *Accidents on Main Rural Highways Related to Speed, Driver and Vehicle.* (Bureau of Public Roads, Washington, DC).

South DR, Harrison WA, Portans I and King M (1988) *Evaluation of the Red Light Camera Program and the Owner Onus Legislation.* Road 35 p. (Traffic Authority, Melbourne, Australia).

Sowerby K (1987) Safety fence criteria for all-purpose dual carriageway roads. *Contractor Report CR 57.* 79 p. (Transport and Road Research Laboratory, Crowthorne, UK).

Stamatiadis N, Taylor WC and McKelvey FX (1991) Elderly drivers and intersection accidents. *Transportation Quarterly 45(3)*, pp 377-390.

Standards Australia (1994) *Australian Standard 1742. Australian Standard Manual of Uniform Traffic Control Devices. Part 2.* 197 p. (SA, Sydney).

Staplin L and Fisk AD (1991) A cognitive engineering approach to improving signalised left turn intersections. *Human Factors 33(5)*, pp 559-571.

Stark RE (1975) Studies of traffic safety benefits of roadway lighting. *Highway Research Record 440*, pp 20-28.

Steadman LA and Bryan RJ (1988) Cost of road accidents in Australia. *Occasional Paper 91.* 119 p. (Australian Government Publishing Service, Canberra).

Stein AC and Johnson WA (1984) Effective signing to reduce truck downgrade runaways. *Proc 28th Conference, American Association for Automotive Medicine*, pp 77-90.

Stein HS (1986) Traffic signal change intervals: Policies, practices and safety. *Transportation Quarterly 40(3)*, pp 433-445.

Stonex KA (1960) Roadside design for safety. *Proc Highway Research Board 39*, pp 120-152. (Highway Research Board, Washington, DC).

Stopher PR and Meyburg AH (1976). Transportation Systems Evaluation. (DC Heath, Lexington, MA, USA).

Storie VJ (1977) Male and female car drivers: Differences observed in accidents. *Laboratory Report LR 761*. 26 p. (Transport and Road Research Laboratory, Crowthorne, UK).

Sudgen R and Williams A (1978). The Principles of Practical Cost-Benefit Analysis. 275 p. (Oxford University Press, Oxford).

Summersgill I (1985) Safety performance of traffic management at major road works on motorways in 1982. *Research Report RR 42*. (Transport and Road Research Laboratory, Crowthorne, UK).

Sumner R and Shippey J (1977) The use of rumble strips to alert drivers. *Transport and Road Research Laboratory Note LR 800*. 29 p. (TRRL, Crowthorne, UK).

Swali LN (1993) The effect of speed cameras in West London. *Proceedings PTRC Summer Annual Meeting, Seminar C*, pp 249-260. (Planning and Transportation Research and Computation, London).

Sweatman PF, Ogden KW, Haworth N, Vulcan AP and Pearson RA (1990) NSW heavy vehicle crash study: Final technical report. *FORS Report CR 92*. 294 p. (Federal Office of Road Safety, Canberra, Australia).

Swedish National Board of Urban Planning and the National Road Administration (1968) *The SCAFT Guidelines*. (Karlshamn, Sweden).

Symons NR and Cunningham JA (1987) Experience with a roadside hazard management program in Victoria, Australia. *Proc New Zealand Roading Symposium, Vol 3*, pp 419-426.

Tanner JC (1953) Accidents at three-way junctions. *J. Institution of Highway Engineers 2(11)*, pp 56-67.

Tanner JC (1958) A problem in the combination of accident frequencies. *Biometrika 45*, pp 331-342.

Taylor GB and Wiltshire PJ (1992) Toucan crossing at Tushmore Gyratory, Crawley. *Traffic Engineering and Control 33(6)*, pp 380-382.

Taylor MAP (1991) *Effect of Right Turn Phases at Signalised Intersections. Part 2, Mobility Performance*. 80 p. (Monash University Accident Research Centre, Melbourne, Australia).

Taylor MAP and Young W (1988) *Traffic Analysis: New Technology and New Solutions*. 353 p. (Hargreen, Melbourne, Australia).

Taylor MC and Barker JK (1992) Injury accidents on rural single-carriageway roads; an analysis of STATS19 data *Research Report 365*. 32 p. (Transport Research Laboratory, Crowthorne, UK).

Taylor WC (1965) Speed zoning: A theory and its proof. *Traffic Engineering 35(4)*, pp 17-19 and 48-51.

Teale GL (1984) Evaluation of the effectiveness of MITERS type projects. *Report CR22*. (Office of Road Safety, Canberra, Australia).

Tenkink EA and van der Horst R (1990) Car driver behaviour at flashing light railroad grade crossings. *Accident Analysis and Prevention 22(3)*, pp 229-239.

Tignor SC (1993) Traffic control devices: Overview, in *The Traffic Safety Toolbox: A Primer on Traffic Safety*, pp 45-52. (Institute of Transportation Engineers, Washington, DC).

TMS Consultancy (1983) *A before and After Road Accident Study of Road Sign Installations*. 17 p. (3M United Kingdom PLC, Bracknell, UK).

Todd K (1988) A history of roundabouts in the United States and France. *Transportation Quarterly 42(4)*, pp 599-623.

Todd K (1991) A history of roundabouts in Britain. *Transportation Quarterly 45(1)*, pp 143-155.

Transit New Zealand (1993) *Safety Audit Policy and Procedures*. 37 p. (Transit New Zealand, Wellington, NZ). 1993.

Transport and Road Research Laboratory (1987) *Guidelines for the Traffic Conflict Technique*. 48 p. (Institution of Highways and Transportation, London).

Transport Research Laboratory (1988) *Microcomputer Accident Analysis Package: Road Accident Report Form*. 20 p. (TRL Overseas Unit, Crowthorne, UK).

Transportation Research Board (1987a) Designing safer roads. *Special Report 214*. 319 p. (TRB, Washington, DC).

Transportation Research Board (1987b) Relationship between safety and key highway features. *State of the Art Report 6*. (TRB, Washington, DC).

Transportation Research Board (1988) Transportation in an aging society. *Special Report 218*. 2 vols. (TRB, Washington, DC).

Transportation Research Board (1993) Human factors research in highway safety. *Transportation Research Circular 414.* 54 p. (Transportation Research Board, Washington, DC).

Travers Morgan Pty Ltd (1991) *Road Features Safety Assessment: Final Report.* 67 p plus Appendices. (Roads and Traffic Authority of NSW, Sydney, Australia).

Travers Morgan (NZ) Pty Ltd (1992) Accident countermeasures: Literature Review. *Transit New Zealand Research Report No. 10.* 94 p. (Transit New Zealand, Wellington, NZ).

Treat JR (1980) A study of pre-crash factors involved in traffic accidents. *Research Review 10(6) and 11(1).* (University of Michigan Highway Safety Research Institute, Ann Arbour, MI, USA).

Triggs TJ (1980) The influence of oncoming vehicles on automobile lateral position. *Human Factors 22(4),* pp 427-433.

Triggs TJ (1981) *Signalised Intersections and Driver Performance.* (Road Safety and Traffic Authority, Melbourne, Australia).

Triggs TJ, Harris WG and Fildes BN (1979) Delineation on rural roads at night: A laboratory-based study of curve direction estimation. *ARRB Internal Report AIR 266-2.* (Australian Road Research Board, Melbourne).

Trinca G, Johnston I, Campbell B, Haight FA, Knight P, Mackay M, McLean JR and Petrucelli E (1988) *Reducing Traffic Injury - A Global Challenge.* 136 p. (Royal Australasian College of Surgeons, Melbourne, Australia).

Troutbeck RJ (1983) Background to proposed NAASRA guidelines for the provision of safety barriers. *ARRB Internal Report 833-1.* (Australian Road Research Board, Melbourne).

Turner DS, Fambro DB and Rogness RO (1981) Effects of paved shoulders on accident rates for rural Texas highways. *Transportation Research Record 819,* pp 30-37.

Turner DS and Hall JW (1994) Severity indices for roadside features. *National Cooperative Highway Research Program. Synthesis of Highway Practice 202.* (Transportation Research Board, Washington, DC).

Twomey JM, Heckman ML and Hayward JC (1992) *Safety Effectiveness of Highway Design Features. Volume 4, Interchanges.* 11 p. (Federal Highway Administration, Washington, DC).

Ungers R and Vincent T (1995) How the road toll can be managed. *Road and Transport Research 4(1)*, pp 6-19. (Australian Road Research Board, Melbourne).

Upchurch JE (1983) Guidelines for the use of sign control at intersections to reduce energy consumption. *ITE Journal 53(1)*, pp 22-34.

van de Watering CF (1993) Road safety policy in The Netherlands. *ITE 1993 Compendium of Technical Papers*, pp 396-400. (Institute of Transportation Engineers, Washington, DC).

van Heystraeten G and Moraux C (1990) Ten years experience of porous asphalt in Belgium. *Transportation Research Record 1265*, pp 34-40.

van Minnen J (1990) Roundabouts: Safe for cyclists too? *Proceedings PTRC Summer Annual Meeting, Seminar G*, pp 247-258. (Planning and Transportation Research and Computation, London).

VicRoads (1994) *Traffic Engineering Manual, Volume 1, Section 7, Speed Zoning Guidelines*. (VicRoads, Melbourne, Australia).

Vincent EN (1978) A trial installation of corner-cube delineators: Calder Highway, Gisborne to Woodend. *Australian Road Research 8(3)*, pp 38-40.

Vis A, Dijkstra A and Slop M (1992) Safety effects of 30 km/h zones in The Netherlands. *Accident Analysis and Prevention 24(1)*, pp 75-86.

VISP Working Group (1994) *Village Speed Control Working Group Final Report*. 73 p. (Department of Transport (UK), London).

Wachtel A and Lewiston D (1994) Risk factors for bicycle-motor vehicle collisions at intersections. *ITE Journal 64(9)*, pp 30-35.

Wainwright WS (1993) One way streets and reversible lanes, in *The Traffic Safety Toolbox: A Primer on Traffic Safety*, pp 141-148. (Institute of Transportation Engineers, Washington, DC).

Walker CD and Lines CJ (1991) Accident reductions from trunk road improvements. *Research Report CR 321*. 15 p. (Transport Research Laboratory, Crowthorne, UK).

Walker JS and Pittam SR (1989) Accidents at mini-roundabouts: Frequencies and rates. *Contractor Report 161*. (Transport and Road Research Laboratory, Crowthorne, UK).

Wallen MA (1993) What makes a good safety management system? *ITE Journal 63(1)*, pp 26-30.

Wallwork MJ (1993) Traffic calming, in Institute of Transportation Engineers *The Traffic Safety Toolbox: A Primer on Traffic Safety*, pp 235-247. (ITE, Washington, DC).

Walsh DJ and Dileo T (1992) A new approach to a black spot identification program for Queensland. *Proc 16th Australian Road Research Board Conference 16(4)*, pp 81-97.

Wambold JC (1988) A field study to establish truck escape ramp designs. *Proc 14th Australian Road Research Board Conference, 14 (4)*, pp 182-198.

Ward H (1992) *Evaluation of Engineering Countermeasures used in Road Accident Remedial Work*. 23 p. (Centre for Transport Studies, University College, London).

Ward H and Allsop R (1982) Area-wide approach to urban road safety: Evaluation of schemes by monitoring of traffic and accidents. *Traffic Engineering and Control 23(9)*, pp 424-428.

Watts GR (1973) Road humps for the control of vehicle speeds. *Laboratory Report LR 597*. (Transport and Road Research Laboratory, Crowthorne, UK).

Westerman HL, Black JA, Brindle RE, Lukovich T, and Sheffield D (1993). Sharing the main street. *FORS Report CR 132*. 90 p plus appendices. (Federal Office of Road Safety, Canberra, Australia).

Wheeler AH (1992) Advanced stop line for cyclists at Oxford, Newark and Bristol. *Contractor Report CR 336*. 22 p. (Transport Research Laboratory, Crowthorne, UK).

Wheeler AH, Leicester MAA and Underwood G (1993) Advanced stop lines for cyclists. *Traffic Engineering and Control 34(2)*, pp 54-60.

Wheeler AH, Taylor MC and Barker JK (1994) Speed reduction in 24 villages: Details from the VISP study. *Project Report 85*. 21 p plus appendices. (Transport Research Laboratory, Crowthorne, UK).

Wickens CD (1984) *Engineering Psychology and Human Performance*. 513 p. (Charles E Merrill Publishing Co, Columbus, OH, USA).

Wigglesworth EC (1978) Human factors in level crossing accidents. *Accident Analysis and Prevention 10(3)*, pp 229-240.

Wigglesworth EC (1990) How can safety be improved at open level crossings? *Australian Road Research 20(4)*, pp 61-75.

Wilde GJS (1982) The theory of risk homeostasis: Implications for safety and health. *Risk Analysis 2(4)*, pp 209-225.

Wilde GJS (1986) Beyond the concept of risk homeostasis: Suggestions for research and application towards the prevention of accidents and lifestyle-related disease. *Accident Analysis and prevention 18(5)*, pp 377-401.

Willet D (1979) *Safety Benefits of Intersection Traffic Lights.* (Main Roads Department, Perth).

Williams AF and O'Neill B (1974) On the road driving records of licensed race drivers. *Accident Analysis and Prevention 6(3)*, pp 263-270.

Willis PA, Scott PP and Barnes JW (1984) Urban safety project: The Reading scheme. *Laboratory Report LR 1117.* 17 p. (Transport and Road Research Laboratory, Crowthorne, UK).

Winnett (1994) A review of speed camera operations in the UK. *Proceedings PTRC Summer Annual Meeting, Seminar J*, pp 265-276. (Planning and Transportation Research and Computation, London).

Wohl M and Hendrickson C (1984) *Transportation Investment and Pricing Principles: An Introduction for Engineers, Planners and Economists.* 380 p. (Wiley, New York).

Wong SY (1990) Effectiveness of pavement grooving in accident reduction. *ITE Journal 60(7)*, pp 34-37.

Wong YD and Nicholson AJ (1992) Driver behaviour at horizontal curves: Risk compensation and the margin of safety. *Accident Analysis and Prevention 2(4)*, pp 425-436.

Woods DL, Rollins JB and Crane LM (1989) Guidelines for using wide-paved shoulders on low-volume two-lane rural highways based on benefit/cost analysis. *Report FHWA/TX-89/1114-1F*, 41 p. (Federal Highway Administration, Washington, DC).

Wright CC, Abbess CR and Jarrett DF (1988) Estimating the regression-to-mean effect associated with road accident black spot treatment: Towards a more realistic approach. *Accident Analysis and Prevention 20(3)*, pp 199-214.

Wright CC and Boyle AJ (1987) Road accident causation and engineering treatment: A review of some current issues. *Traffic Engineering and Control 28(9)*, pp 475-479.

Yamanaka H and Odani M (1991) Measures for traffic calming in residential areas. *The Wheel Extended 73.* pp 24-32. (Toyota Motor Corporation, Tokyo).

Young AE (1983) Skid resistance and accident prevention in London. *Report ATWP 79.* (Accident Analysis Unit, London).

Zaal D (1994) Traffic law enforcement: A review of the literature. *FORS Report 53*. 188 p. (Federal Office of Road Safety, Canberra, Australia).

Zegeer CV (1982) Highway accident analysis systems. *National Cooperative Highway Research Program Synthesis of Highway Practice 91*. 69 p. (Transportation Research Board, Washington, DC).

Zegeer CV (1986) Methods for identifying hazardous highway elements. *National Cooperative Highway Research Program: Synthesis of Highway Practice 128*. 80 p. (Transportation Research Board, Washington, DC).

Zegeer CV (1993) Designing for pedestrians, in *The Traffic Safety Toolbox: A Primer on Traffic Safety*, pp 187-202. (Institute of Transportation Engineers, Washington, DC).

Zegeer CV and Council FM (1992) *Safety Effectiveness of Highway Design Features. Volume 3, Cross Sections*. 23 p. (Federal Highway Administration, Washington, DC).

Zegeer CV and Council FM (1993) Highway design, highway safety and human factors. *Transportation Research Circular 414*. pp 20-34. (Transportation Research Board, Washington, DC).

Zegeer CV and Deacon JA (1987) Effect of lane width, shoulder width, and shoulder type on highway safety, in *State of the Art Report Number 6: Relationship Between Safety and Key Highway Features*, pp 1-21. (Transportation Research Board, Washington, DC).

Zegeer CV and Deen RC (1978) Green extension systems at high speed intersections. *ITE Journal 48(11)*, pp 19-25.

Zegeer CV, Deen RC and Mayes JG (1981) Effect of lane and shoulder widths on accident reduction on rural two-lane roads *Transportation Research Record 806*, pp 33-43.

Zegeer CV, Hummer J, Herf L, Reinfurt D and Hunter W (1987) Safety cost-effectiveness of incremental changes in cross-section design. *Report No. FHWA/RD-87/094*. 89 p. (Federal Highway Administration, Washington, DC).

Zegeer CV, Opiela KS and Cynecki J (1982) Effect of pedestrian signals and signal timing on pedestrian accidents. *Transportation Research Record 847*, pp 62-72.

Zegeer CV, Reinfurt DW, Hummer J, Herf L and Hunter W (1988) Safety effects of cross-section design for two-lane roads. *Transportation Research Record 1195*, pp 20-32.

Zegeer CV, Stewart J, Council FM and Reinfurt D (1991) Cost-effective geometric improvements for safety upgrading of horizontal curves. *Report FHWA-RD-90-021*. (Federal Highway Administration, Washington, DC).

Zegeer CV, Twomey JM, Heckman ML and Hayward JC (1992) *Safety Effectiveness of Highway Design Features. Volume 2, Alignment*. 14 p. (Federal Highway Administration, Washington, DC).

Zegeer CV and Zegeer SF (1988) Pedestrians and traffic control measures. *National Cooperative Highway Research Program: Synthesis of Highway Practice 139*. 76 p. (Transportation Research Board, Washington, DC).

Zogby JJ (1994) Highway safety management: Past and current practice. *TR News 173*, pp 22-25. (Transportation Research Board, Washington, DC).

Zogby JJ (1995) Personal communication.

# Index